The Riot and the Dance

THE RIOT AND THE DANCE

DR. GORDON WILSON

ILLUSTRATED BY FORREST DICKISON

Gordon Wilson, *The Riot and the Dance: Foundational Biology*

Published by Canon Press
P.O. Box 8729, Moscow, ID 83843
800.488.2034 | www.canonpress.com

Cover design by James Engerbretsen. Cover illustrations by Forrest Dickison.
Interior design by Laura Storm Design.
Printed in the United States of America.

Library of Congress Cataloging-in-Publication Data
Wilson, Gordon, PhD.
The riot and the dance : foundational biology / Dr. Gordon Wilson.
pages cm
Audience: Grade 9 to 12.
ISBN 978-1-59128-123-8
1. Natural history--Textbooks. 2. Biology--Textbooks. 3. Natural history--Religious aspects--Textbooks. 4. Biology--Religious aspects--Textbooks. I. Title.
QH47.W57 2013
508--dc23

2013026480

18 19 20 21 22 23 10 9 8 7 6 5 4

To my lovely wife Meredith,
my helpmeet, joy, and crown

CONTENTS

PART 1: THE LIVING CELL

PART 2: DIVERSITY OF LIFE

PART 1

THE LIVING CELL

PART 1

INTRODUCTION

This odd title *The Riot and the Dance* warrants an explanation among readers who may find themselves puzzled. Therefore, it is my first duty in the Introduction to explain the cogitations that produced it. So here goes.

There are a number of ways that both 'riot' and 'dance' can be viewed. First, the creation is cursed due to Adam's sin. The beautiful dance was "subjected to futility." The enemy "death" invaded. This curse of God was ushered in through predators, parasites, and pathogens. This is one meaning of "the riot," and it looms large in almost every nature documentary made. Animals killing each other may seem normal, but it's not beautiful or good in any sense. Death is the last enemy to be destroyed.

But even before the fall, it is probable that animal movement and plant placement or dispersal did not conform to our tidy sense of spatial organization. Wildebeests of the Serengeti aren't marching lock step to the beat of a drum, and the arrangement of trees in the wilderness isn't in rows. Both appear haphazard, so in this sense "riot" refers to the apparent chaotic pattern of plant placement and animal movement in a given habitat.

At the same time, there is also a divinely choreographed dance at a much deeper level (that's why it's beautiful). And these elements of a dance are still clear even amidst the riot of the fall. This includes the flow and cycling of energy and nutrients in an ecosystem (the biogeochemical cycles) and the dynamic rhythms of nature. This includes the changing seasons, blooming flowers, courting behaviors, and mutualism. All of these are remnants of a dance once perfect at creation. With the advent of death the original dance was deformed but it hasn't been blotted out altogether.

For example, on the molecular or cellular level the movement of molecules due to Brownian motion is seemingly chaotic. Even if we could see the molecules from the windows of the Magic School Bus, their movements would still look like a riot. But when we step back and look at what is really happening—metabolic pathways, DNA replication, RNA transcription, protein translation, mitosis, and meiosis—it is a wonderfully intricate series of dances that clearly proclaims the wisdom and majesty of God.

A second question readers may have is this: why do we need another biology text when it seems there are countless books of a similar nature? Granted, there are a lot of textbooks out there, but most have a thoroughgoing evolutionary worldview, and that won't do. This book is unashamedly creationist and seeks to honor the Author of life at every opportunity (see Appendix B).

There is a great need for reformation in the area of science education. I will pick on evolutionary science education first. One fundamental problem is that most (not all) science texts have a layout and text that is sterile and objective, lacking personality or aesthetic appeal. Unfortunately, many students who are forced to partake of their recommended high school or undergraduate allowance of biology receive only a mound of disconnected facts about the living world ("I call this data dumping"), with most of the wonder and beauty sucked out of it by the leech of naturalism. Many students probably marvel at how biology teachers and writers (Christian or not) manage to retain any interest in the subject matter when they dole it out with about as much enthusiasm as a server in a prison cafeteria dishing up lukewarm gruel.

If any attempt is made to highlight the magnificence of nature, all glory, honor, praise, and thanksgiving must fall upon the naturalistic gods named time, matter, energy, laws of chemistry, mutation, and (of course) natural selection. This is an abomination and a flagrant insult to the Lord of all Creation. Creation has beauty, complexity, and diversity that proclaim an infinitely wise and omnipotent Creator, but the cosmos's existence is regularly and dogmatically attributed to mindless matter begotten from nothing. This is not only ultimate foolishness, but also blasphemy (whether deliberate or inadvertent). This can be likened to teaching an art survey class and refusing to acknowledge the genius of the masters or to mention their names; and then, adding insult to injury, proclaiming that any apparent design of Michelangelo's David was really the result of wind and water erosion on marble.

Some (not all) Christian biology textbook writers mimic the aforementioned secular pedagogy and teach this glorious subject with materialistic descriptions and definitions. They may praise and honor God with enthusiasm (which I appreciate) but it doesn't solve the sterile "data dump" writing style and layout.

I hope to accomplish something different here. My goal is not just to present the subject matter but rather to *teach* it. Consequently, this book is rife with analogies, illustrations, and anecdotes serving as handles to get a grip on difficult concepts or simply to make the experience enjoyable. I don't presume this book is the ultimate solution to the 'boring biology' problem, but my hope is to usher in the 'love of learning' in biology. The natural revelation of creation is so much more magnificent than any of the works of the masters, and shouldn't be taught as a pile of dry facts we're supposed to learn (and then forget), hoping to check off the required course list for high school or college. When science is taught as just another subject to put on the transcript instead of a new way to see the glory of God, attempting to learn the pile of facts is about as much fun as eating gravel.

Instead, as with all subjects, the life sciences should be taught to bring glory to God, and should also be taught as a subset of theology simply because they are the study of God's natural revelation (as I mentioned earlier). By studying nature, we are studying the direct handiwork of God, and His creation gives us great insights into His creative character. His artistry and engineering are so wonderfully evident when pondering the biological systems spanning all levels, from molecules, cells, and organs to organisms and ecosystems, to list just a few examples. One who is called and privileged to teach our God's creation—its beauty, unity, complexity, and diversity—should strive to teach it so that students will not only enjoy the experience, but will begin to respond with reverence, wonder, praise, and thanksgiving toward the Lord of all Creation.

Gordon Wilson
Moscow, Idaho

CHAPTER 1

A SMIDGE OF CHEMISTRY

To grasp the spectacular world of a living cell, it's important to start with a few basic facts about the physical stuff cells are made of. This quick overview is not a substitute for a proper chemistry class, but it might prime the pump for taking one. If you've had one already, this will be a good review of some of the main concepts. I'm not trying to help you out in your chemistry class; I'm simply giving some foundational knowledge so you won't be lost when I discuss the chemical building blocks of cells.

Most people have heard of atoms, but have never seen one. It is hard to conceive of something so small that even if you could shrink down to the size of a single microscopic cell, you would still have trouble seeing one with your puny naked eye.

Just what is an atom, exactly? An **atom** is the smallest part of an element. Well, that helps a lot. What's an element? An **element** is a substance that has distinct chemical properties and cannot be broken down into simpler substances by normal chemical means. For example, oxygen is an element because you can't break it down into simpler substances. You can have fewer atoms of oxygen, but when you get to one atom, it can't be separated into smaller parts and remain oxygen.

Why is an atom the smallest part of an element? Because if you split an oxygen atom in two, you don't get two halves of an oxygen atom, you get an array of subatomic particles that compose atoms—particles called neutrons, protons, and electrons. This will become clearer when we discuss how the arrangement and number of these particles determine the identity of a particular element. For now, let's hit a few more basic definitions. A **molecule** is simply a group of two or more atoms hooked together by some kind of chemical bond. (We will discuss types of bonds later.)

Tinker toys always make helpful illustrations. A tinker toy item called a spool represents an atom (Figure 1.1). Any stick represents a chemical bond. (These sticks are a bit long to illustrate bonds, but work with me.) If you use sticks to put two or more of these spools together, you have a crude model of a molecule.

Figure 1.1 Tinkertoys

Some molecules only involve two atoms (such as hydrogen gas), but many molecules are quite large compared to the size of one atom.

Many molecules, especially those with three or more atoms, are composed of atoms of different elements. If a particular molecule has two or more elements in it, it is a called a **compound.** For example, the most familiar of all substances, water (H_2O), is a compound because it has two elements in it: two atoms are hydrogen (H) and one atom is oxygen (O).

Carbon dioxide (CO_2) is also a compound containing the elements carbon (one atom) and oxygen (two atoms).

Glucose is a larger molecule containing three elements (carbon, hydrogen, and oxygen) and twenty-four atoms. It has six carbon atoms, twelve hydrogen atoms, and six oxygen atoms (Figure 1.2).

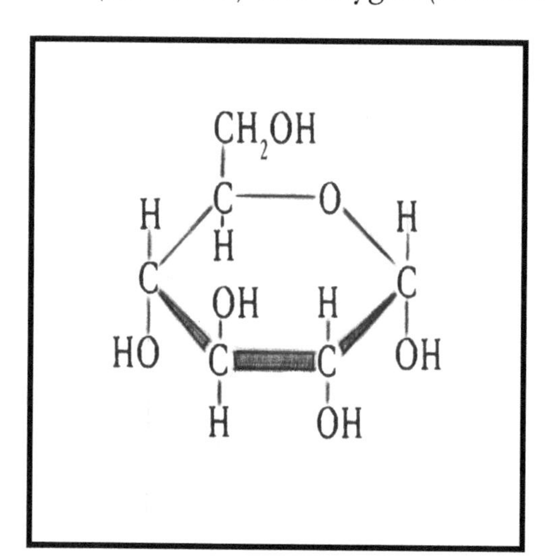

Figure 1.2 Glucose Molecule

THE ATOM

My deepest apologies to my chemist friends, but since this is very basic chemistry serving only as a springboard into biology, I am not interested in the relevance of some of the smaller particles like positrons, quarks, and neutrinos. I'll let the chemistry and physics teachers trouble over them. I'm sticking to the basics.

As I said before, atoms are exceedingly tiny. You might think a flake of dandruff is tiny, but cells are even tinier (a small flake of dandruff is composed of thousands of skin cells). But atoms are wicked tiny; so tiny that cells are gargantuan compared to them. If one of those skin cells was the size of the Houston Astrodome, an atom would be roughly the size of a marble or golf ball. No, this comparison isn't necessarily one hundred percent to scale mathematically, but you get the idea of the differences between these three types of "tiny."

The basic format of an atom is as follows. The **nucleus** is in the center of the atom and is composed of neutrons and protons. Both of these subatomic particles have about the same mass—mass which is arbitrarily set at one amu (atomic mass unit, or Dalton). The **proton** has a positive electrical charge while the **neutron** is neutral; it has no electrical charge. **Electrons** push the limits of how tiny things get. They have a negative electrical charge and weigh in at .008 amu or 8/1000th of an amu. The electrons zip around the weighty nucleus like gnats around your hot, sweaty head on a sultry day in Virginia. The main difference is that the electrons don't crash into the nucleus like gnats do to your sticky skin. Instead, they have very organized orbital patterns around the nucleus. The atom has one or more **energy levels** or **shells** in which electrons flit about. There may be one or more **orbitals** per shell and a maximum of two electrons can fit in an orbital. The first shell, which is closest to the nucleus, contains only one orbital, so only two electrons max can fit in the first shell. The larger second shell, which is farther away from the nucleus, has four orbitals (two electrons per orbital). Therefore, it can fit a maximum of eight electrons. (The figure does not show the technical details about the shapes and patterns of the orbitals within each shell. To avoid confusion, the circles represent the shells whereas pairs of electrons in each shell represent the individual orbitals.) The third shell, even farther away, has four orbitals which also can fit eight electrons. (Adding more than eight electrons into other orbitals is possible, but it is also beyond our scope, so if you want to know, check out a chemistry textbook.) Above is the structure of a chlorine atom (Figure 1.3).

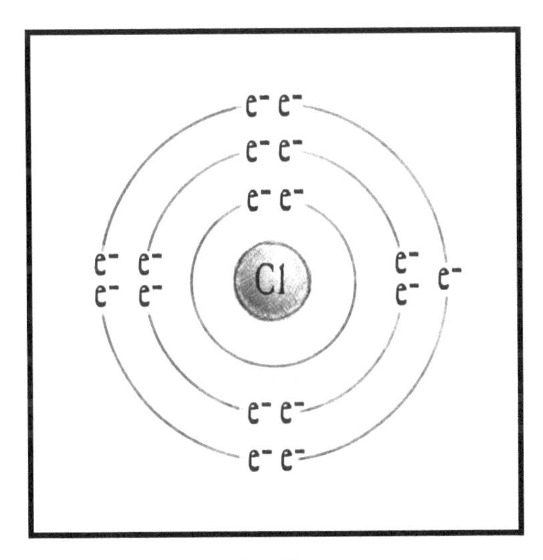

Figure 1.3 Chlorine atom

ATOMIC NUMBER, MASS NUMBER, AND ISOTOPES

The **atomic number** simply is the number of protons in an atom. The number of protons gives the atom its identity (refer to Appendix 3 for the entire periodic table of elements). For example, if the atomic number is one, it is hydrogen, period. If it is two, then it is helium; if it is six, then it is carbon, and so on. The atomic weight (or mass) number is the total number of protons plus neutrons. For instance, the atomic weight of the most common form of carbon is twelve: six protons and six neutrons. Some rarer forms of carbon have an atomic weight of thirteen; six protons and seven neutrons. Another form has an atomic weight of fourteen and therefore it has six protons and eight neutrons. In short, the number of neutrons can vary without changing the identity of the element. These different flavors of an element that have a variable number of neutrons in their atomic nuclei are called **isotopes**. The three forms of carbon (carbon 12, 13, and 14) I just mentioned are carbon isotopes.

TYPES OF BONDS

To figure out the nature of bonding, as well as which types of atoms are apt to bond and which aren't, it is good to understand a few rules of thumb about the atomic structure of a particular element.

The number of electrons equals the number of protons if the atom is electrically neutral. Given a neutral atom, this means that you automatically know the number of electrons if you know the atomic number (number of protons).

By way of reminder, electron orbitals are full when they have two electrons. The first shell contains one orbital and therefore can only fit a max of two electrons. The second shell is composed of four orbitals (two electrons per orbital) and can therefore fit eight electrons. In the third shell, eight electrons can fit in the first four orbitals, although more electrons can be added into different types of orbitals (but we won't worry about that).

The Octet Rule

Another important fact is that atoms are most stable when their outermost shell is filled to the max with electrons (eight electrons in the atoms we will consider). Obtaining an octet is the main driving force for bonding between most atoms. Electrical neutrality for an atom is not a goal, preference, or driving force, and is readily surrendered to obtain an **octet**. Bonding is the way most atoms obtain the stable octet configuration; hence, most matter is in molecule form.

IONIC BONDING

An atom with an electric charge is called an **ion**. You might be wondering how an atom becomes an ion. Since electrically neutral atoms aren't usually stable, they rob or share electrons from other atoms at the first opportunity in order to obtain an octet for their outer (**valence**) shell. In **ionic bonding**, certain kinds of atoms rob one or more electrons (to fulfill the octet) and consequently make themselves negatively charged. The atom that was robbed of electrons has lost one or more negative charges and winds up being positively charged. Since the robber becomes negatively charged (**anion**) and the robbed becomes positively charged (**cation**), they stick together.

Figure 1.4 below illustrates the ionic bond forming a familiar substance—sodium chloride or table salt. The sodium atom has an atomic number of

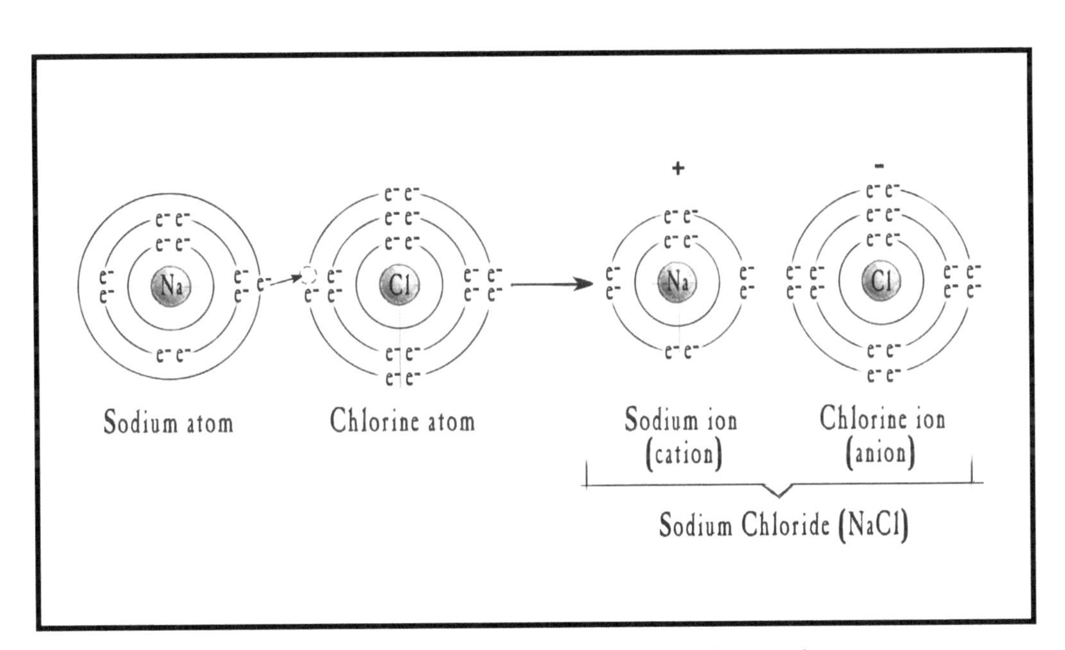

Figure 1.4 Ionic bond of Sodium Chloride (NaCl)

11, which means that it has eleven protons. Since the number of electrons must equal the number of protons in an electrically neutral atom, the sodium atom has eleven electrons (e-) dispersed among its shells.

If you recall the capacity of each shell, two electrons fit in the first shell, while eight electrons (4 orbitals and two e- in each) fit in the second shell (2 + 8 = 10). But a neutral sodium atom has eleven electrons, so the last electron winds up all by its lonesome in the third shell. Since neutral atoms are very inclined to get an octet at the first opportunity, the sodium gives its outer lone electron to the first taker. In this instance, chlorine is the taker.

The chlorine atom has an atomic number of 17, hence seventeen protons and seventeen electrons. If we were making a chlorine atom, we would load two electrons in the first shell, eight in the second shell, and seven in the third shell.

You might begin to see that this here is a very amicable arrangement for sodium and chlorine atoms. If chlorine simply swipes the lone electron from sodium's outermost shell, it now has an octet, but the robbery also grants the sodium a happy octet. Sodium now has ten electrons (two in the first shell and eight in the second). But because sodium's proton number hasn't changed (11), it has eleven positive charges and only ten negative charges (after the loss of its lone electron), and the atom (cation) has a net +1 charge. Because chlorine's proton number hasn't changed either (17), it has seventeen positive charges but also eighteen negative charges after swiping sodium's lone electron. This gives the chlorine a net -1 charge (it is now called a chloride anion). Because these two ions are oppositely charged, Na (+1) and Cl (-1) stick together, resulting in an ionic bond.

COVALENT BONDING

In many cases, atoms bond in such a way that electrons are shared rather than transferred. The outermost electrons are called valence electrons and these are the ones involved in sharing. Thus, a bond formed through the sharing of valence electrons is termed a **covalent bond.**

Let's consider water, H_2O. Oxygen has an atomic number of 8. Therefore, it has 8 protons in the nucleus and 8 electrons in the shells. The first shell fits only two electrons and the remaining six electrons fit into the second shell composed of four orbitals. This part is a bit tricky. The electrons distribute themselves among the four orbitals much like the way six cards are dealt between four players (a full hand is two cards in this analogy). If you do that, what happens? Because the cards are dealt in a circle, two players will get a full hand but the other two players will receive just one card apiece. (If that doesn't make sense, deal six cards to 4 people and it will.)

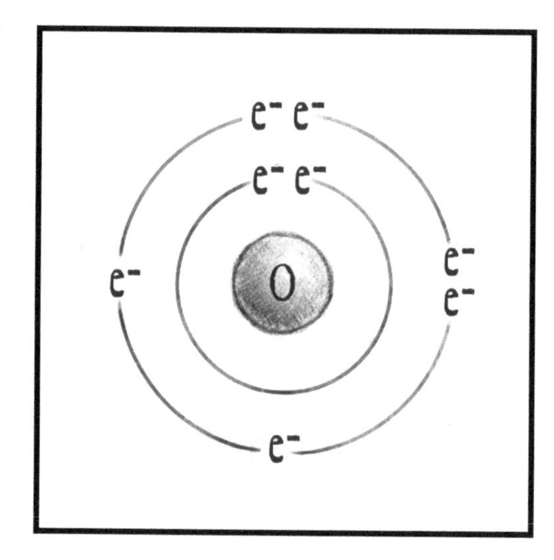

Figure 1.5 Oxygen atom

Similarly, the oxygen atom would have two orbitals containing two electrons each, and two orbitals containing one electron each. It doesn't wind up with three orbitals each with two electrons and one orbital with none (see Figure 1.5).

The hydrogen atom has an atomic number of one. According to the way God wants matter to behave, hydrogen has one electron in its one and only orbital (it would be more stable with two). Oxygen, remember, has four outer orbitals, two of which are short one electron. If the oxygen atom shares its two single-electron orbitals with the single electron orbitals of two hydrogen atoms, all three atoms will successfully fill each other's electron needs (see Figure 1.6). As Rocky Balboa so profoundly said with that rich Philly accent in Rocky I, "She's got gaps, I got gaps, together we fill gaps, ya know what I mean."

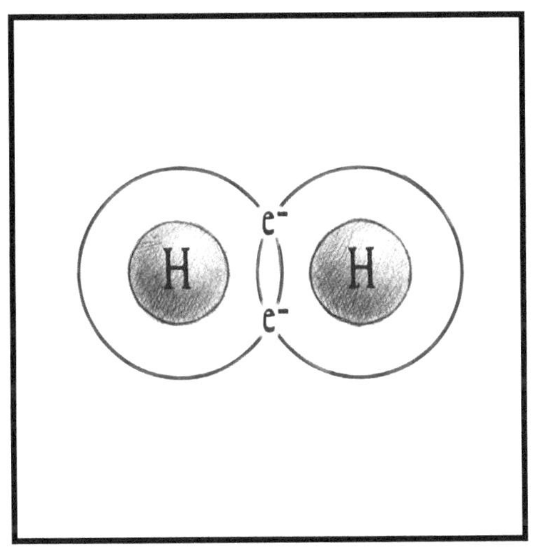

Figure 1.6 Hydrogen molecule

There are two types of covalent bonds that are based on the equity of electron sharing: **non-polar** and **polar covalent bonding**. The non-polar covalent bond is formed when there is a more "communistic" electron distribution. The atoms involved have an equal pull on the shared electrons and consequently the electrons are equally distributed between the two or more atoms. There is no polarity of charges across the molecule; i.e., there isn't one part of the molecule that is more negative and one part more positive.

On the other hand, the polar covalent bond is formed when there is a more "capitalistic" electron distribution. The atom(s) with the greatest pull (higher electronegativity) on the shared electrons will cause the electrons to swarm about them more than the weaker (low electronegativity) atom(s).

This lopsidedness of electron distribution causes a polarity of charges across the molecule. The atoms with a preponderance of electrons will have a slightly negative charge and the short-changed atoms will have a slightly positive charge.

Water serves as a good example of polar covalent bonds. The oxygen has a greater pull on the electrons, giving the oxygen atom a partial negative charge and the two hydrogen atoms wind up with partial positive charges. Because the oxygen's two full and unshared orbitals are on the same side of the atom, the negative electrons repel the hydrogen atoms, giving the molecule a bent appearance (Figure 1.7).

I like to compare the water molecule to the head of Mickey Mouse. Mickey's head is the oxygen (with a partial negative charge) and the two ears are the hydrogen atoms (with a partial positive charge). Keep in mind that this is not the same as ionic bonding. The electrons are still shared (albeit unequally). In ionic bonding, there is outright robbery (transfer of electrons); no sharing. In polar covalent bonds, the hoggish atoms only get partial rather than complete negative charges, as is the case with ionic bonds.

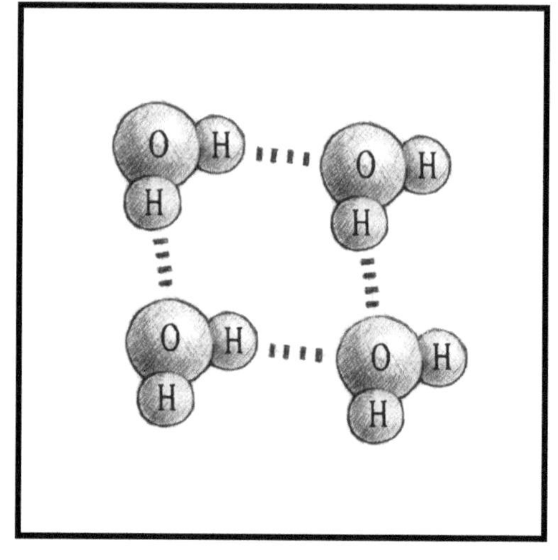

Figure 1.7 Hydrogen bonds between water

HYDROGEN BONDING.

The stage is now set for understanding the nature of **hydrogen bonding.** Because polar molecules have atoms which are partially negative and atoms that are partially positive, it is logical to assume (given the chemical axiom that opposite charges attract) that areas of partial positive charges might exert a pull for negatively charged areas on other molecules. Again, the best example of this is water. Above in Figure 1.7, you see the oxygen atoms forming hydrogen bonds (dotted lines) with hydrogen atoms of other water molecules.

Hydrogen bonds can also form between polar areas within the same molecule, given that the molecule is large enough to allow bending. Hydrogen bonds are responsible for forming and maintaining bends and kinks within large molecules (Figure 1.8). They can also form connections between large molecules (Figure 1.9).

Figure 1.8
Hydrogen bonds within large molecules

The relative strengths of these bonds are as listed:

- Covalent bonds (strongest)
- Ionic bonds (intermediate)
- Hydrogen bonds (weakest)

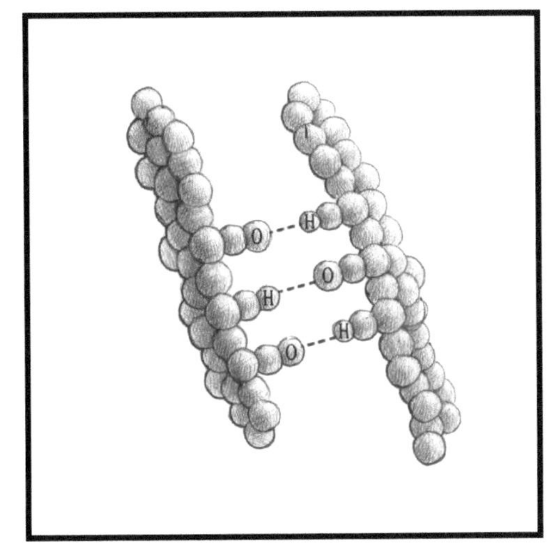

Figure 1.9
Hydrogen bonds between large molecules

THE IMPORTANCE OF WATER

Since water looms large in the economy of life, I thought it would be good to inculcate the characteristics of water that are particularly relevant. First, because water is a polar molecule, it readily forms hydrogen bonds with itself and other polar molecules. Also, ionic compounds, when placed in water, readily dissolve because the polar water molecules are attracted to the positive and negative ions (Figure 1.10). This attraction can be shown by a simple experiment. Comb your hair to give the comb a static charge. Then hold the comb next to a thin stream of water coming from the faucet. Watch the stream of water bend toward the charged comb.

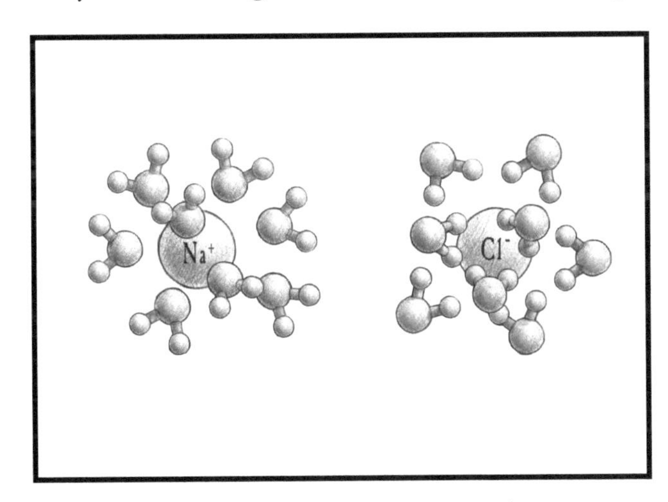

Figure 1.10 Water molecules attracted to ions

On the other hand, non-polar substances (such as oils) don't dissolve in water, because there are no charged areas on the molecules for the water to orient toward.

Because water hydrogen-bonds with itself, it gives water a cohesive property. Water likes to stick to itself. Young basketball players employ this property frequently when they moisten their fingers and the ball so they can palm it. When we see a drop of water on the counter top, it forms a little dome. This is because the water molecules are forming as many hydrogen bonds as possible, causing them to huddle up into a tiny mound of water.

The reason it's so intimidating to jump into the water from a lofty height is the fact that water doesn't separate from itself easily due to all those hydrogen bonds. Belly flops are so painful because the broad surface of your belly doesn't break all those hydrogen bonds as quickly and smoothly as we would like. When your belly breaks those bonds, it leaves a stinging reminder of the collective power of hydrogen bonding.

Water is also a very effective temperature stabilizer. In chemistry terms, it has a high *specific heat capacity.* In simple terms, it takes a lot of energy to heat water up, but once it has that energy, it hangs onto it quite well. This means it takes a longer time for it to cool down compared to other substances like metal and alcohol. The implications of this are very important because the water's specific heat is largely responsible for how fast creatures heat up and cool down within their environment.

Lastly, water is the solvent of biological life. We and every living creature are very wet on the inside (and I don't just mean blood). Creatures are made of cells, the vast majority of which are essentially very tiny, exceedingly complicated water balloons. Even the crannies between cells are filled with an aqueous (water-based) solution. All the enzymes, organelles, and other cellular machinery within cells do their job in a watery solution called the cytoplasm. Consequently, most of the processes of biological life are designed to work in and harmonize with the chemistry of water.

ACIDS, BASES, AND SALTS

This could quickly slip beyond the scope of this text, but I should mention a few biologically relevant things about acids, bases, and salts.

An **acid** is any substance that gives off hydrogen ions. By the way, a hydrogen ion (H+) is simply a proton. This is because a hydrogen atom has one proton (in the nucleus) and one electron in the first orbital. When the electron is stripped away, all that's left is a positively charged proton so a hydrogen ion and proton can be used interchangeably. The chemistry is quite complex, but when H+ ions get too concentrated, they can be quite troublesome to the normal processes of the cell. Super high concentrations wreak havoc upon the cell, so it is important for cell biologists and biochemists to understand the chemistry of H+ ions in the life (or death) of a cell and to be able to accurately measure H+ ion concentrations.

I don't particularly want to get into definitions of moles and molar concentrations; you can consult a chemistry text if you're curious for more details. Suffice it to say that molarity is a measure of a substance's concentration when dissolved in water. In this case, we are concerned about H+ ion concentrations. 1.0 M (molar solution) is extremely concentrated. Scientific notation of 1.0 M would be written as 1×10^0 M. If we are referring to the concentration of H+ in an acid solution, we use the pH scale, which is exponential (i.e., based on the negative of the exponent of the molar concentration). For instance, a very strong acid would be 1×10^0 M solution. The pH would be 0. (Although it is beyond the scope of this text it is worth mentioning that the pH of some substances can go way below pH 0. Chemists have custom-made a super acid that has a pH of -31, which is 100,000 billion billion billion times more acidic than pH 1.) If, however, the concentration of H+ ions was 0.1 M, the scientific notation would be 1×10^{-1} and the pH would be simply 1. Notice that 1.0 M is ten times more concentrated than 0.1 M. Consequently, pH = 0 is ten times more acidic than pH = 1. Again, 0.01 M written in scientific notation is 1×10^{-2} M. What would be the pH? It would simply be pH = 2. And since 0.1 M is ten times more concentrated than 0.01 M, then pH = 1 is ten times more acidic than pH = 2 and so on. The pH scale ranges from 0-14. Acids have concentrations of H+ ions ranging from 1.0 M to 0.000001 M, or 1×10^0 M to 1×10^{-6} M. The pH range would be 0–6 (actually up to 6.9). Hydrogen ion concentration of 0.0000001 or 1×10^{-7} M or pH = 7 is said to be neutral. Pure, distilled water has a pH of 7. This means that the H+ concentration is equal to the hydroxide concentration (OH-). Solutions with H+ concentrations lower than 0.0000001 M (or 1×10^{-7} M) have pH values greater than 7 and up to 14. These are said to be basic or alkaline (see Figure 1.11 on the next page).

Now that I've mentioned basic or alkaline, you might wonder if there are substances called bases. Just as acids are substances that give off H+ ions, **bases** are substances that combine with or absorb H+ ions. When they do this, they take them out of solution, thus lowering the concentration of H+ ions further (which raises the pH). As I mentioned earlier, what bases and acids exactly do at the molecular level to the molecules that make up living cells would quickly get complicated, so suffice it to say that extremes in pH badly damage living tissue (with few exceptions). That's why we don't bathe in battery acid or oven cleaner (a base). There is one notable exception: People who use hair remover are using a pretty strong base, but this, of course, does not wash hair; it dissolves it.

All aqueous liquids have a pH. The closer they are to a neutral pH (pH = 7), the friendlier they are on most varieties of human flesh. Years ago, shampoo advertisements made a big deal about their product being pH balanced. Most people didn't have a clue what that meant, but shampoo

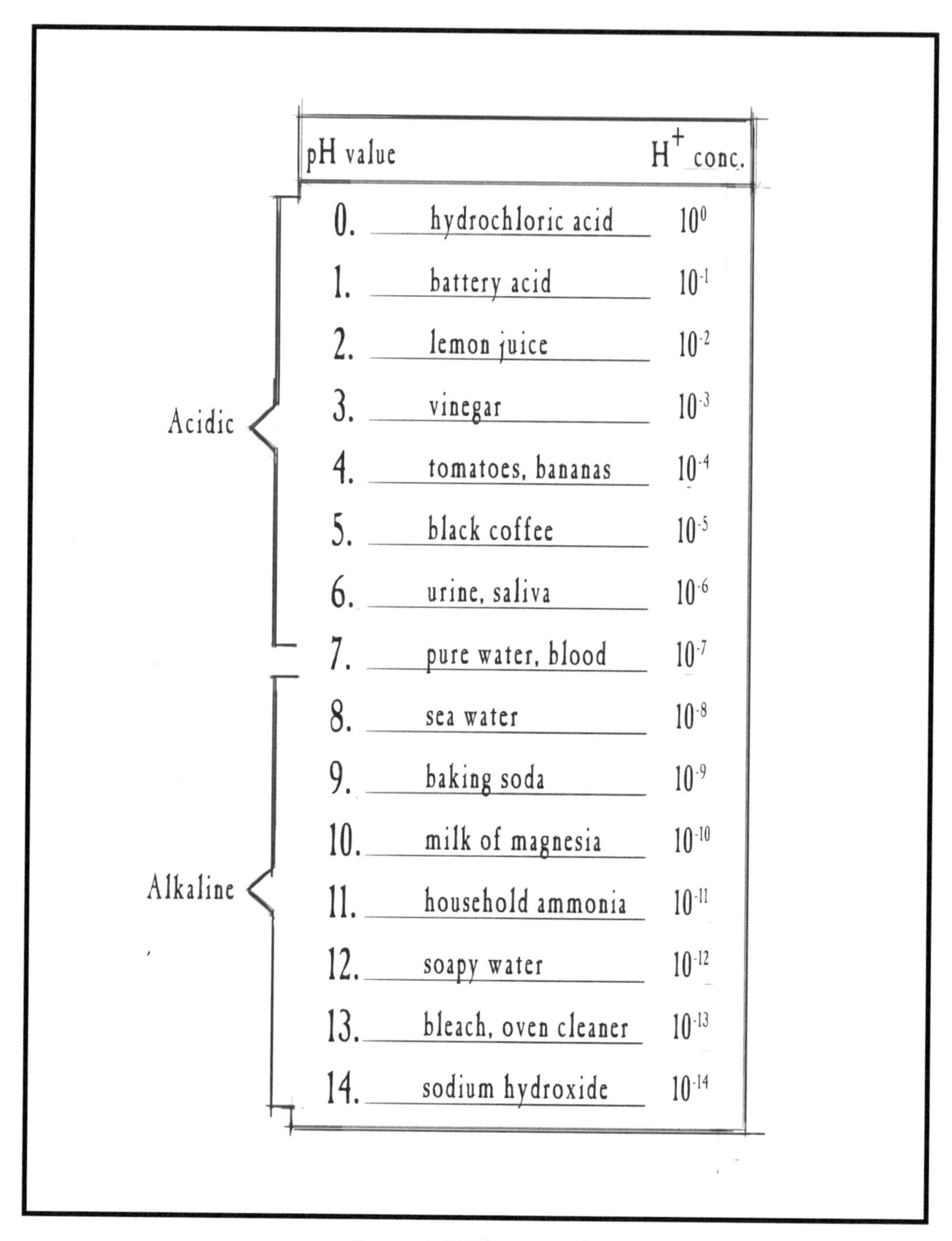

Figure 1.11 The pH scale

manufacturers said it with so much pride that it was accepted by consumers as a good thing. And it is a good thing. The phrase "pH balanced" simply means that its pH is at or near neutral (7), which means that it is gentle on your hair like pure water.

Salts are defined as any substance resulting from mixing equal amounts of an acid and a base. A typical example of this would be mixing HCl (hydrochloric acid) with a strong base like NaOH (sodium hydroxide). What happens is a replacement reaction. The H+ ions separate from (dissociate from) the Cl- ions and the Na+ ions dissociate from the OH- ions. Then they recombine with the other's partner. The Na+ and Cl- ions pair off to form NaCl (table salt) and the nasty H+ ions pair off with equal quantities of nasty OH- ions, forming innocent water (H_2O). There are many other examples of different kinds of acids and bases combining to form water and other kinds of salt, but we'll stop there.

Buffers are wonderful chemicals that do a great service either in the lab or within our bodies. Basically, they ride the brakes in any change in pH. In other words, if a buffer is in solution when an acid is added, the pH will not drop as fast or as far. The same is true if a base is added; if a buffer is there, the pH won't rise as fast or as far. A buffer in an acid solution will absorb H+ ions (like a base), but a buffer will release H+ ions (like an acid), counteracting the base in an alkaline solution.

Years ago, when I was a lab technician in Dr. Scott Minnich's bacteriology lab (you may have heard of him if you've watched some Intelligent Design videos), one of my jobs was to make various solutions of specific concentrations and pH. As I was dissolving something in a beaker on the stir plate, I had to bring the pH down to something like pH 5. An electronic pH meter with its probe dangling into the solution would give me an instant digital readout of the current pH. I would use concentrated HCl to bring the pH down. If no buffer was in the solution, one carefully added drop of HCl acid would cause the pH to plummet (to my dismay) far below pH 5. Then I would have to raise the pH with NaOH. I would often overshoot the desired pH because strong acids and bases would cause the pH to change too quickly. It was like using a sledge hammer on a thumb tack. Try that without putting it in too far. But if a buffer was in the solution, I could drip away with the HCl acid and slowly bring down the pH to the desired value. We also have a built-in buffering system in our bodies.

Our blood is supposed to be right around pH 7.2 and if it deviates too much in either direction (while still inside your body), your nervous system is toast. H_2CO_3 (carbonic acid) is in our blood plasma and helps maintain our blood pH at healthy levels. If our blood gets too alkaline (pH >7.3), then H_2CO_3 dissociates into H+ and HCO_3- and our pH goes down to pH ~ 7.2. On the other hand, if your blood slightly drops below pH ~ 7.2 (not far, even pH 6.8 kills people), then the HCO_3- (bicarbonate) absorbs H+ ions to become H_2CO_3, thus raising the pH.

CHAPTER 1: REVIEW QUESTIONS

Make sure you know how to spell the terms.

1. A substance that has distinct chemical properties and cannot be broken down into simpler substances by normal chemical means is a(n) ______.

2. The smallest unit of an element is a(n) ______.

3. Two or more atoms bonded together is a(n) ______.

4. A molecule containing two or more elements is a(n) ______.

5. The two subatomic particles contained in the nucleus of an atom are ______ and ______. What are their charges?

6. The subatomic particles contained in the shells orbiting the nucleus are the ______. Charge?

7. Atomic number is the number of ______.

8. Atomic weight or mass number is the sum of ______ and ______.

9. Draw an oxygen atom (atomic number: 8).

10. Draw a water molecule (H_2O) showing orbitals and shared electrons (atomic number of hydrogen: 1).

11. A complete transfer of electrons from one atom to another resulting in oppositely charged atoms sticking together is called a(n) ______ bond.

12. When atoms are joined together because they are sharing electrons it is called a(n) ______ bond.

13. In a polar covalent bond how are the electrons being distributed in the molecule?

14. In a non-polar covalent bond how are the electrons being distributed in the molecule?

15. Weak attractions between partially positive charged atoms and partially negative charged atoms within the same molecule or between different molecules are called ______ bonds.

16. Water's cohesive property is due to its ability to ______ bond with itself.

17. The pH scale is a measure of a substance's ______ ion concentration.

18. A pH of 7 is termed ______. Below pH 7 is considered ______ and above 7 is considered ______.

19. A move from pH 6 to pH 5 has made the solution ______ times more acidic.

20. Substances that resist changes in pH are called ______.

CHAPTER 2

BIOMOLECULES

THE CHEMICALS OF LIFE

This chapter is an attempt to introduce you to the basic chemicals that make up cells. For many people, there is a disconnect between *cells* (which are comprehensible—you can see them under the microscope) and *molecules* (which often seem abstract, kind of like math—you can't see molecules under the microscope). But I hope to explain the connection between cells and the molecules that form their very fabric. The relationship between molecules and a cell is no different than the relationship between nails, screws, boards, drywall, carpet, tiles, wires, piping, shingles, siding, etc . . . and a house. A house's very existence depends on the existence and proper arrangement of its various parts.

Other than water, there are four basic categories of biomolecules that form the vast majority of a cell's substance: **carbohydrates, lipids, proteins,** and **nucleic acids** (DNA and RNA). But before we discuss them, I want to look at what I call the "Tinkertoy" rules for the various elements found in biomolecules.

Carbon (atomic number 6) has six protons and (if neutral) six electrons. This means that two electrons are in the first shell and four electrons are in the second shell. Remember that they distribute themselves equally (like dealing cards) so that one electron goes into each orbital. As a result, carbon can share electrons (covalent bond) in four places. Tinkertoy rule for carbon: 4 bonds.

Oxygen (atomic number 8), as we have seen, has eight electrons; two in the first shell and six in the second shell, with two filled orbitals and two half-filled orbitals available for covalent bonding. Tinkertoy rule for oxygen: 2 bonds.

Hydrogen (atomic number 1), has one electron in its one and only shell where it can covalently bond with one other atom. Tinkertoy rule for hydrogen: 1 bond. Nitrogen (atomic number 7) has seven electrons; two in the first shell and five in the second shell. They are distributed as evenly as possible among four orbitals; therefore, two electrons are in one orbital and one in each of the other orbitals. This means it can bond covalently in three places. Tinkertoy rule for nitrogen: 3 bonds.

Phosphorus (atomic number 15) has fifteen electrons; two in the first, eight in the second, and five in the third, but in this case, the electrons spread out with one electron in five orbitals. Consequently, phosphorus can covalently bond in five places. Tinkertoy rule for phosphorus: 5 bonds.

Lastly (at least for our purposes—we could go on), there is the element sulfur. Sulfur (atomic number 16) has sixteen electrons; two in the first, eight in the second, and six in the third. This makes for a similar arrangement of electrons as oxygen in its outer (valence) shell; i.e., two filled orbitals and two half-filled orbitals available for covalent bonding. Tinkertoy rule for sulfur: 2 bonds.

These Tinkertoy rules help us to understand how many bonds can form between atoms of certain elements. This will be useful as you begin to memorize and draw the structures of certain biomolecules.

CARBOHYDRATES

We have all heard of carbohydrates during our frequent blathering about food, nutrition, or health. We may have simply picked up the term mindlessly reading nutrition labels on our cereal boxes, attempting (perhaps vainly) to amuse ourselves while eating alone. The reason we all hear about carbohydrates in these contexts is that carbohydrates are the primary fuel source for most living creatures. They generate energy within biological internal combustion engines known as cells and the mitochondria within cells. Carbohydrates can also serve as structural support of cells and tissues, particularly in insects, plants, and fungi.

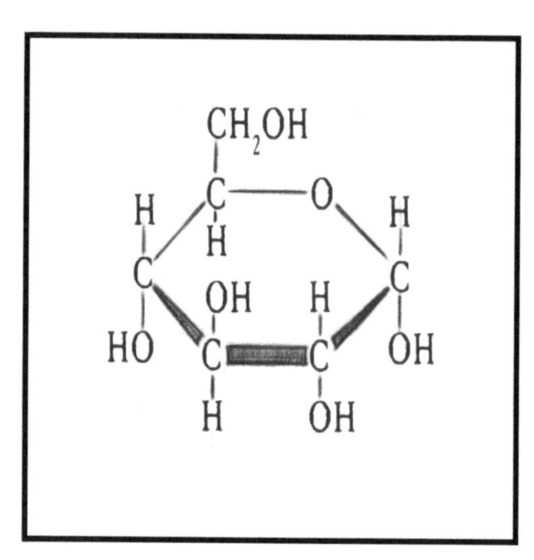

Figure 2.1 Glucose

Now let's examine them from a chemical perspective. The basic building block, or simplest unit, of all carbohydrates is a **monosaccharide** (a simple sugar). There are many different kinds but the most common and well known is glucose. **Glucose** has the molecular formula of $C_6H_{12}O_6$. Figure 2.1 is the structural formula.

Notice that each atom in this compound (more than one element) follows its own TinkerToy rule. Each carbon atom has four bonds; each oxygen atom has two bonds, and each hydrogen atom has one bond. Because they have a lot of carbon and hydrogen atoms, they are aptly named carbohydrates (don't ask me why oxygen isn't in the name). Although glucose is the only one you have to memorize, Figure 2.2 is an illustration of fructose, another kind of monosaccharide.

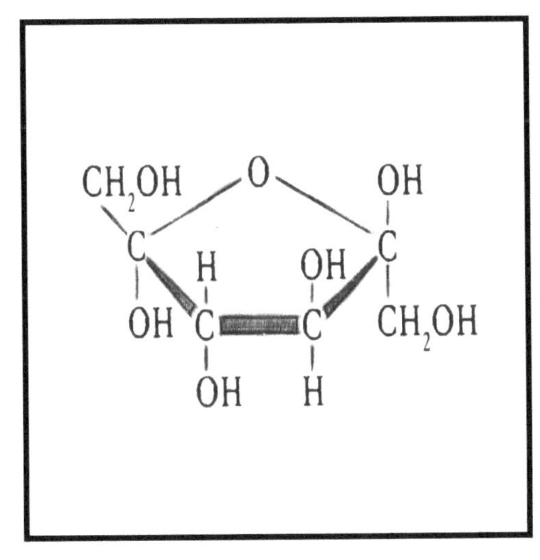

Figure 2.2 Fructose

Another type of carbohydrate is a **disaccharide**, which is formed by linking two monosaccharides together. A chemical reaction must take place for the two monosaccharides to be linked (refer to Figure 2.3). Basically, the hydrogen (in the box) on the left monosaccharide is hooked to an OH (hydroxyl group also in a box) on the right monosaccharide. The OH plus the

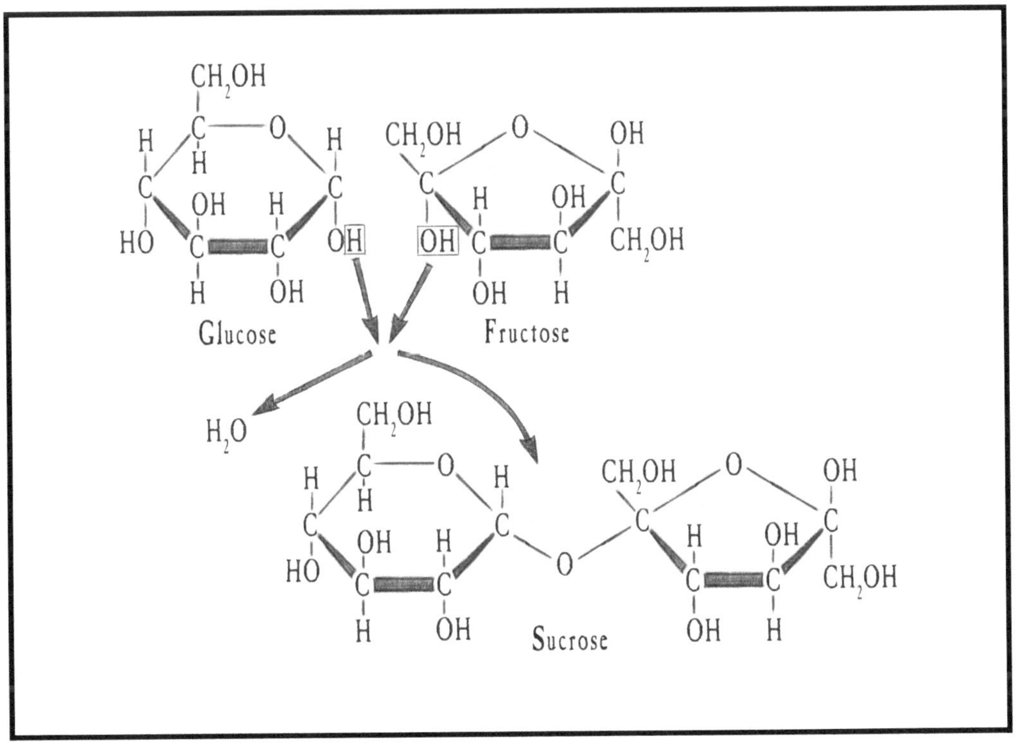

Figure 2.3 Dehydration synthesis

H forms water (H_2O). The two monosaccharides are joined together covalently between two adjacent carbon atoms with an oxygen in the middle. Because water is removed and a bigger molecule is formed in the reaction, it is called a **dehydration synthesis** reaction. And the covalent bond linking the two monosaccharides together is called a **glycosidic linkage.**

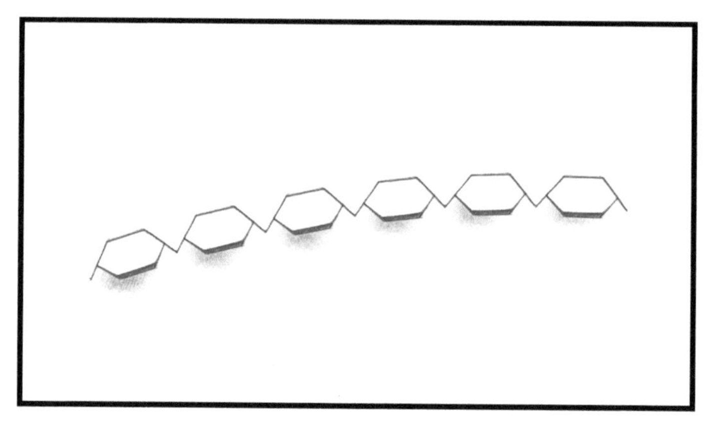

Figure 2.4 Starch

If the reverse reaction occurs—if water is split into OH and H and placed back in their original positions (thus breaking the glycosidic linkage)—it is called a **hydrolysis reaction.** This particular disaccharide is composed of two different monosaccharides, glucose and fructose, and is called **sucrose**—or table sugar.

Complex sugars are composed of many monosaccharides (usually the same kind) linked together by glycosidic linkages to form chains (often the monosaccharide is glucose). If the chain length is a few to less than a hundred, it is referred to as an **oligosaccharide** (oligo = few). If the chain is one hundred or more monosaccharides long, it is called a **polysaccharide.** There are a few household polysaccharides we are familiar with. **Starch** is a type of polysaccharide composed of a linear chain of glucose units and is primarily used for food storage in plants (Figure 2.4). In starch, the glycosidic linkages have a fancy designation of α (1, 4). This refers to the orientation of the glucose units with respect to each other.

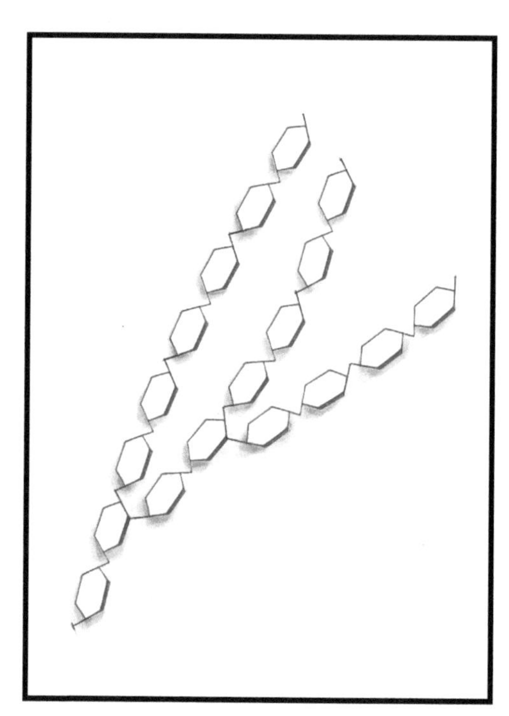

Figure 2.5 Glycogen

Glycogen (also known as animal starch) is a less familiar polysaccharide, but is used as short term food storage in animals (Figure 2.5). Surplus blood sugar (glucose) after a meal is taken out of circulation at the liver and chained up to form glycogen. This is like your checking account (stored but easily accessible). If you skip lunch, your body makes a withdrawal from the glycogen account in the liver bank to maintain normal blood sugar levels (spending money) until dinner time. It is very similar to plant starch except that the glucose chains are highly branched.

Lastly, **cellulose** is another polysaccharide that is a linear chain of glucose units but is not used for food storage in plants (Figure 2.6). It is used extensively as structural support in plant tissues and is the main component in plant cell walls. The glycosidic linkage is of a different nature and is called β (1, 4).

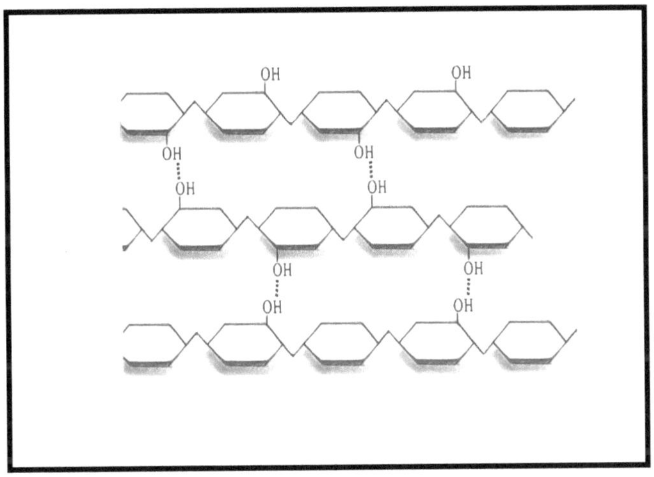

Figure 2.6 Cellulose

Because of this different linkage, the normal enzyme that digests starch is completely incapable of digesting cellulose. Although many animals and people don't make the enzyme which digests cellulose, many herbivores do house microbes in their guts which secrete the appropriate enzyme, enabling them to digest the cellulose and absorb glucose into their blood. Think about it . . . if we had that enzyme we could take the edge off of our hunger in class by snacking on notebook paper (paper is essentially cellulose purified from wood cell walls). By the way, digesting any polysaccharide is the process by which an enzyme performs hydrolysis (go back and see what it means) on the glycosidic linkages. In other words, the enzyme is breaking apart the polysaccharide chain into its monosaccharides units.

LIPIDS

The lipids are another major group of biomolecules. These include the neutral lipids (fats, oils, and grease), waxes, and steroids. There is another type that is usually only mentioned among biologists, and they are called phospholipids.

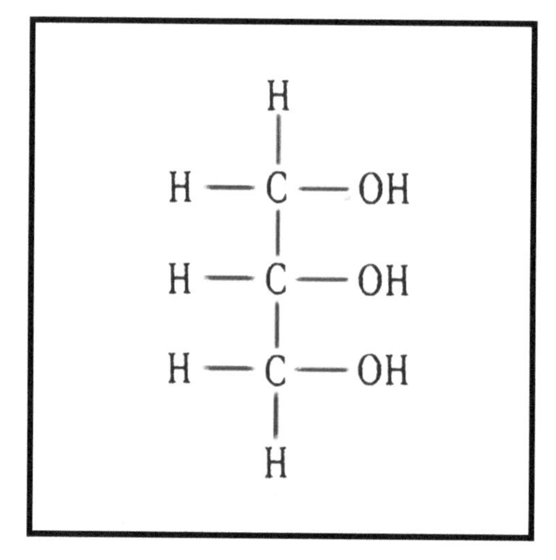

Figure 2.7 Glycerol

In the economy of life, lipids are indispensable. Neutral lipids (they don't have a charge) are commonly called oils, fats, and grease (glycerides). They primarily function as food storage molecules. If food is wanting, our bodies mobilize fat reserves to burn for our energy needs. I compared glycogen (the polysaccharide stored in the liver) as a checking account—stored but easily accessible. Fats and oils are more like a savings account—not as easily accessible. We draw on them for fuel when the other accounts are approaching our minimum balance threshold.

First, let's look at the chemical structure of a fat molecule (also known as a glyceride). There are two basic components of the glyceride—glycerol and fatty acids. These two molecules are not a glyceride unless they are bonded together. The **glycerol** is a linear chain of three carbon atoms with three OH groups on one side and hydrogen occupying the rest of the bonding sites. Figure 2.7 is the structural formula of glycerol.

The **fatty acid** is a longer linear molecule that ranges from four to eighteen carbons long. Except for one end, the carbon chain is covered with hydrogen. The end that isn't covered with hydrogen has a double bond to oxygen and a single bond to OH. Below is the structural formula of an eight-carbon fatty acid.

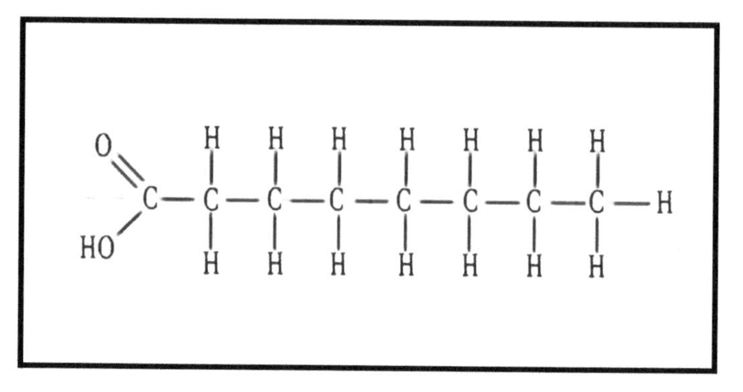

Figure 2.8 Eight-Carbon fatty acid

We still don't have a glyceride. These two molecules have to be hooked together first. You may recall that two monosaccharides are linked together by a dehydration synthesis reaction by producing H_2O from one OH group and a hydrogen atom forming a linkage between the two molecules where the OH groups used to be. The leftover oxygen remains in the middle of the linkage.

Since there are three available OH groups on the glycerol, three fatty acids can be mounted on the glycerol. If they are bonded together, they are no longer considered a glycerol and a fatty acid. It is now called a glyceride. If only one fatty acid has been mounted, it is a **monoglyceride**; if two, then a **diglyceride**; if three, then a **triglyceride**. To the right is the structure of a triglyceride.

```
     H       O   H    H    H    H    H
     |       ||  |    |    |    |    |
  H—C—O—C—C — C — C — C — C—H
     |           |    |    |    |    |
     |           H    H    H    H    H
     |
     |       O   H    H    H    H    H
     |       ||  |    |    |    |    |
  H—C—O—C—C — C — C — C — C—H
     |           |    |    |    |    |
     |           H    H    H    H    H
     |
     |       O   H    H    H    H    H
     |       ||  |    |    |    |    |
  H—C—O—C—C — C — C — C — C—H
     |           |    |    |    |    |
     H           H    H    H    H    H
```

Figure 2.9 Triglyceride

As in carbohydrates, these bonds can be broken by hydrolysis, which is simply the reverse of dehydration synthesis.

You may have never heard of phospholipids, but countless phospholipid molecules comprise most of the fabric of our cell membranes (the flexible boundary of every one of our sixty to a hundred trillion cells). A **phospholipid** is similar to a diglyceride (a glycerol plus two fatty acids) except that it has a unique molecular group with a positive and negative charge dangling off of the third carbon. Below is the structure of a phospholipid. (Note the positively charged nitrogen and negatively charged oxygen.)

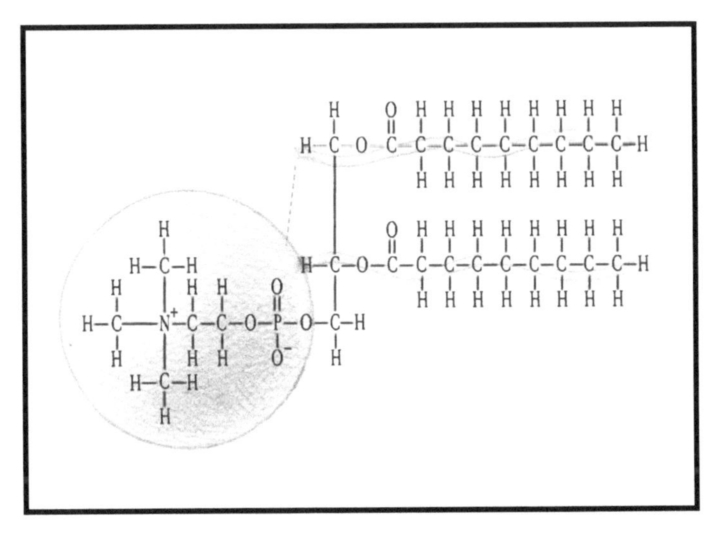

Figure 2.10 Phospholipid

This charged group bestows a dual nature on the phospholipid. The fatty acids are very nonpolar, which makes them exceedingly unfriendly with water. Consequently, they are termed "hydrophobic"—water-fearing. But the charged portion of the phospholipid is friendly toward water and readily forms hydrogen bonds with it. Thus, this portion is termed "hydrophilic"—water-loving. Below is a simplified cartoon of a phospholipid.

This dual nature makes phospholipids highly suitable for forming cell membranes. The interior fluid of cells is called **cytoplasm** and is water-based (aqueous). The exterior is also aqueous. If a lot of phospholipids are thrown into water, their dual nature causes them to form two-layer phospholipid membranes. The hydrophobic tails (the fatty acid portion) all get together and form a water-free area while the hydrophilic heads (the unique charged portion) all face the water—on either the inside or the outside of the membrane. This arrangement can be spontaneous (phospholipids thrown into water) or built and arranged by the metabolism of the cell. Either way, the chemistry of phospholipids causes them to naturally retain this arrangement.

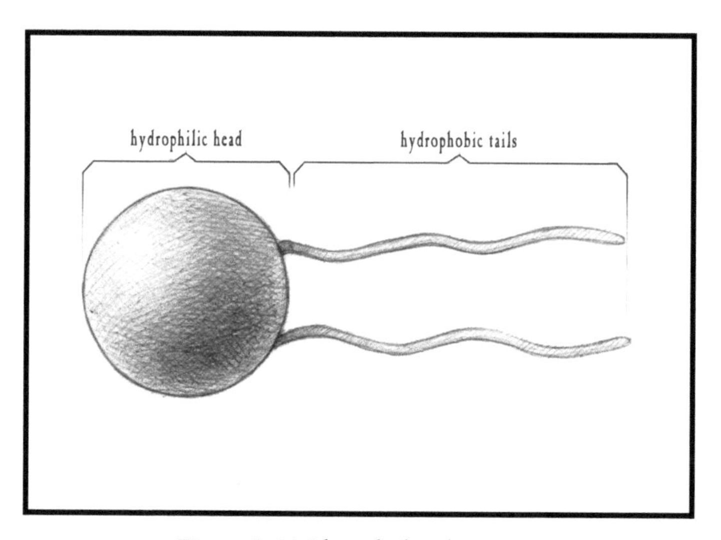

Figure 2.11 Phospholipid cartoon

In the cartoon to the left, the hydrophilic heads are represented by the little balls and the hydrophobic tails are represented by the short lines in the interior of the **phospholipid bilayer**. Inside and outside is water.

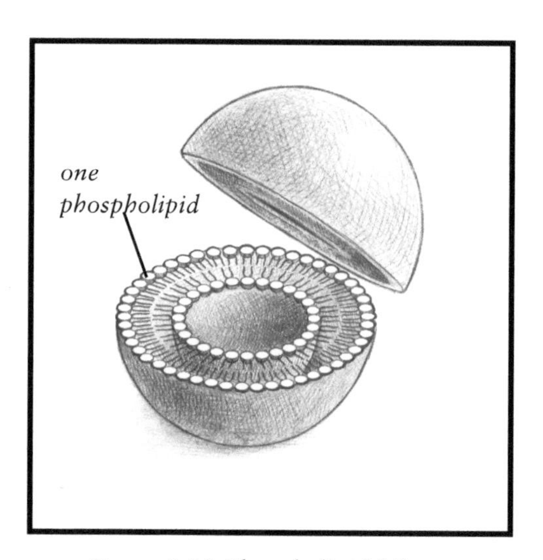

Figure 2.12 Phospholipid bilayer

Another biologically important lipid that I will mention here is wax. Waxes have a variety of functions, but they are generally involved in whole or in part as a water-proofing substance by both plants and animals. This water-proofing is, of course, due to the hydrophobic nature of the hydrogen-coated carbon chain. Wax molecules are structurally similar to fatty acids.

The last lipids on my list are the steroids. Briefly, steroids have two general functions. The first is hormonal (chemical messengers). Several hormones are steroids. Secondly, cholesterol (a steroid) plays a role in the structure of cell membranes. All steroids consist of four carbon rings and a hydrophobic tail of some sort. Figure 2.14 is the structure of cholesterol, which often serves as a precursor to many other steroid hormones.

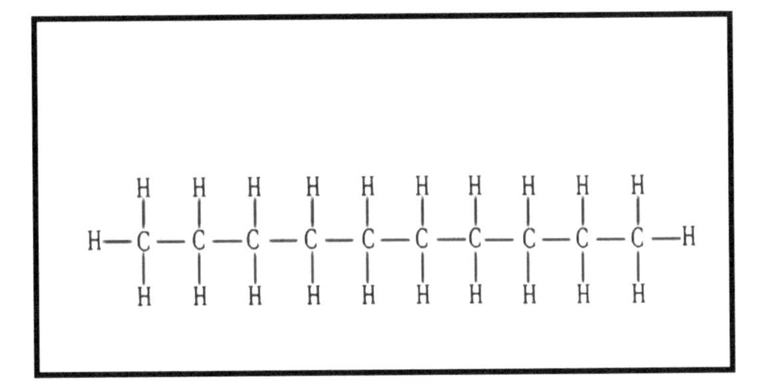

Figure 2.13 One type of wax

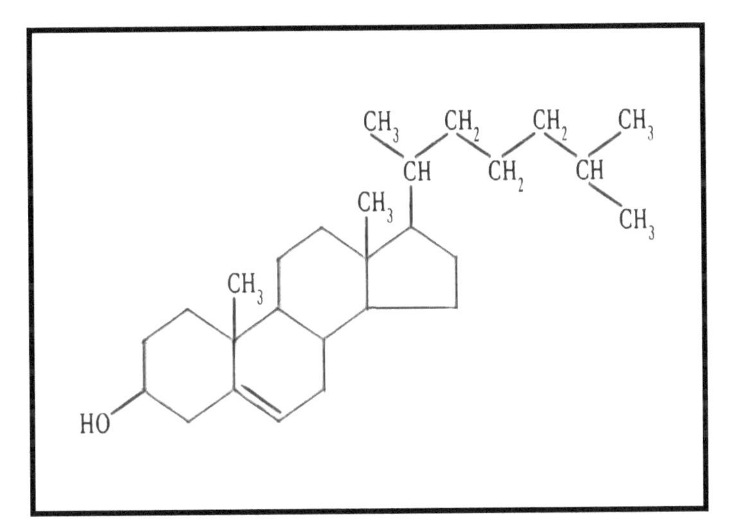

Figure 2.14 Cholesterol

PROTEINS

Now, without carbohydrates and lipids, life would simply be impossible. In fact, all the biomolecules described in this text are essential to life in countless ways. Nevertheless, if I had to pick the MVB (most valuable biomolecules) that are responsible for a lot of the architecture and operations of the cell, I'd have to pick proteins.

Proteins are uber-important in the economy of a cell. If I compared a cell to a factory, certain proteins would be the internal structural supports, some would be transport cables, others would be molecular machines (motors, transport vehicles, pumps, mechanized gates, etc.). But the factory employees that run the whole show are also proteins—special kinds of proteins called enzymes.

First, let's examine the protein's structure. The building block or basic unit of proteins is the **amino acid**. Figure 2.15 is a generalized amino acid.

H
H
O
H—N—C—C—OH
R
Amino Group
Side Chain
Carboxyl Group

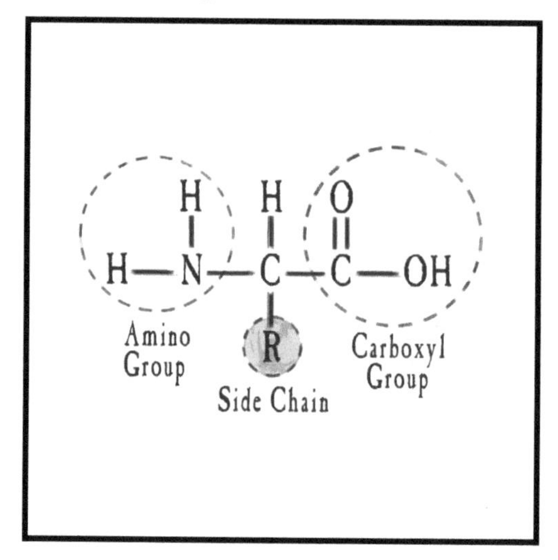

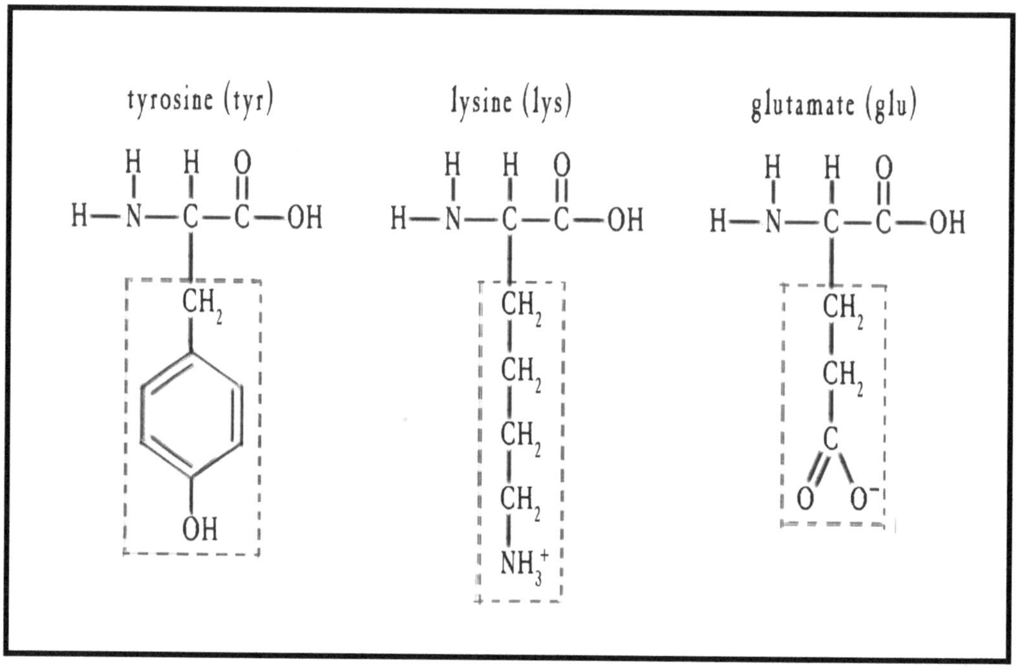

Figure 2.15 Generalized amino acid

There are 20 different kinds of amino acids found in proteins but they all have the upper portion in common: the amino group, the alpha-carbon, and the carboxyl group. The R-side chain is where each type of amino acid differs from each other.

Below in Figure 2.16 are examples of three different kinds of amino acids.

Just like carbohydrates and lipids, amino acids can be linked together

tyrosine (tyr)
lysine (lys)
glutamate (glu)

Figure 2.16 Three amino acids

by dehydration synthesis reactions to form chains. The bond linking two amino acids together is called a peptide bond. In Figure 2.17, the peptide bond is boxed.

Two amino acids joined together are called a **dipeptide**, three are called a **tripeptide**, and so on. A few hooked together are an **oligopeptide**. When there are fewer than one hundred amino acids but you don't feel like counting them, it's a **polypeptide.** If it has one hundred or more amino acids, then it's considered a **protein.**

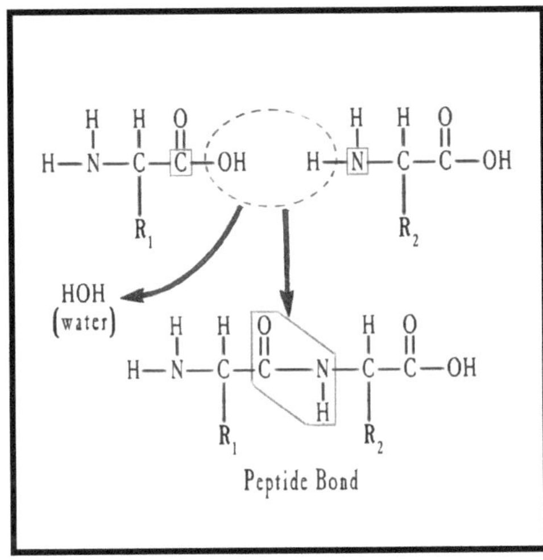

Figure 2.17 Peptide bond formation

Because proteins have an enormous array of functions as mentioned above, these long chains are certainly not homogeneous. Proteins aren't long straight molecules. The R group side chains have a variety of different chemical properties ranging from hydrophobic to hydrophilic, negative to positive, etc.; plus they can be ordered in countless ways. Because each type of amino acid has these chemical differences, the order of amino acids greatly affects how the protein folds on itself and how it interacts with its chemical environment. For instance, different amino acids along the chain may hydrogen bond with each other forming bends and kinks in the chain.

One type of amino acid (cysteine) has an SH group on it. If two SH groups from cysteines on different parts of the chain come in contact with each other, they can react and form a covalent bond called a disulfide linkage, thus putting a semi-permanent hairpin kink in the chain.

Some of the folding patterns form corkscrew sections in the chain called alpha helices. Other parts of a protein may form a number of zigzag stretches lined up parallel to each other. Hairpin turns between these zigzag stretches allow them to be parallel to each other. Hydrogen bonds form in a number of places along these stretches, thus stabilizing these patterns. This arrangement is called a beta-pleated sheet.

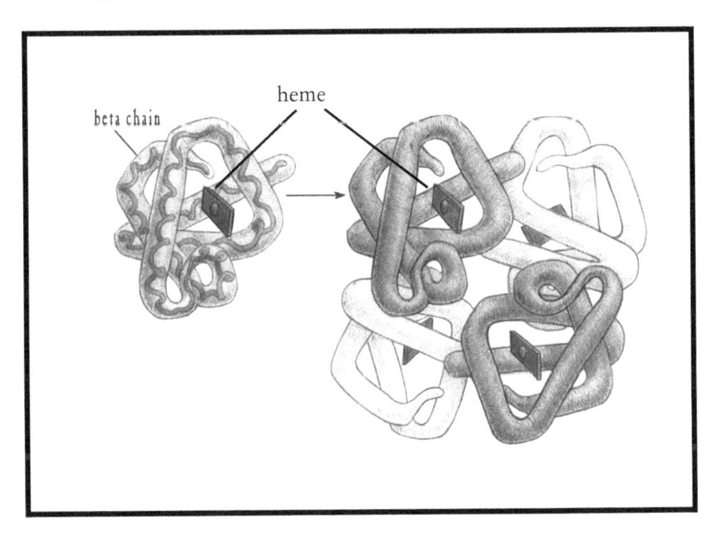

Figure 2.18 Hemoglobin

So the sequence of amino acids in the chain determines how the protein will fold (loops, hairpins, alpha helix, beta-pleated sheet). The various folding patterns of the entire protein determine its overall three-dimensional shape and its shape determines its function. This is easy to understand if we consider tools. A screwdriver, a hammer, and a saw each has a particular 3D shape and their shape determines their function.

To really drive this point home I will discuss one familiar protein called hemoglobin. It is the protein that fills our red blood cells and carries and delivers oxygen to the body. A large protein as far as proteins go, hemoglobin is actually made of four protein chains hooked together to form a bigger 4-part protein. There are two alpha chains (each having 141 amino acids) and two beta chains (each having 146 amino acids). The amino acid sequence of each chain, how the chains are fitted together, and how the chains are hooked to the oxygen-carrying 'heme' group give hemoglobin its particular 3D shape. This, in turn, determines the job of hemoglobin as an oxygen-carrier.

The total number of amino acids in hemoglobin is 574. If even one amino acid is replaced by another with different properties, it may slightly or greatly alter the shape of the protein, which will then slightly or greatly diminish (or enhance) its oxygen-carrying ability. This demonstrates how the sequence of amino acids is paramount in determining a protein's function. Even seemingly insignificant changes can greatly hinder its function. In fact, many congenital defects are the result of one wrong amino acid within an otherwise correct sequence of many amino acids.

Here is an incomplete list of jobs that proteins are responsible for:

- Structural components (keratin, collagen, etc.)
- Oxygen and CO_2 transport (hemoglobin)
- Long-distance chemical messengers (protein hormones)
- Short-distance chemical messengers (protein neurotransmitters)
- Immunity (antibodies)
- Membrane transport (membrane proteins)
- Metabolic (synthetic and digestive) reactions (enzymes)
- Locomotion (flagellar proteins)
- Muscle contraction (contractile proteins)

The list goes on and on.

NUCLEIC ACIDS

The last major group of biomolecules that we will cover is the nucleic acids. This group includes the familiar DNA and RNA. It has become household knowledge that these famous biomolecules are "genetic blueprints" loaded with genetic information. In modern parlance, they are genetic software coding for how an organism is to be constructed from the ground (one cell) up. All this is true as far as it goes, but since we're here, we get to dig into more details.

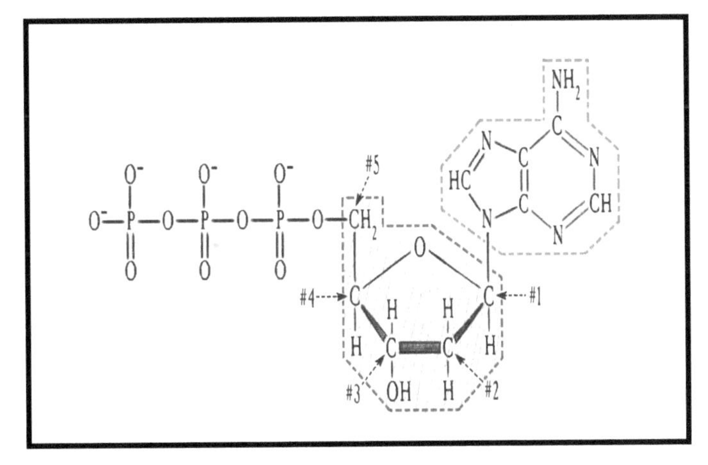

Figure 2.19 Nucleotide

Let's begin as we usually do—with the building blocks. Both DNA and RNA are composed of basic units called **nucleotides**. The one complicating factor to nucleotides is that they are composed of yet three smaller building blocks: a simple sugar or monosaccharide (ribose or deoxyribose) (red), a phosphate (PO_4-) (yellow), and nitrogenous base (blue).

There are five different types of nitrogenous bases: adenine, thymine, guanine, cytosine, and uracil. These three molecules are hooked together to generate a nucleotide (see Figure 2.19). (Note that a fully formed nucleotide will have three phosphates. This is necessary because the covalent bonds between the phosphates have a lot of energy and that energy is used to link nucleotides together).

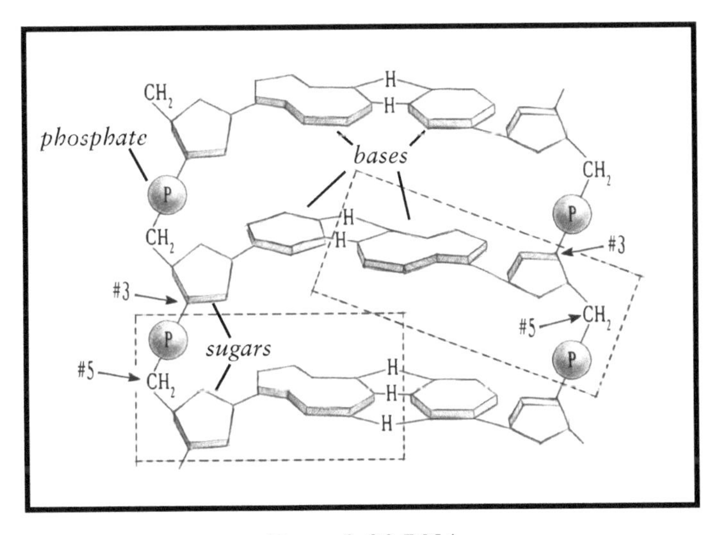

Figure 2.20 DNA

Nucleotides are linked together to form long DNA or RNA chains. Note that the phosphate is attached to the #5 carbon (on its own sugar) but the free end of the phosphate attaches to the #3 carbon of the next nucleotide's sugar. The boxed areas contain one nucleotide each (Figure 2.20).

This is DNA. Note that this kind of nucleic acid is double-stranded (two chains of nucleotides running side by side). The nitrogenous bases dangle to the side of each strand and hydrogen bond with the adjacent nitrogenous bases of the neighboring strand, thus forming something like rungs on a ladder. The poles of the ladder are the alternating sugars and phosphates formed from a chain of nucleotides. RNA is put together similarly except that the sugar is slightly different; it has one different nitrogenous base (uracil instead of thymine), and it is usually single-stranded. We will discuss DNA and RNA in more detail later on in the book.

Besides using nucleotides as building blocks for our genetic software, we use one nucleotide as cellular 'rechargeable batteries'. We call it ATP or Adenosine Triphosphate. There will be more on this wonderful molecule later.

Lastly, we use modified nucleotides to make molecules called NADH, NADPH, and $FADH_2$. Their full names are mouthfuls, so I will leave them abbreviated. For now, suffice it to say that they are used extensively to shuttle electrons around in important metabolic processes like cellular respiration and photosynthesis. Again, I will burden you with these wonderful details later on.

This ends my introduction of the four classes of major biomolecules. Keep in mind that there are many other essential molecules for life that don't fit neatly (or at all) into these four classes of biomolecules. For instance, cofactors and coenzymes come to mind off the top of my head. But it's important for me to limit the content of this text (for your sake and mine) so that you can learn these things without being completely overwhelmed.

CHAPTER 2: REVIEW QUESTIONS

1. What are the 'TinkerToy rules' for carbon, hydrogen, oxygen, nitrogen, phosphorus, and sulfur?

2. Name the four main biomolecule categories.

3. Name the building blocks of each of the above groups.

4. Name one example of a disaccharide.

5. Two examples of polysaccharides.

6. Draw glucose, glycerol, a fatty acid, an amino acid, and a stick figure of a nucleotide (using a circle for the phosphate, a pentagon for the sugar, and a rectangle for the nitrogenous base).

7. Draw glucose doing a dehydration synthesis reaction with another glucose forming a disaccharide. Label the glycosidic linkage.

8. Draw a glycerol doing a dehydration synthesis reaction with a fatty acid to form a monoglyceride.

9. Draw a stick figure of a phospholipid and label the hydrophobic tails and the hydrophilic head. Why is the head hydrophilic?

10. Draw a short section of a phospholipid bilayer.

11. Draw an amino acid doing a dehydration synthesis reaction with another amino acid to form a dipeptide. Label the peptide bond.

12. A chain of 60 amino acids is called a ______.

13. Draw hydrolysis reactions separating the disaccharide, the monoglyceride, and the dipeptide.

14. Using the stick figure form of a nucleotide, draw four nucleotides hooked together.

15. Describe how the sequence of amino acids relates to the function of the protein.

16. Name five different types of jobs done by proteins.

17. Name two functions of nucleotides other than storing genetic information.

CHAPTER 3

A SHORT HISTORY OF MICROSCOPY

A SHORT HISTORY OF DISCOVERING THE CELL AND OTHER MINUTE CREATURES

The invention of the compound microscope (around 1600) is tangled up with the invention of the telescope, which is understandable since they both work similarly. For the record, although Galileo is sometimes credited with the invention of the telescope, it was really one of the following Dutch spectacle-makers: Hans Janssen, his son Zacharias Janssen, or Hans Lippershey. Unfortunately none of these chaps ever published scientific observations with the use of their invention. Galileo, inspired by the invention of these Dutchmen, was able to construct a higher quality telescope of his own in 1609. However, he wasn't particularly interested in the little world about him. He was much more inclined to turn this wonderful instrument toward the heavens, which changed the course of astronomy forever. While most were preoccupied with astronomical and military applications of the telescope, there were men who turned their attention to the diminutive rather than distant. I am not sure how or exactly when the microscope was invented but it is generally assumed that it was some sort of jerry-rigging of a telescope. Credit for the first published microscopic illustrations goes to an Italian scientist named Francesco Stelluti. Stelluti published his engravings of the bee and the weevil in 1630, and they are the first biological illustrations as seen through a microscope.

A few decades later in England, an amazing scientific virtuoso named **Robert Hooke** developed a microscope of his own based on the principles he learned from previous inventions. In 1665 he published his drawings and descriptions of his various microscopic subjects, ranging from insects, sponges, and cork tissue, in a book called *Micrographia*. Figure 3.1 is a picture of his microscope.

His most well-know contribution to biological terminology is the term 'cell' which he coined in the pages of his book. When he examined cork tissue under the microscope he noticed that the cork tissue was composed of many square or rectangular chambers which reminded him of the little rooms in a monastery (the Latin word for little rooms is *cellulae*). He thus applied the term 'cell' to these compartments, and it definitely stuck.

Antony van Leeuwenhoek will also hold a place in the history of microscopes but keep in mind that he did not invent them either. He was Robert Hooke's contemporary and was born in Delft, Holland in 1632 to a couple who were well-off tradespeople and members of the Reformed Church. His father was a basket-maker and his mother a brewer. When he was sixteen years old he was sent to a shop in Amsterdam to learn the trade of linen-draper (a dealer in cloth and sometimes in clothing and dry goods). He learned the trade well and eventually returned to Delft in the mid-1600s where he married, bought a house and shop, and opened his own business as a draper and haberdasher (a dealer in men's clothing and accessories). Before 1668 he learned how to grind lenses and started to make simple microscopes to view the Lilliputian world around him. This new hobby was inspired by looking at Robert Hooke's illustrated book *Micrographia*.

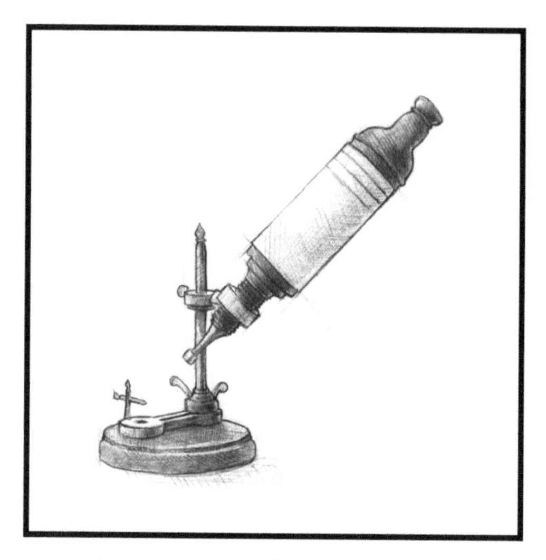

Figure 3.1 Hooke's microscope

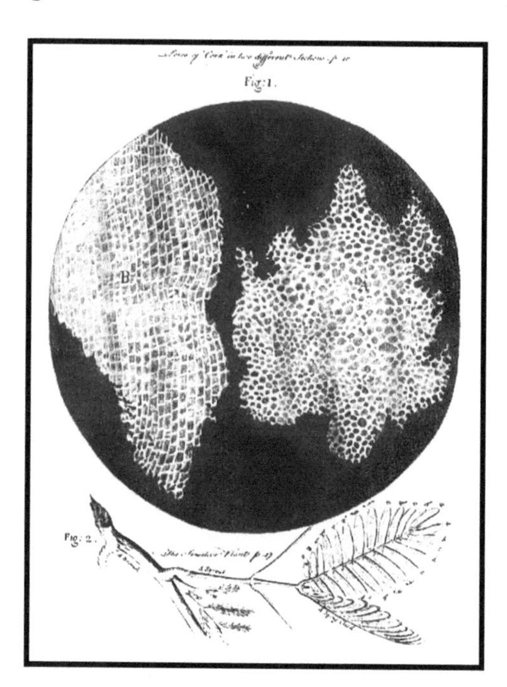

Figure 3.2 Hooke's drawing of cork cells

Even though Hooke's microscope was compound (two lenses) it had certain yet-unsolved technical problems that limited magnification to about 20 to 30 times. Somehow, Leeuwenhoek's lens grinding skill enabled him to build a microscope (with a single lens!) that was able to magnify objects over 200 times. This is amazing, since it's really not a compound microscope. It's really a tiny magnifying glass mounted in a brass plate. To look through it, you put your eye very close to the lens as if you were looking through a tiny keyhole in a miniature brass door. Specimens were mounted on an adjustable sharp point on the other side of the lens. A picture of his microscope is shown below.

This simple yet powerful design coupled with his patience, extraordinary eyesight, and finesse at adjusting the lighting, opened up a world of microbes which he affectionately called animalcules. His descriptions and sketches (he actually hired an artist to draw them) included what we know today as nematodes, rotifers, algae, protozoa, blood cells, sperm cells, and even bacteria. It wasn't until almost 200 years later that compound microscopes were improved enough to clearly observe bacteria. Excited at his own discoveries, Antony van Leeuwenhoek sent his descriptions to the Royal Society. The Royal Society asked Robert Hooke to confirm the Dutchman's observations, which he did. Hooke was quite impressed that Leeuwenhoek's simple contraption surpassed his own compound microscope in magnification and clarity. However, he was not keen on using it. He found it difficult to use and offensive to his eye. I've looked through a replica of Leeuwenhoek's scope myself, and I agree with Hooke. Although he was a member of the Royal Society and became a scientific hero of Holland, keep in mind that all his biological contributions were done as a hobbyist. He continued his work as a draper but also did some work as a surveyor and wine assayer. He even spent some time as a minor city official. He lived in the same house he bought in the 1650s for the rest of his long life and died in 1723 at the age of 90. If you would like to know more about this fascinating man, read *Antony van Leeuwenhoek and His 'Little Animals'* by Clifford Dobell.

Figure 3.3 Antony van Leeuwenhoek

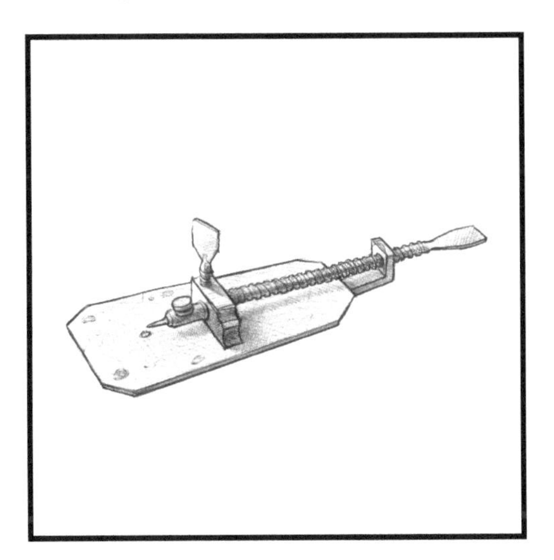

Figure 3.4 Leeuwenhoek's microscope

For the next 200 years no sudden jumps occurred in the field of microscopy. There was, however a gradual and steady advancement in the science of optics and the mechanics of microscope design and the technical limitations in magnification were overcome. Nonetheless, microscopes were not much more than a curiosity and a hobby for those who took some interest. There was an awareness of microbes from the time of Leeuwenhoek but no one seriously considered these animalcules as having tremendous human significance.

Thanks to the advancement in microscope design, biology began to pick up a lot of momentum in the mid to late 1800s. While Louis Pasteur, Robert Koch, and others were figuring out that many diseases were caused by certain microbes (germ theory), two German biologists were microscopically studying the fundamental nature of animal and plant tissue. These men were **Theodor Schwann** and **Matthias Schleiden**. Theodor Schwann was a German physiologist who made several important biological discoveries and is considered the father of cytology (the study of cells). Over dinner (a great place for sharing ideas) he was discussing his research with a botanist by the name of Matthias Schleiden. They both found that their observations in animal tissue (Schwann) and plant tissue (Schleiden) had a common theme which they decided to distill as the **cell theory** in 1839.

Today we take these facts for granted, but during this exciting time of discovery, all of biology was on the frontier and all biologists were pioneers. The two major tenets supported by a preponderance of their observational evidence is that 1) all living things are composed of cells and 2) cells were the fundamental structural and functional unit of all living things. About 20 years later another German biologist (though he trafficked in many other disciplines) by the name of **Rudolf Virchow** also contributed a third tenet to the cell theory. He proposed that all cells arise from pre-existing cells. Ironically, this tenet has to be disputed by both creationists and evolutionists regarding the very first cell or cells. Creationists believe that when God created life, all the cells composing living creatures did not come from pre-existing cells. They came from nothing (*ex nihilo*) or from some rearrangement of pre-existing matter by the power of God. Naturalistic evolutionists argue that all life arose from one or a few single-celled life forms which somehow assembled themselves from non-living matter by naturalistic processes in the primordial soup. But, with regard to day-to-day biology, neither worldview takes issue with the third tenet.

This has been a very brief history of biology focusing on the advent of the microscope, but if you're a history buff and want more of this sort of thing, I would like to direct your attention to two good books dealing particularly with the history of microbiology that make the story come alive: *Microbe Hunters* by Paul de Krief and *Microbes and Men* by Robert Reid.

CHAPTER 3: REVIEW QUESTIONS

1. What other invention was closely associated with the microscope?
2. Who was the English scientist who coined the term "cell"? What Latin word is cell derived from? Why did he pick that term?
3. Who was the Dutchman who viewed microscopic life with a microscope of his own making? In what century did he make these observations? What did he call these life forms?
4. What are the three tenets of the Cell Theory?
5. Who were the three men who composed this theory?

CHAPTER 4

INTRODUCTION TO CELL BASICS

When you observe a cell from your body (say one of your cheek cells) under a typical light microscope, three basic parts become apparent: the **cell membrane**, **cytoplasm**, and **nucleus**. The cell membrane is the edge or boundary of the cell which plays a vital role in the import of oxygen and nutrients and export of cell products and waste. The cytoplasm is the fluid of the cell in which many other functional compartments (organelles) are submerged. Lastly, the nucleus is the master control center of the cell in which is housed the DNA (the biomolecule that bears all the genetic software programs of the entire organism).

There are two general cellular formats that God created for composing all organisms. The first is the **prokaryotic cell**. This is the cell type of bacteria and blue-green algae. These cells are usually smaller than 10 μm and do not possess membrane-bound organelles or a membrane-bound nucleus. They do have DNA but it is not surrounded by a nuclear envelope. Many different processes occur in the cytoplasm of the prokaryotic cell but they manage to keep things running smoothly without compartmentalizing the cell as eukaryotic cells do. The prokaryotic cell can be likened to a one-room school house, in that grades K-12 can be going on in the same room at the same time and still get the job done. The **eukaryotic cell**, on the other hand, is usually larger than 10 μm, has a membrane-bound nucleus and membrane-bound organelles. These organelles compartmentalize the various 'goings on' in the cell such as transport, digestion, energy production, and manufacture. These different processes are quite specialized and require their own set of enzymes which work more efficiently if physically separated from other entirely different processes. As a prokaryotic cell is like a one-room school house, the eukaryotic cell is like a university. All the different classes occur in different classrooms (or different classes in the same room at different times). It would be a drag if you were trying to learn Biology, Calculus, and English Lit at the same time in the same room.

The separation of different classes is a good thing and so is the separation of different processes within the cell. This type of compartmentalized (eukaryotic) cell makes up the fabric of all other life forms such as single-celled protozoa, algae, fungi, plants, and animals.

CELL SIZE

Why are cells so small? I should point out a few exceptions. Some cells can be seen with the naked eye (mostly plant cells), others are exceedingly long but microscopically thin (some neurons), and some are simply huge like the yolk of a bird's egg (consider an ostrich egg yolk). But there is a reason why most eukaryotic cells fall within the microscopic range of 10 to 100 μm (one thousand micrometers equals one millimeter). Actually there is more than one reason but I will discuss an important physical constraint that necessitates their small size. Suppose we have a sphere that is 0.5 cm in diameter. Its surface area would be 0.79 cm^2 and its volume would be 0.06 cm^3. Keep in mind that diameter is one dimension, surface area is two dimensions, and volume is three dimensions. If we simply double our sphere's diameter to 1.0 cm, what happens to the surface area and the volume? The surface area will be 3.14 cm^2 and the volume will be 0.52 cm^3. Compare the numbers and look at what occurred. Although we only doubled the diameter, the surface area of 3.14 cm^2 is almost four times greater than the original surface area of 0.79 cm^2. If we triple the original diameter to 1.5 cm, the surface area will be 7.07 cm^2 (almost nine times the original surface area), but the volume will be 1.77 cm^3 (which is almost 30 times the original volume of 0.06 cm^3). What are the implications of this? The cell is a living entity and as such it needs nutrients for fuel and raw materials for the manufacture of its goods. It also requires oxygen to burn its fuel for energy and needs to rid itself of various wastes including carbon dioxide. In other words, there is a lot of stuff that needs to get in and a lot of stuff that needs to go out (import and export). The cell membrane constitutes the surface area of the cell and serves as the import/export surface of the cell. If we increase

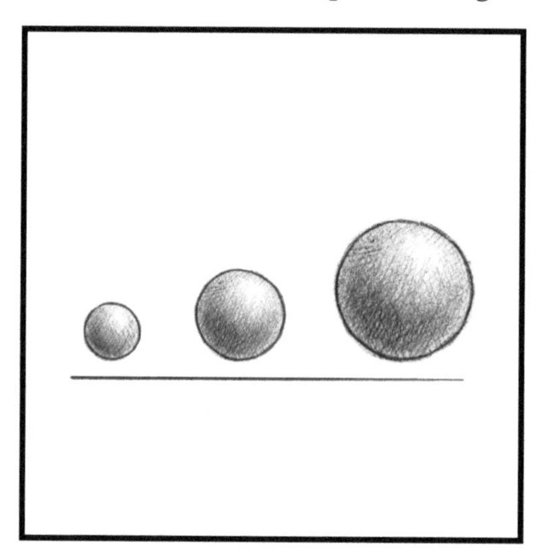

Figure 4.1 Surface-to-volume ratio

the cell diameter, the volume and the surface area (cell membrane) increases, but the volume increases to a much greater degree than the surface area. Look at the table below: three times the diameter, nine times the surface area, and thirty times the volume. Since cells die if they don't have their metabolic demands met, an overly big cell will have an inordinately large mass (mass is directly related to volume) that is proportionally way too big for its own cell membrane to meet its metabolic demands . . . so, consequently, cells are dinky. The only way for cells to be large and get around this problem is for them to have a shape that maximizes surface area and minimizes volume, or has very low metabolic demands. In other words, long, skinny, or branching cells.

diameter (cm)	0.5	1.0	1.5
surface area (cm^2)	0.79	3.14	7.07
volume (cm^3)	0.06	0.52	1.77
surface-to-volume ratio	13.17:1	6.04:1	3.99:1

Another reason cells are small is that there is a greater potential for division of labor. If you were made of ten cells each being the size of a volleyball, even if there was no surface area to volume problem, you would be . . . well . . . severely limited in your activities. You couldn't think, talk, walk, see, taste, eat, touch, or hear, just to name a few. Trillions of small cells allow you to have many different kinds of cells which can form a variety of tissues, these different tissues can form organs, and different organs can form organ systems, and different organ systems are all wonderfully integrated to form a body that enables you to do everything you do.

CELL MEMBRANES

Cell membranes are wonderful dynamic linings that form the boundary of each cell. As I mentioned earlier, biomolecules called phospholipids are an essential ingredient that form a large portion of cell membranes. They interact with the watery interior and exterior of the cell such that the hydrophilic heads of all the phospholipids line the inner and outer surface of the cell membrane while all the hydrophobic (fatty acid) tails form the inside of the membrane. But cell membranes are not 100% phospholipids. Many different proteins are imbedded in various ways in the phospholipid bilayer like icebergs floating in a sea with its two parallel surfaces facing away from each other (work with me here). Some of the icebergs may span the layer of water and poke out of both surfaces. Other icebergs might poke out of the outer surface or out of the inner surface. The phospholipid bilayer (like the layer of water) is fluid, so the proteins bob and drift about the phospholipid ocean; they aren't locked rigidly in one place. Because the proteins are surrounded by phospholipids just like pieces of tile are surrounded by plaster in a mosaic, this understanding of the cell membrane has been named the **fluid mosaic model** ('fluid' because the phospholipids are fluid unlike the plaster in a real mosaic). The functions of these membrane proteins will be discussed after we describe how substances naturally move about in both gaseous and aqueous environments.

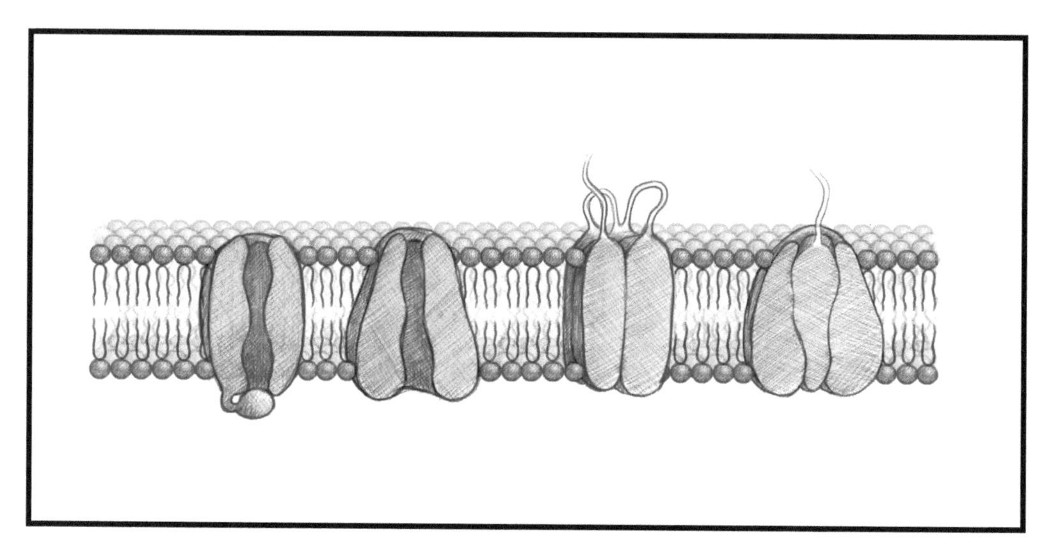

Figure 4.2 Cell membrane

DIFFUSION

To really get a handle on how cells work on such a tiny scale, it is essential to know some of the physical principles that God has established governing the behavior of gases and fluids. But first I would like to lay some philosophical groundwork, while mentioning the 'big britchiness' of science. Science is very useful and has done great things and made great discoveries that have benefited mankind in countless ways. However, when science describes how matter behaves (gravity, light, magnetism, electricity, etc.) and harnesses it to man's benefit, we must constantly remind ourselves that science has not at all explained why matter does what it does at the atomic and molecular level. Science describes and measures fundamental properties of matter but does not explain them. For instance, on earth a falling object accelerates toward the earth at 9.8 meters per second squared. This is a very useful piece of information for aeronautical science but this description doesn't tell us a single thing about what gravity is. We are in the same boat regarding all fundamental properties of matter. I could go on and on about the wonderful technologies have been established by accurately describing, measuring, and manipulating physical properties, but in the end we are doing just that . . . "describing, measuring, and manipulating." We still cannot explain them. It would be best to say that the fundamental properties of matter behave that way because God created these properties to behave in a certain predictable way such that we can scientifically study and harness them in many practical ways. We say protons are positive and electrons are negative and that opposites attract. Good for us! What's positive? What's negative? Why do opposites attract? We could even say that all physical properties are God's magic. Not arbitrary and capricious magic, but normal, ordinary, measurable, predicable, and usable magic. Magic, in this sense, doesn't mean we can't study it with the scientific method. It simply means that we can't explain matter's behavior at the most fundamental level. And that should point us to God. John 1:1-3: "In the beginning was the Word, and the Word was with God, and the Word was God. He was with God in the beginning. Through him all things were made; without him nothing was made that has been made." Colossians 1:17: "He is before all things, and in him all things hold together."

Please keep the above in mind as I describe the process of diffusion. It helps to know that diffusion is one of the most familiar processes that we observe on a daily basis. Putting on deodorant or perfume, steeping tea bags, or smelling a road kill skunk half a mile down the road are several ways that we've all experienced diffusion. **Diffusion** is the movement of a substance from an area of high concentration to an area of low concentration. Let's take our dead skunk as an example. In the vicinity of the unfortunate mammal there is a high concentration of stink molecules. Your nose, a half mile away, has a low concentration of stink molecules. These nasty molecules diffuse from the area of high concentration toward your nose (and in every other direction) until the odor molecules have evenly dispersed themselves over a vast area (at that point the concentration is so low no one can smell it). If the skunk was in a closed room the stink molecules would eventually diffuse until the molecules are evenly distributed such that the concentrations are equal in every part of the room. When this occurs **equilibrium** has been reached. Diffusion occurs because molecules have an innate ability to randomly move about in three dimensions (this is one of those properties that we can describe and name but we can't explain). This movement is called **Brownian motion**. There are three major factors affecting diffusion rates.

1. If the thermal energy (temperature) of the substance is increased, then Brownian motion increases; if the thermal energy is decreased, then Brownian motion decreases. In other words, if it's hot, diffusion speeds up, and if it's cold, diffusion slows down. I suppose that's why we say 'chill' if we want someone to slow down mentally or physically. To demonstrate this principle put one tea bag in a glass of calm boiling hot water and at the same time put another tea bag in a glass of calm ice cold water (do not jerk the bags around) and watch the diffusion rates. Which glass of water got the tea molecules diffusing quickly? By the way, the water is also diffusing from high to low. Outside the tea bags the water concentration is high and in the tea bags the water concentration is low. The water diffused into the tea bags from high to low just like it's supposed to.

2. The second factor that affects diffusion rate is concentration. This is intuitively obvious. Suppose a young lady lacking discretion puts on perfume in a Baptistic style (i.e., by immersion). In this case the concentration of perfume is exceedingly high on the surface of her body, and (you guessed it) the diffusion rates are much faster. In fact, it only takes just a second or two for everyone in the room to be bowled over by the invisible yet rapidly advancing plume of perfume molecules. Conversely, a small dab (a lower concentration) of perfume doesn't diffuse nearly as fast.

3. The third factor is molecular size. If a substance has a large molecule size (more atoms), then the diffusion rate will be slower. Although this is less intuitively obvious it is easy to remember. Who usually moves faster on the basketball court, the big guys or the little guys? Yes, the little guys. So remember that in the same way substances composed of small molecules diffuse faster under the same conditions as substances of larger molecular size.

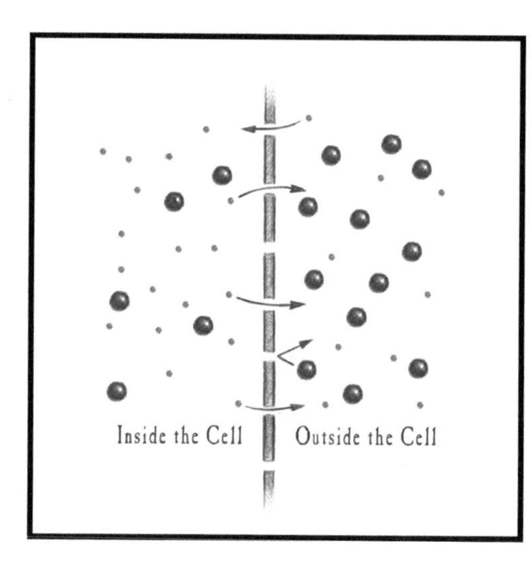

Figure 4.3 Osmosis

OSMOSIS

When a solid, liquid, or gas is dissolved in water (or some other liquid) the latter is referred to as the **solvent** and the dissolved substance is called the **solute**. Together they form a **solution**. Example: Kool-aid powder is the solute, water is the solvent, and Kool-aid drink is the solution. If the atoms or molecules are not locked up in a crystalline lattice or the temperature is not absolute zero (at absolute zero there is no Brownian motion), every substance moves from high to low concentration (there are other factors that interfere with diffusion like electrical charges, polarity, etc.). This means diffusion also applies to water (the biological solvent). When water diffuses across a semipermeable membrane (from high to low water concentration) it is referred to as **osmosis**. The semipermeable membrane can be artificial like dialysis tubing or be a natural cell membrane (phospholipid bilayer with membrane proteins). **Semipermeable** means that some substances can freely pass through the membrane while other substances cannot. This is usually because some molecules are too large to pass through the tiny openings. In Figure 4.3, the small particles represent water, the vertical line with openings in it is the semipermeable membrane, and the larger particles represent some solute (say glucose) that cannot pass through the membrane. These molecules are constantly moving due to Brownian motion. In their perpetual random wanderings the water (small) is able to pass through the membrane because it can fit through the openings, but the glucose (large) can't fit through the openings. In the figure, which side has a higher concentration of water? If you chose the left side you are smarter than the average bear. Now if we apply the principle of diffusion to water, which way will the water move (remember that substances move from an area of high concentration to one of low concentration). Since water is higher on the left side and lower on the right, and the water is small enough to pass through the openings, there will be a net movement of water from the left side to the right. Do you follow me so far? If not, read it again. Now suppose the left side was a portion of a cell, the right was the outside of the cell, and the semipermeable membrane was the cell membrane. Since the water will mostly move from left to right it would mean that the cell would be losing water.

TONICITY

Tonicity refers to the concentration of the solute in water outside the cell. In Figure 4.3, the outside of the cell has a higher concentration of the solute, glucose (large dots). This condition would be called **hypertonic** because the solute is high (hyper) outside the cell (keep in mind that wherever the solute concentration is relatively high, the water concentration is relatively low). As I mentioned earlier, the water would move out of the cell, so we can conclude that cells placed in a hypertonic solution would lose water. An easy way to remember that cells lose water when placed in a hypertonic solution is that the 'e' in 'hyper' looks like a shriveled cell. This shriveling of cells due to the loss of water is called **plasmolysis**. On the other hand, if the solute concentration on the outside of the cell is low (**hypotonic**) (say pure water) relative to the cell's innards (which has all sorts of dissolved stuff in it), which way will the water move? If the outside is pure water (no solutes or very low solutes), the concentration of water is high relative to the inside of the cell, and the water will flood into the cell. Consequently, the cell swells due to the influx of water. (The 'o' in hypotonic resembles an inflated cell.) If the cell has no exterior wall to prevent the over-inflation of the cell, the cell will continue to swell and eventually explode. This is called **cytolysis**. **Hemolysis** is a special term given to the cytolysis of red blood cells. In an **isotonic** solution the solute concentration is the same (*iso*) inside and outside which means that the water concentration would be the same on both sides. Water still moves across the membrane, but there is no net flow of water in or out, and thus the cell stays the same size. Tonicity is extremely important in the lives of cells. The medical profession has learned to be mindful of tonicity (among other things) when dealing with living tissues. For instance, if an IV solution is dripping into a patient's blood stream, it is important that the fluid is isotonic. If the tonicity is too low or too high, hemolysis or plasmolysis can quickly destroy red blood cells.

Turgor pressure is another term which needs mentioning when discussing the effects of tonicity in plant cells. I will discuss the cell wall in plant and a variety of other non-animal cells in more detail later, but I need to mention a few cell wall facts to understand tonicity regarding plant cells. Cell walls are located on the outside of cell membranes and are, to varying degrees, more rigid than the cell membrane. This arrangement is like a trash can (cell wall) is to its plastic trash bag lining (cell membrane). Cell walls are also much more permeable and non-selective than cell membranes. If plant cells are placed in a hypotonic solution, water will flow, as usual, into the cells. But instead of expanding until they burst (cytolysis), the cell wall, like a tire wall resisting the outward expansion of the inflating inner tube, prevents the cell from over-inflating and bursting. We pump up our bicycle tires with air to make them more firm and rigid. In the same way, if we put plant cells into a hypotonic solution, the cells will inflate until they become very firm. They won't undergo cytolysis because the cell wall allows the cell to become more pressurized without popping than cells lacking a cell wall. The pressure within the cell due to the influx of water is called turgor pressure. Turgor pressure is similar to PSI tire pressure except the former is water pressure and the latter is air pressure. When plant cells are plump and firm because of high turgor pressure, they are said to be **turgid**. At the familiar level, crisp celery is the result of all its plant cells being turgid. When a plant wilts, that means its plant cells have lost their turgidity. In other words, they have lost too much water (plasmolysis) due to soaking in a hypertonic solution or they have lost water through evaporation. Technically the cells are said to have a low turgor pressure or to have lost their turgidity. This would correspond to flat or almost flat tires.

MEMBRANE FUNCTION

Since diffusion and osmosis are a given, membranes must be designed in such a way to harness the innate Brownian movement of substances to regulate what is going in and out. I mentioned earlier that the cell is like a factory and the cell membrane is its link to the outside world, whether it is air, water, blood, or other neighboring cells. A cell is not autonomous and independent: It must get rid of carbon dioxide and other wastes so it won't poison itself, and it must also export many products that it makes. Moreover, it has to bring in oxygen and nutrients. Some of the nutrients are used for energy production and other nutrients are used as raw materials for the manufacture of cellular products. In short, the cell membrane is responsible to direct all the hurly-burly traffic of all these imports and exports.

Simple diffusion refers to any molecules that have the size and properties that allow them to sneak right across the phospholipid bilayer. This movement can either be going into the cell or leaving it. The word 'diffusion' implies that these molecules are going from a high concentration to a low concentration or *with the concentration gradient*. This phrase is useful because it concisely communicates that a substance is moving from high to low rather than low to high concentration. When a bicycle

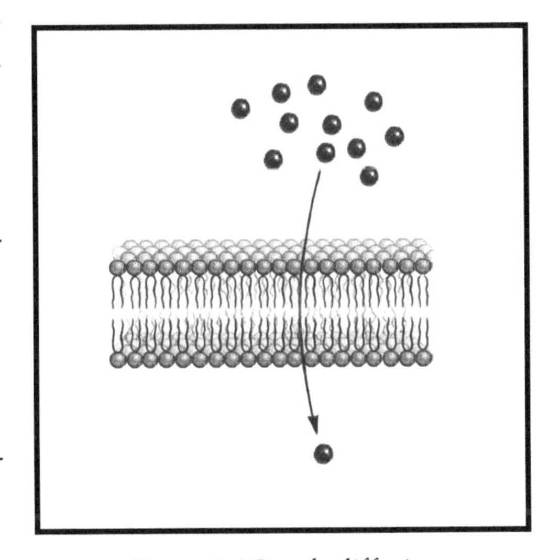

Figure 4.4 Simple diffusion

rolls down hill, it is rolling from high to low elevation, or *with the elevation gradient,* and requires no energy input. Similarly, simple diffusion does not require an input of energy—the movement occurs spontaneously (like a bicycle coasting downhill). The word 'simple' refers to their route through the membrane. They don't require a membrane protein that forms some fancy doorway or gate. They simply zip right across the phospholipid bilayer like mice through a chain link fence. In order for molecules to get directly through the phospholipid bilayer they must be pretty small, non-polar and/ or electrically neutral such as oxygen and carbon dioxide (Figure 4.4).

Water, although it is relatively small (only three atoms), cannot cross a membrane by simple diffusion because it is too polar. The hydrophobic fatty acid interior of the phospholipid bilayer can't abide polar molecules. Consequently, water must use a protein that is designed to form a channel through the membrane. Other molecules have gates that are designed more like a revolving door that receives the molecule on one side, rotates, and deposits the molecule on the other side. This type of diffusion is called **passive transport** or **facilitated diffusion.** Passive refers to the fact that no energy is required to move the molecule across the membrane. Since the molecule is *flowing* from high to low concentration, (like water through a dam) the cell doesn't need to expend any energy to move the molecule across. Like simple diffusion, the movement is *with the concentration gradient*, but unlike simple diffusion, the molecules are too big or too polar to sneak across. (It doesn't matter how high the dog concentration is inside a kennel. Dogs don't diffuse through chain link fences; they require a gate or door. Once the door is provided, the higher the concentration of dogs inside, the faster the 'diffusion' will be exiting the kennel.) In the same way these larger molecules require some sort of protein to transport them (or facilitate their diffusion). In Figure 4.5 (above), the black triangles represent larger or polar molecules unable to move by simple diffusion. The gray blobs are protein molecules that span the phospholipid bilayer and form a channel through which the large molecules can pass.

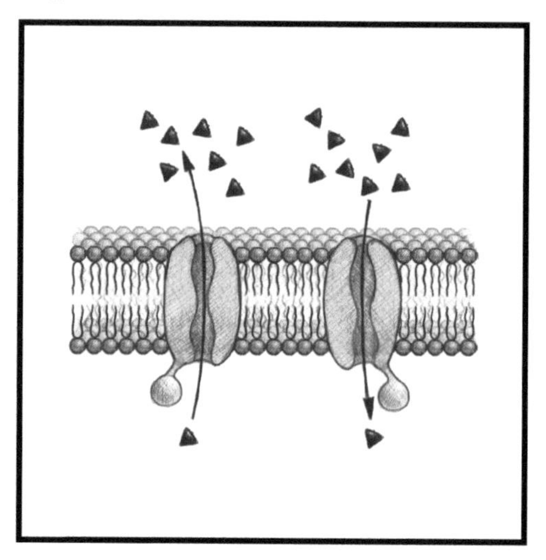

Figure 4.5 Active transport (left) & passive transport (right)

Active transport refers to the movement of molecules that, for one reason or another, need to be moved from an area of low concentration to an area of high concentration. In other words, they need to be moved *against the concentration gradient.* Thus active transport is not diffusion in any sense of the word, because it is movement *against the gradient.* If we refer to the bicycle analogy, pedaling uphill is *against the gradient* and requires an input of energy from your leg muscles chugging away. If molecules are to be pushed *against the gradient* then energy must be expended. In the economy of the cell, the energy currency is usually in the form of ATP (portable and rechargeable battery-like molecules). An ATP molecule delivers enough energy to the carrier or channel protein to pump the molecules across a membrane. You could also think of this as a toll gate. But instead of coin payment, it is ATP (Figure 4.5, left).

ENDOCYTOSIS AND EXOCYTOSIS

When people and other things come in and out of buildings, most of the movement takes place through doors. Think of passive and active transport as doorway movement, the latter being a tollgate. But some things are too big to get through a door. Buildings designed to move big items in and out have loading docks. Cells of course don't have loading docks, but they are designed to move large molecules or even bigger stuff across their membranes. Stuff that is too big to use a protein channel or carrier requires a fancy process called exocytosis or endocytosis.

If one considers all the proteins required and what they do, it would be mind-boggling and way beyond the scope of this text. However, a simplified overview is quite easy to grasp. In **endocytosis**, a large molecule or even a cell that is to be transported across the membrane attaches to certain protein receptors. This triggers the membrane to form an inpocketing where the attachment occurred. The inpocketing grows deeper and deeper. The inpocketing is often at the tip of a large extension of the cell called a pseudopod (outpocketing of the cell membrane). Or two or more pseudopods ooze out and surround the object to be endocytosed. So whether it's just an inpocketing or an inpocketing with surrounding

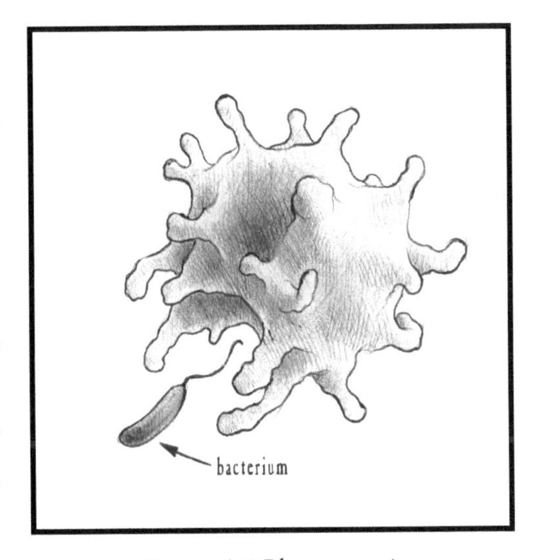

Figure 4.6 Phagocytosis

pseudopods engulfing the object, eventually the cell membrane at the rim of this depression constricts and completely engulfs the object. The membrane that once was part of the cell membrane is now a completely internalized vesicle. There are two forms of endocytosis: **phagocytosis** (cell eating) and **pinocytosis** (cell drinking). These differ from each other more in degree than in kind. During phagocytosis a cell is attempting to engulf entire cells or cell fragments for food, so the process is accomplished at a much larger scale. An example of phagocytosis is when one of our patrolling white blood cells encounters a bacterial cell (Figure 4.6). When it recognizes it as foreign, it completely engulfs and digests it. I will describe the digesting part later.

If the cell is bringing in large dissolved molecules that are too small to be considered phagocytosis but too big to bring in by passive or active transport, it is called pinocytosis (Figure 4.7).

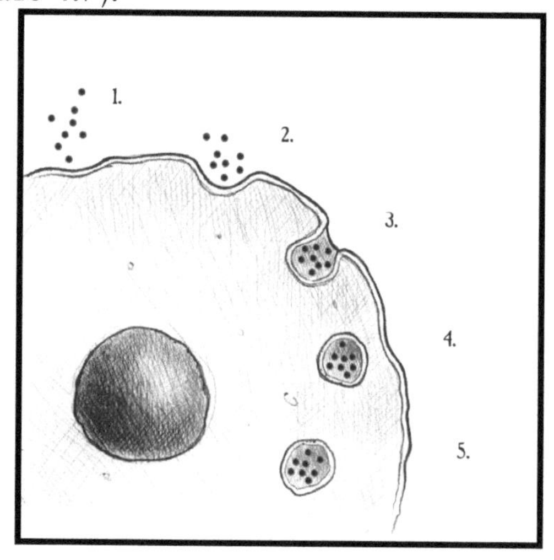

Figure 4.7 Pinocytosis

Exocytosis is essentially the reverse of endocytosis. Exo refers to 'out.' We get the word 'exit' from the same root. In this case, some internal contents need to be ejected as waste or exported as a product needed outside the membrane. The material must be packaged within a vesicle which is then transported to the cell membrane (by internal motor proteins along gondola-like protein cables). The vesicle membrane then fuses with the cell membrane, becoming one. The contents of the vesicle are now released to the outside (Figure 4.8).

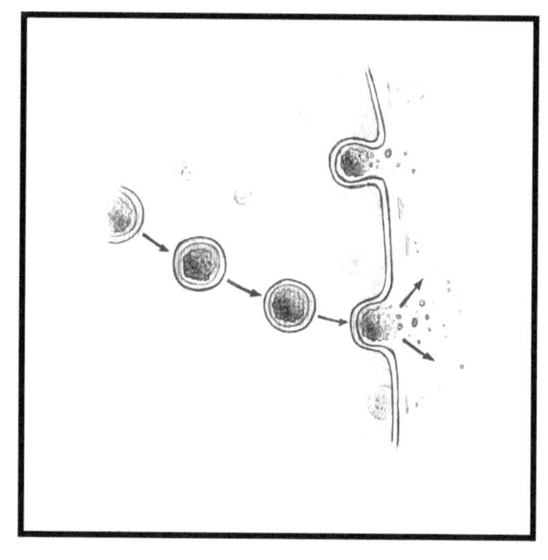

Figure 4.8 Exocytosis

Now that you know something about how substances move about and how cells transport them across membranes, we can explore the dynamic inner-workings of a cell. Keep in mind that there is no such thing as a Platonic cell in the realm of forms—cells in a body are rarely generic. They are usually quite specialized in their occupation, doing some very narrow set of jobs. A multicellular creature (usually made of millions to trillions of cells) exercises division of labor in that all the activities needed to maintain life are parceled out to different cell types, each doing a different function. A unicellular organism has to be proficient at all the activities needed for life. To name a few, it needs to move around to obtain food, maintain proper temperature and moisture, excrete waste, and reproduce itself. We sometimes speak of one-celled critters as simple. Nothing could be further from the truth. If anything, they are more complex than any one of our body cells because they have to do it all. Because multicellular creatures have many different cell types each doing different jobs it is understandable that these cell types will differ a lot in their internal and external structure and function. There are certain 'common denominator' characteristics that all cells share, but beyond that cells will differ in their size and shape and how they connect with their neighbors. The function of a certain cell type is in part often dependent on the three-dimensional layout of the tissue. For example epithelial cells are designed to line internal and external surfaces, so consequently each cell will be attached to their neighboring cells tightly in patterns reminiscent of brickwork, tile floors, shingled roofs, and siding. It is also very important what the cells are doing functionally. This means that different cell types will vary in the kinds of biochemical processes that are occurring within their innards. This means that different cell types will differ in the numbers and ratios of the various organelles they contain. Even among the organelles shared among all kinds of cells, they often differ in how and what substances they are making and exporting. In short, because groups of cells (tissues) have a variety of different jobs ranging from storing and secreting substances, to providing structural support (cartilage and bone), to lining surfaces, to generating movement (muscle cells), to communicating with others cells (neurons), vast differences in the architecture and activities of cells are required. These differences would be brought to light in a human body textbook. For now, it is important to highlight the standard features of all cells and a few features that may be unique to certain cells but are nonetheless important in understanding life.

CHAPTER 4: REVIEW QUESTIONS

1. How do prokaryotic cells differ from eukaryotic cells regarding: A nucleus? Organelles? Size?

2. What life forms have prokaryotic cells? What life forms have eukaryotic cells?

3. Why can't cells be big? What thing becomes too small relative to the increased mass?

4. Using stick figures for phospholipids and blob-like shapes for proteins; draw a small section of a biological membrane.

5. Define diffusion.

6. What fundamental property of matter causes diffusion?

7. How does concentration, temperature, and molecular size affect diffusion rate?

8. Define osmosis.

9. A substance that is dissolved in a solvent is a ______.

10. If a plant cell is placed in a hypertonic solution, it will lose/gain (circle one) water. This condition is called ______. When this occurs what happens to the turgor pressure?

11. Movement of a substance across a membrane, through a protein gate but against a concentration gradient is called ______.

12. The engulfing of a food particle by a cell so that a food vacuole is formed within the cell containing the food is ______.

CHAPTER 5

ORGANELLES

OF THE EUKARYOTIC CELL

In my overview of the eukaryotic cell I will liken it to a factory. Cells are not static, they are very dynamic—like a factory. They are carrying out many different activities, and they require the energy and materials to do so. They bring in raw materials, and with them build many different products using various machines. They also need design templates to manufacture the various products to be made. They need employees (factory workers) that run, maintain, and operate the machinery. They need transport vehicles to carry raw materials as well as partially or completely assembled products around or out of the cell. Because of these similarities I will use factory terminology to summarize the functions of the important organelles or organelles common to all cells.

CYTOPLASM

Cytoplasm is simply the fluid of the cell (cyto = cell; plasm = fluid). As I mentioned before, cells are very complicated microscopic water balloons. It is the watery or gel-like matrix in which the organelles move about or are suspended in. It is 80-95% water with many dissolved biomolecules in it. Among these molecules are important ions, biomolecules used for fuel or for raw materials needed for manufacturing products, and the biomolecules that function as the factory workers. The latter are the mighty enzymes (catalytic proteins) performing many of the demolition or manufacturing reactions in the cell. There are hundreds of different kinds of enzymes and each has a very specialized job description. An assembly-line worker that screws in one kind of bolt is a good approximation of one kind of enzyme. I will discuss enzymes later on in more detail.

NUCLEUS

The **nucleus** is a relatively large organelle that is often in the middle of the cell but may be situated off to the side depending on the type of cell. It is exceedingly important in that it contains all the genetic information of the cell. In factory-speak, it would be the executive offices where all the design blueprints are stored. Of course the blueprints themselves are not made into a particular product. Rather, the information in the blueprints are scrupulously followed by the production engineers and 'whatever the plans' specify is made into a tangible product like a car engine. In the cell, the design blueprints are contained on the biomolecule called DNA. As a quick preview, the tangible product is protein. Later we will discuss the nitty-gritty of how the DNA code is translated into protein. The boundary of the nucleus is called the **nuclear envelope**. We have mentioned previously the substance of biological membranes (phospholipid bilayers). Well, the nuclear envelope is a two-ply phospholipid bilayer, that is, a bilayer of bilayers. This envelope is also perforated. The inner and outer bilayers connect to form openings over the surface of the envelope giving it a whiffle-ball appearance. These holes allow, among other things, the movement of RNA ('xeroxed' copies of certain sections of the blueprints, i.e., DNA) out of the nucleus (executive offices) and into the cytoplasm (the factory floor). This enables the various cellular factory workers to have access to the blueprints so that they can build the product according to code (genetic code, that is).

As I have said, just about everything inside living things is wet. That also goes for the nucleus. The watery fluid of the nucleus is called the **nucleoplasm**. The DNA and other important molecules are dissolved in the nucleoplasm. So what is DNA, actually? Many people have heard the term chromosome but aren't sure how it relates to DNA. You are probably familiar with the term 'skein' if you have anybody in your family that knits. If not, here you go: a skein is a sausage- shaped bundle of yarn coiled up in an orderly fashion so as to minimize tangling as it's unwound. Your chromosomes are like miniature skeins of DNA. You have 46 chromosomes (skeins of DNA) per nucleus. You have a double set of genetic information since you received an entire set from your father's sperm (23 chromosomes) and an entire set from your mother's egg (23 chromosomes). Recall when we discussed biomolecules, DNA is an exceedingly long molecule made of millions of nucleotide building blocks. It is a double helix with two chains of nucleotides twisted around each other such that the nitrogenous bases in the middle form the 'rungs' between the chains. With high powered microscopes it is possible to see a darkly stained area within the nucleus which is called the **nucleolus**. This is an area that is actively engaged in the manufacture of certain parts of ribosomes.

RIBOSOMES

We will get into the details on ribosomes later on, but for now, suffice it to say that **ribosomes** are complex assembly platforms for making proteins. The RNA ('xeroxed' copies of certain sections of DNA blueprints) move out into the cytoplasm and are fed through ribosomes. As the RNA instructions are 'read' by the factory workers (enzymes) at the ribosome, the RNA nucleotide sequence specifies the sequence of amino acids to be hooked together. This is a quick overview of how DNA codes for life. DNA codes for RNA, which in turn codes for proteins. The types and amount of proteins made in a particular cell determine the structure and function of that cell. Getting back to the factory cell analogy, the blueprints (DNA) not only code for much of the structural parts of the cell factory but also the functional parts. In other words, certain sections of the DNA code for factory machines, for much of the supporting framework of the building, and also for the factory employees (enzymes). (These employees aren't hired on from the outside; they are factory-made employees.)

ENDOPLASMIC RETICULUM

After a piece of RNA is fed through a ribosome and a brand new protein is made, it is not necessarily 'ready to roll'. It may require further processing in one or more cellular assembly lines. One of the first organelles that a protein usually enters is a maze-like network of membranes filled with many enzymes designed to manipulate and modify a new protein. This organelle is called the **endoplasmic reticulum** (ER) (endo=inner; plasm=fluid; reticulum=network). The ER enzymes stick various molecules on specific parts of a protein chain so that it will be equipped to carry out its particular function when it is finally deployed (for example, an oligosaccharide chain may be tacked on the new protein so that it can serve as an identification sticker on the cell's surface). The ER may also attach a molecule that serves as a 'mailing address' so that the protein can be delivered to the correct location in the cell (another organelle which will act like another assembly line) for further processing. If the protein is complete and 'ready to roll,' it is then delivered to its final destination for deployment. If the ER is heavily

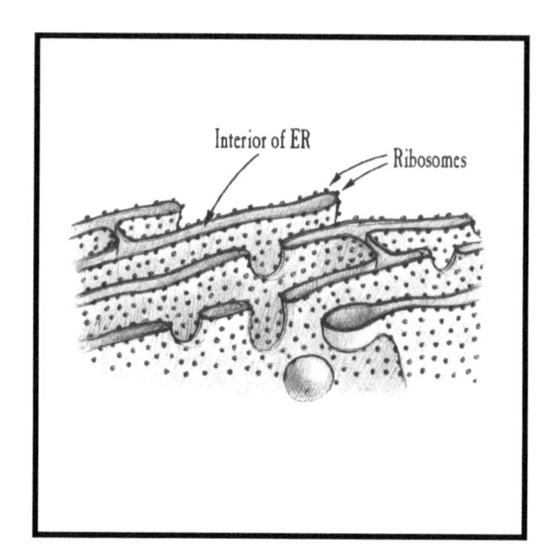

Figure 5.1 Rough endoplasmic reticulum

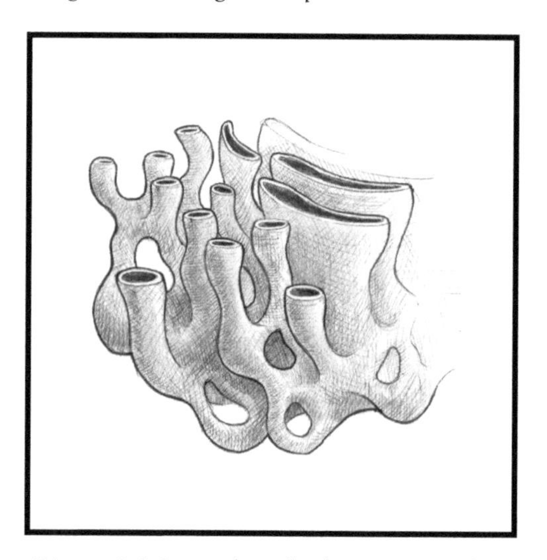

Figure 5.2 Smooth endoplasmic reticulum

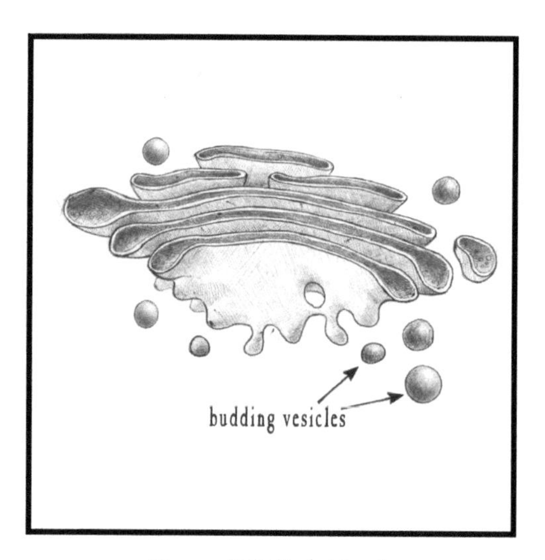

Figure 5.3 Golgi body

involved in processing freshly made proteins from ribosomes, its outer surface will be peppered with ribosomes. When electron micrographs (photographs taken through an electron microscope) reveal a bumpy surface on the ER due to its generous coating of ribosomes, it is called **rough ER** (figure 5.1).

Another endoplasmic reticulum that is not studded with ribosomes is called the **smooth ER** (figure 5.2). Because it lacks ribosomes, it is not as heavily involved in protein processing as is the rough ER, but it may be involved in the further modification of proteins received from the rough ER. The smooth ER typically has a team of enzymes designed to either manufacture lipids from scratch or remodel existing lipids.

GOLGI BODY

The **Golgi body** (figure 5.3) is a peculiar organelle that looks like a stack of deflated beanbags. They have several functions, one of which is protein processing. When thus occupied, the Golgi body receives membrane-bound packages loaded with proteins (from either the rough or smooth ER) that still need a few final touch-ups before they are turned loose as fully functional proteins. For instance, the Golgi body makes final modifications to glycoproteins (proteins with carbohydrate side chains) from the rough ER. In plants, Golgi bodies often have enzymes that are employed in the manufacturing of cellulose (a common polysaccharide) from glucose units (a common monosaccharide). If you recall, the reaction which hooks glucose units together is called a *dehydration synthesis* reaction. Cellulose is the major ingredient of plant cell walls. Virtually every plant cell has a cell wall outside of its cell membrane. This means that plant Golgi bodies are quite busy manufacturing plant cell wall material (cellulose). Once cellulose is made in the Golgi body, it must be packaged in a vesicle and shipped to the cell membrane to be dumped outside of the cell. This is accomplished by the aforementioned process called exocytosis. In Figure 5.4, cellulose is being exocytosed from a vesicle made at the Golgi body.

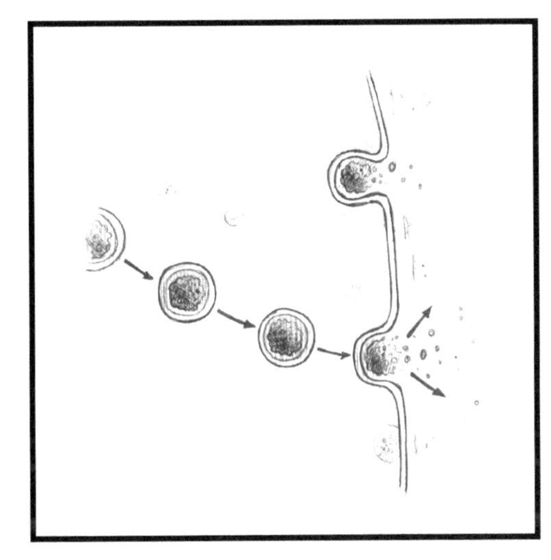

Figure 5.4 Exocytosis of cellulose

When a particular cell needs to make and export digestive enzymes, again, exocytosis is the preferred method by which its enzymes exit the cell. In short, the Golgi body is involved in modifying, packaging, and shipping various biomolecules to other organelles or the cell membrane.

LYSOSOMES

It is not good to keep facts about these various organelles in completely separate vacuum-sealed compartments in your brain. As you have already seen, some organelles are closely related, interact with each other, or produce one another. Lysosomes are one such example of the latter: **lysosomes** are begotten by the Golgi body if the Golgi was engaged in the manufacture of digestive enzymes. Once the digestive enzymes are ready to be deployed, the Golgi body buds off a vesicle (a lysosome) filled with a variety of digestive enzymes designed to hydrolyze (break apart) most of the major biomolecules. Lysosomes receive a shipping address so that the cellular transportation system (more on this later) will ship it to its proper destination. Some of these destinations include the cell membrane (exocytosis). An example of this is found in cells lining your digestive tract. As chewed up steak, mashed potatoes, and gravy leave your stomach, bazillions of cells lining the inner surface of the small intestine actively dump (exocytose) digestive enzymes into the lumen (empty space) of the intestine. How? These cells had been diligently manufacturing digestive enzymes in their Golgi bodies, and they packaged those enzymes up in lysosomes and sent them to the cell membranes that face the lumen. Gazillions of lysosomes are then exocytosed (imagine them exocytosing their digestive enzyme contents). The enzymes are dumped out of the cell and into the lumen in which the food is sloshing along. The proteins, carbohydrates, lipids, and nucleic acids that compose the bulk of the steak, mashed potatoes, and gravy are attacked by the digestive enzymes. Eventually the meal is liquefied because the enzymes digest almost everything down to the basic building blocks (amino acids, monosaccharides, monoglycerides, fatty acids and glycerol, etc).

Sometimes the lysosomes have a destination within the same cell. Certain organelles get too old and shabby, becoming a liability to the cell's proper functioning. For instance, if a mitochondrion has too many miles on it, its diminishing performance makes it a candidate for forced retirement and demolition. Consequently, a lysosome is shipped to it, it fuses with the mitochondrion, the digestive enzymes break it all down, and its nutrients are used by the cell as needed.

If a cell (often unicellular organisms or a white blood cell) phagocytoses a food particle, the resulting vesicle is called a **food vacuole**. Of course the food particle needs to be digested for it to be of any use to the cell, so once again, it's a job for a lysosome. The lysosome is shipped to the food vacuole and fuses with it. The enzymes then wreak havoc on the food particle, digesting all the biomolecules down to their basic building blocks. Another interesting use of lysosomes is programmed cell death (apoptosis). When we were tiny embryos within our mother's womb, our hands looked like paddles because our fingers were stuck together. In a highly regulated process, the cells that form the webbing between our fingers undergo *programmed cell death.* In other words, the lysosomes release their destructive brew within the cytoplasm resulting in cell death and disintegration. When certain cells do this between the fingers, the fingers physically separate. It is much more complex than it sounds, but that is the gist of it. The last use I will mention later when I discuss food vacuoles.

MITOCHONDRIA

Within each cell are usually dozens of jelly-bean shaped organelles called mitochondria. For some reason this is the organelle that many students vaguely recall from their high school biology class. It does have a nice ring to it. We will discuss some of the metabolic reactions that occur in its innards later on. But for now, these organelles are power plants of the cell generating a usable form of energy for most cell activities that require energy. All electrical power plants require an external energy source, whether it is the burning of coal or the flow of water through the turbine within a hydroelectric dam. In the eastern US there are many coal-powered plants that produce a lot of energy for that part of the country. In fact, many personal computers are run from the electricity produced by burning coal. The point I'm making is a computer may be coal powered, but not by shoveling coal into the disc drive and lighting a match to it. The burning of coal releases heat energy, but it has to be first converted into a usable form of energy (electricity). It also has to be converted to a usable form of electricity that is compatible with the power cord on the computer. The energy currency used by the cell, as mentioned earlier, is ATP, not a Snickers bar (although a Snickers bar may ultimately power your cells). In short, whether it is a unicellular creature or a cell within a multicellular creature, cells need energy (just like your computer) if they are to do anything (like keep you alive). Food (like coal to the power plant) is ultimately the source of energy for cells (usually sugars and lipids), but this food is not in the right form for the cell to use directly. The cell must first convert the energy stored in food and harness that energy to make ATP. Most burning requires oxygen.

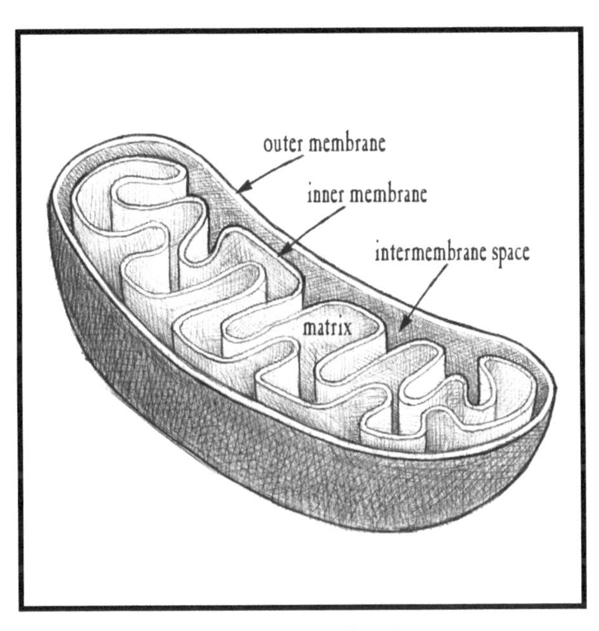

Figure 5.5 Mitochondrion

Whether wood, coal, oil, gas, or food is burned, oxygen is necessary for the combustion to occur. Consequently, all your cells (particularly the mitochondria) need a constant supply of oxygen to burn food and make ATP. Then the mitochondria 'burn' the sugars and lipids into biological exhaust, which are CO_2 and H_2O.

Power plant: oxygen + coal →→ smoke and ash + energy (electricity)
Mitochondrion: oxygen + food →→ CO_2 + H_2O + energy (ATP)

By the way, your respiratory system is your exhaust system and your mouth and nose are your exhaust pipes or smoke stacks. That means (are you ready for this?) a large part of your food is ultimately exhaled out of your mouth and nose. Yes, you lose weight by just breathing. Part of the burning process occurs in the cytoplasm, but it's finished in the mitochondria. During this burning process, the energy in the food (sugar and lipids) is released and captured by the mitochondrion. During the 'burn,' the mitochondrion is charged up like a miniature acid battery which is then able to produce ATP (high energy) from ADP and P (low energy). An analogy of this would be like a battery recharger (the mitochondrion) recharging dead batteries (ADP and P) into fully charged batteries (ATP). The details will come later (whether you like it or not). Of course the battery recharger needs to get energy, so that's why it is plugged into the wall. The mitochondria get their energy by burning food, so that's why you eat: so your mitochondria can 'recharge' their batteries (ATP).

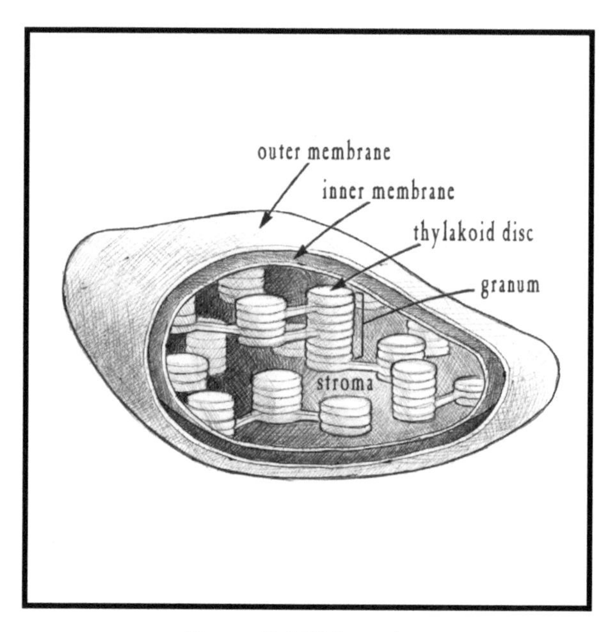

Figure 5.6 Chloroplast

CHLOROPLASTS

Chloroplasts are bright green organelles that are responsible for carrying out the amazing process of photosynthesis. Consequently they are found in photosynthetic organisms like plants, algae, and blue-green algae. The major reason why most stems and leaves are green or greenish in appearance is that most of the cells in them are jam-packed with chloroplasts. Chloroplasts are green because their internal membranes are loaded with the green pigment called chlorophyll. In most respects chloroplasts do the exact opposite of the mitochondria. While mitochondria burn sugars (and lipids) into CO_2 and H_2O to generate ATP, chloroplasts, conversely, use the sun's energy (and ATP) to build sugars from the simple ingredients of CO_2 and H_2O. See how their ingredients and products are just the reverse, except that sunlight is in the place of ATP as the energy.

Mitochondrion: oxygen + food →combustion→ CO_2 + H_2O + energy (ATP) (Burning sugar releases energy)

Chloroplast: CO_2 and H_2O + energy (sunlight) → building → sugar + oxygen (by-product) (Building sugar requires energy)

What is really amazing about plants (and other photosynthesizers) is that they can make the vast majority of their body out of thin air! Yes, they do need a few minerals from the soil, but these are miniscule amounts compared to their entire mass. Most of their tissues (which include many different types of compounds) are predominantly derived from glucose, the basic product of photosynthesis. Glucose is constructed from two colorless and odorless compounds that came out of thin air, CO_2 and H_2O. The CO_2 is a small percentage of the atmosphere and H_2O is also in the atmosphere. Of course the H_2O condenses to form clouds, the clouds produce rain, the water goes into the soil, then into the plant roots, up their stems, into their leaves, into their plant cell's chloroplasts, and lastly reconfigured (along with CO_2) into the glucose. Think about it: a California Redwood is primarily made from thin air through the magic of photosynthesis.

VACUOLES

Vacuoles are a 'catch all' term for any membrane-bound organelle having a variety of sizes and shapes that share the function of storage container for a variety of contents. The content varies because different cell types have different needs to store many different substances. For instance, fat cells are ministorage vats for lipids, so they have relatively large vacuoles completely filled with triglycerides. (These are called lipid vacuoles.)

After an ameba phagocytoses a smaller critter (often bacteria) for food, it becomes encased in a membrane. The resulting vesicle containing the victim is called a food vacuole. This prey item needs to be digested, so the next order of business is to ship a lysosome to this food vacuole. When the lysosome contacts the food vacuole, it fuses with it. The digestive enzymes then flood around the miniature prey and it is promptly reduced into a nutrient soup. This soup is then absorbed across the vacuole membrane and into the cytoplasm for the ameba's sustenance. After these goodies are absorbed, some waste may remain within the vacuole. At this point the vacuole is storing waste and is thus renamed **waste vacuole** (I hope I didn't insult your intelligence). The waste vacuole needs to do a 'dump run' which consists of the vacuole being transported to the cell membrane for *exocytosis*, thus dumping the waste outside the cell.

Because non-woody plants don't have a skeleton to hold themselves up, they need to maintain high fluid pressures (turgor pressure) within their cells. When this is necessary, plant cells often have large central vacuoles that hold mostly water to maintain a fairly high internal pressure which makes the cells turgid.

Yet another type of vacuole belongs to certain unicellular critters which live in freshwater environments. They have a specialized container called a **contractile vacuole.** Because they live in a hypotonic environment, they are constantly absorbing water by osmosis. Recall that this is because the water concentration is high on the outside compared to the water concentration on the inside (more solutes dissolved in the cytoplasm). Water flows from high to low along its concentration gradient, causing the cell to gain water. This would continue until the cell bursts (cytolysis) like a water balloon left on the faucet too long. But the contractile vacuole is essentially a nano-water-bailing machine or sump pump. Minute membranous canals absorb excess water throughout the cell and deliver it to the contractile vacuole. When it inflates to a certain volume, contractile proteins surrounding the vacuole contract, squeezing the vacuole much like the muscles surrounding your distended bladder cause you to lunge for the bathroom. This forces the water to the outside world through a tiny membranous canal linking the contractile vacuole to the cell membrane, ridding it of excess water. This regularly occurs since the cell is constantly gaining water by osmosis.

Figure 5.7 Cytoskeleton

CYTOSKELETON

As the name implies, the **cytoskeleton** is the skeleton of the cell. Our bones form a skeleton which grants the rest of our flesh a supporting framework to hold us up and provide a system of levers enabling us to move. Without it we would be a big pile of quivering flesh, which would soon die. In much the same way, the cytoskeleton forms a supporting framework within the cell granting the cell a certain shape. Another analogy would be tent poles. These wonderful, lightweight, flexible rods can be fitted together to form an internal (don't think of external tent poles) framework to grant a certain shape to the tent. This web-like cytoskeleton gives this nerve cell (neuron) its peculiar shape (Figure 5.7).

In addition to the cytoskeleton granting a certain shape to the cell, the cytoskeleton can also provide a system of cellular cables along which vesicles, vacuoles, and other organelles get ferried around the cytoplasm like trolleys or gondolas (Figure 5.8).

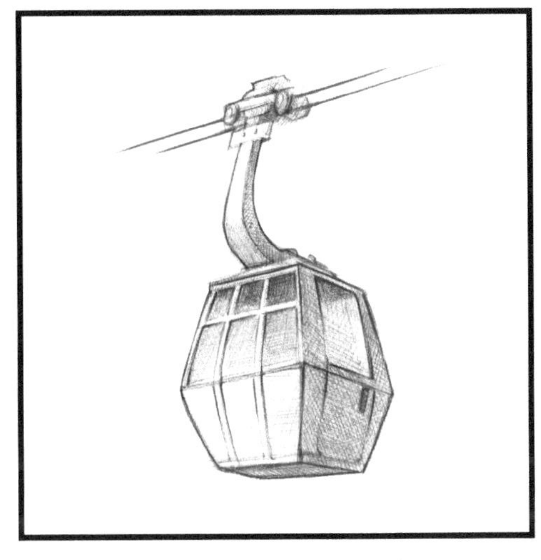

Figure 5.8 Gondola analogy

There are a number of different kinds of cytoskeletal fibers. I will briefly mention three. As I've mentioned before, proteins are ubiquitous and of paramount importance in the economy of the cell, so it's not surprising that the cytoskeleton is made of protein.

MICROTUBULES

Microtubules are the largest of the three cytoskeletal elements. They have an appropriate name because they are small and are hollow like a tube. They are made of many repeating units of a type of protein called tubulin. Each tubulin protein is actually two polypeptide chains hooked together to form a single subunit. Each tubulin subunit fits together with other tubulin subunits much like Legos fit together. Their 3D shape causes them to fit together to form long hollow tubes or cylinders. These long microtubules serve the cell by being the aforementioned trolley or gondola cables for the movement of organelles and, during mitosis, chromosomes. Microtubules also form the internal framework of the locomotive organelles called flagella and cilia. Both flagella and cilia have a similar parallel arrangement of 20 microtubules. There are two single microtubules in the flagellum center and nine sets of paired microtubules surrounding them. This set of tubules is referred to as the 9 + 2 arrangement, and it doesn't just serve as a cellular skeleton; it actually forms a dynamic motor in which the microtubules (which are tethered together by another protein called nexin) are forcefully ratcheted past each other by motor proteins called *dynein*. This ratcheting past each other while still being loosely tethered will cause the whole system of microtubules to bend. And this bending back and forth causes the well known wriggling movement of flagella and cilia, which enables a free cell to swim or a fixed cell to sweep something past.

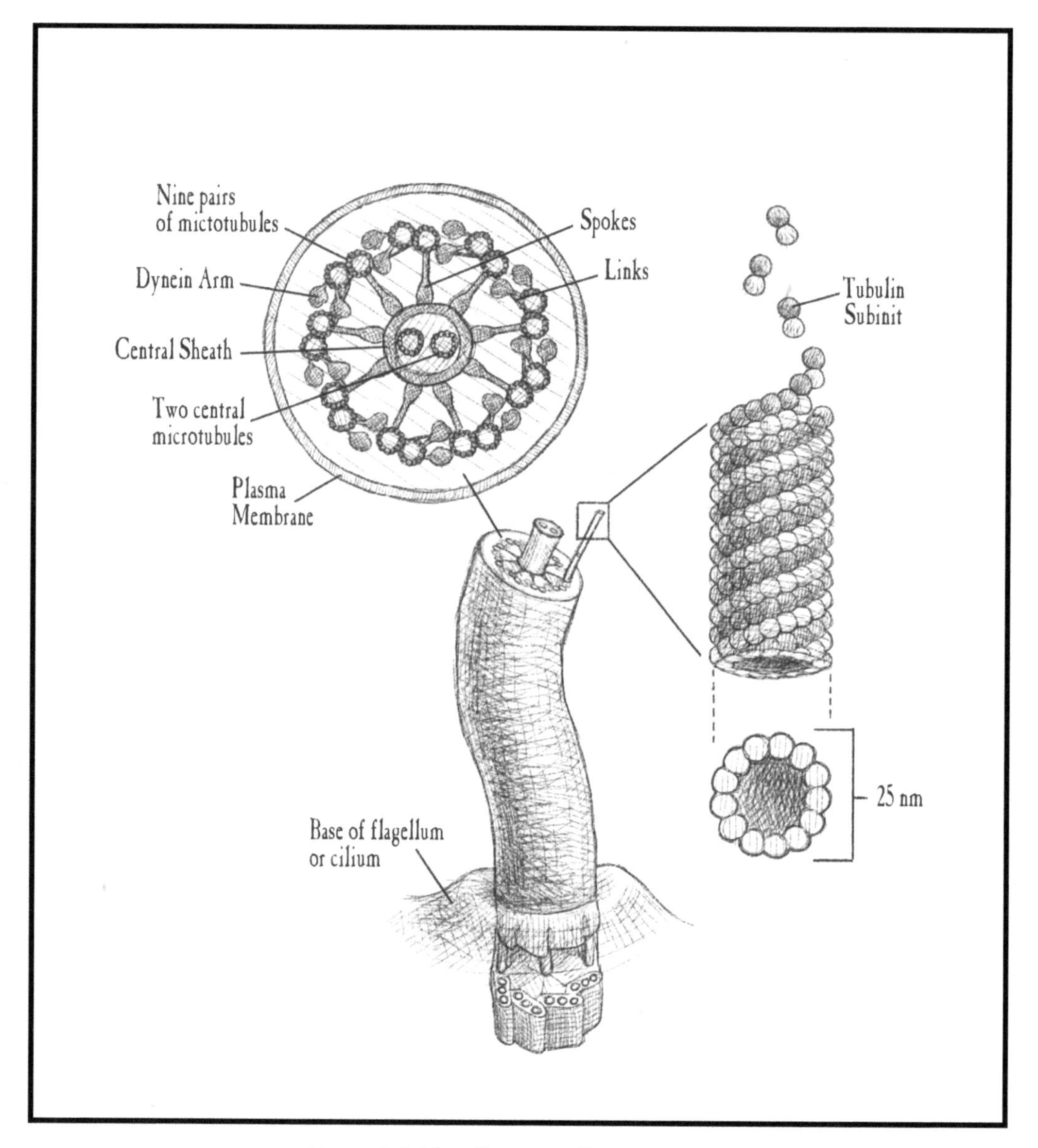

Figure 5.9 Flagellum or cilium structure

INTERMEDIATE FILAMENTS

These tiny tent poles are 1/2 to 1/3 the diameter of microtubules and appear to only have structural roles that help shape the cell rather than provide transportation services like microtubules do. **Intermediate filaments** are not composed of globular proteins, but rather of long fibrous proteins bundled and twisted together like fibers in a rope.

MICROFILAMENTS

Microfilaments are the smallest of the cytoskeletal elements, but are one of the most abundant and widespread proteins in the cytoplasm of eukaryotic cells. Depending on its form, a **microfilament** can simply serve as a structural framework in a cell (tent poles) or be a very important team member in the complex contraction system within all types of muscles cells. It is also found in other nonmuscle motility systems in other cells. The main component in microfilaments is the globular protein called *actin*. One actin protein is called a subunit. Many actin subunits chain together like pop-it beads. Two chains of actin subunits are braided together to form a microfilament.

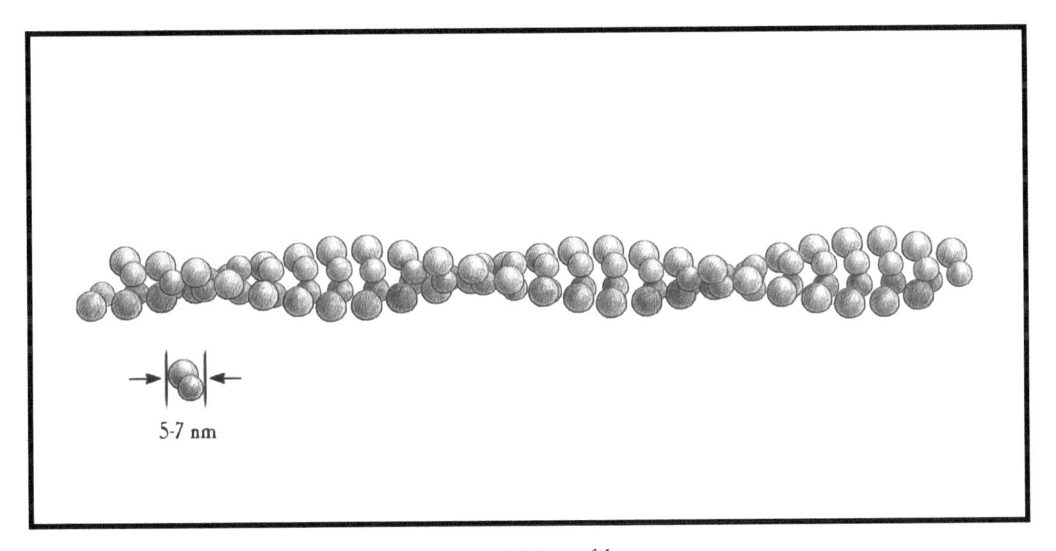

Figure 5.10 Microfilament

CELL WALL

Cell walls, if present, are found outside the cell membrane. They provide external rigid or flexible support for the cell. A simple model for this would be a trash can with a plastic trash bag lining it. The trash bag is the flexible cell membrane. The trash can, which is holding up the bag and giving it shape, is the cell wall. Since cells are filled with fluid cytoplasm, it would be more akin to a trash bag filled with water within the trash can. Without the can, the water-filled bag would bulge out to form a roundish water balloon. However, inside the can the water-filled bag would exert pressure on the

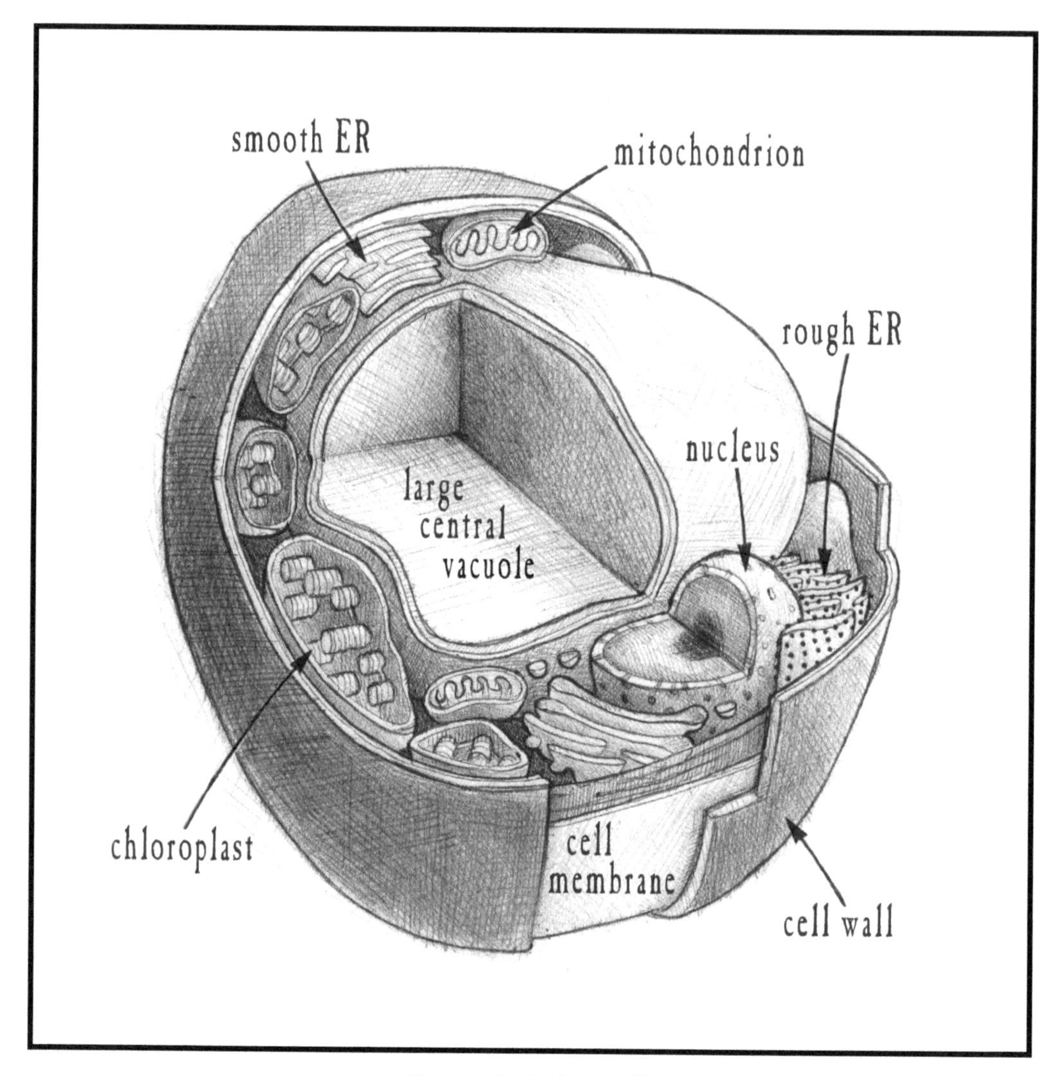

Figure 5.11 Plant cell

trash can walls but would still conform to the shape of the can. If the can is rectangular, then the bag will be as well. Plant cells, fungal cells, bacterial cells, and algal cells all have cell walls and because these are very diverse groups, it is no surprise that the main materials making up the cell walls are different. Most cell wall material is a polysaccharide of some stripe. Plants and most types of algae have cell walls made mostly of *cellulose*. Fungal cell walls are made of the polysaccharide *chitin*. There is another unique polysaccharide cross-linked with short oligopeptides called *peptidoglycan*. This stuff makes up bacterial cell walls. Animal cells don't have cell walls. The fact that plant tissue in salad is somewhat crisp testifies to the fact that its cells have cell walls. The higher the water pressure is within the cell wall, the more turgid the cell becomes. Recall the analogy of air pressure in a tire. The air pressure (psi) would be like the water (turgor) pressure within each cell. The inner tube containing the air would be like the cell membrane containing the cytoplasm. The thicker, more rigid tire would be like the cell wall. The higher the turgor pressure, the more crisp the salad. The satisfying crunch comes from both the semi-rigid cell walls as well as the turgor pressure contained within each cell. When you bite, say, a celery stick, your teeth are rupturing myriads of cell walls, and consequently these cells, under high pressure, are popping. The satisfying crunch of celery is actually the sound of thousands of cells exploding under pressure. When we eat meat (muscle tissue) it is not crunchy (if we don't leave it on the grill too long) because the muscle cells don't have cell walls. Therefore muscle cells can't be under pressure. If they were, they'd pop.

Compared to cell membranes, cell walls are much more rigid. This enables cell walls to provide structural support and to resist varying degrees of mechanical stress. The degree of support and strength depends upon each cell wall's composition and thickness. For example, wood cell walls are much more rigid because they are thicker and have a solidifying compound called *lignin* mixed in with the cellulose. This makes wood cells much stronger than ordinary plant cells and provides enough mechanical support to allow trees to grow very tall. Nevertheless, cell walls are also much more porous than cell membranes.

In other words, they are stronger but leakier. Many substances can pass right through them. By analogy, plastic screening is much more flexible than a chain link fence, but it is also much more selective about what substances can pass through it. Pea gravel is stopped by a thin, flexible screen but it can fly right through a sturdy chain link fence.

OTHER STUFF OUTSIDE CELLS

If it is not cell membrane or cell wall and it is outside the cell, it is called **extracellular material**. This stuff is also very diverse in form, function, and composition. It is usually a mix of polysaccharides and proteins and can be found in plants, animals, fungi, protists, and bacteria.

In bone, the cells are not packed together. Rather an extracellular mix of protein (collagen) and a solidifying compound called hydroxyapatite [$Ca_{10}(PO_4)_6(OH)_2$] provides a fairly rigid matrix surrounding all the bone cells. It is kind of like lots of little water balloons (bone cells) embedded in concrete (extracellular material).

The arrangement is similar in cartilage except that the extracellular material is much more flexible. It has much of the same protein (collagen) but doesn't have the hydroxyapatite to make it rigid. It would be more comparable to water balloons (cartilage cells) embedded in Jell-O (extracellular material).

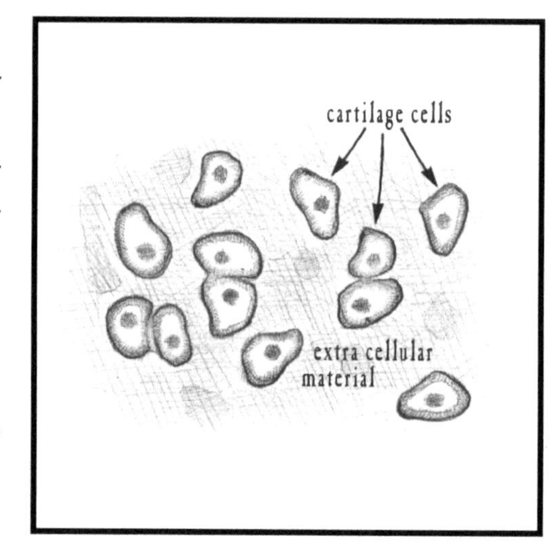

Figure 5.12 Cartilage

In the two examples above, neither had cell walls, but they still had extracellular material. However, on the surface of leaves, the cells have not only cell walls (like all good plant cells) but also extracellular material called a cuticle. This stuff is high in wax content, among other things, and is thus quite water-proof. The cuticle overlays the surface of cells like a fresh coat of wax on a tile floor. Leaves are high in water content, so without the waxy cuticle the water would evaporate from the leaf very quickly, causing the leaf to wilt and die unless it was watered constantly.

STITCHING CELLS TOGETHER

Multicellular creatures, though made of millions, billions, or trillions of cells, are knit together so that they don't burst into a cloud of cellular dust in the face of a stiff wind. It would be a drag if our bodies disintegrated in the bathtub like a sand castle at high tide. Why don't they?

Fortunately God equipped us to stitch our cells together as we develop from a one-celled zygote to a many trillion cell adult. The stitching is accomplished by special membrane proteins on adjacent cells that hook together, thus riveting the cells together wherever the proteins are. These are called **tight junctions.** Another group of proteins forms a tunnel called a **gap junction** that spans both membranes of the adjacent cells. This isn't just riveting the cells together: it also creates a corridor through which cytoplasm can flow from one cell to the other without ever leaving a cell. This would be analogous to a single door jam spanning the adjacent outer walls of two townhouses, so that you could walk from one home to the other without going outside. Another type of junction looks like protein 'buttons' mounted on the inside surface of two adjacent cells (the buttons are lined up) and fibrous proteins stitch one 'button' to the other, linking the two cells to together. This type of junction is called a **desmosome.** (Keep in mind that there are several kinds of desmosomes, tight junctions, and gap junctions.) The significance of gap junctions become apparent once we realize that cells need to chemically communicate with each other. This communication enables cells, tissues, and organs to work together as coordinated and integrated wholes. And these wonderfully integrated wholes we call creatures. But we'll save that realization for another day.

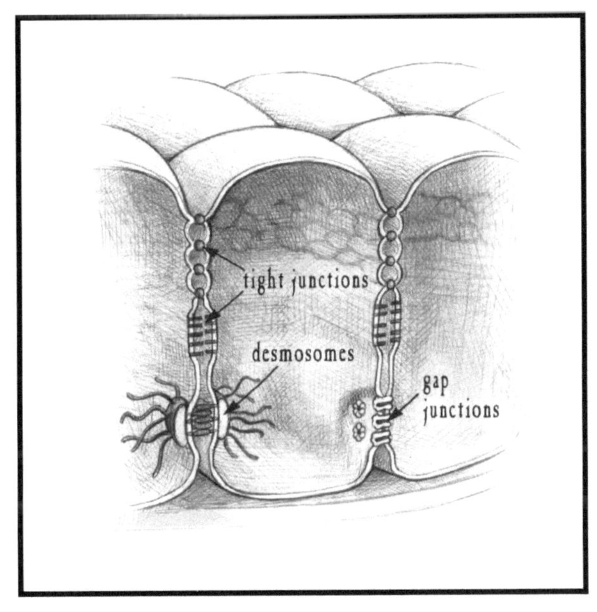

Figure 5.13 Cell junctions

CHAPTER 5: REVIEW QUESTIONS

1. The ______ contains the vast majority of DNA and is covered in a ______ -layered envelope containing pores.

2. ______ are tiny organelles used in the construction of proteins.

3. The ______ is involved in the modification of newly made proteins.

4. The fluid of the cell is called the ______.

5. The organelle that 'burns' food to make ATP for the cells' energy needs is the ______.

6. The organelle that captures sunlight energy to make glucose out of carbon dioxide and water is the ______.

7. The organelle involved in modifying, packaging, and shipping various biomolecules to other organelles or the cell membrane is the ______.

8. An organelle that contains digestive enzymes for the demolition of various biomolecules is the ______.

9. Various proteins that form internal 'tent poles' or form internal transport rails throughout the cell are called the ______.

10. The semi-rigid supporting framework outside the cell membrane is called the ______.

CHAPTER 6

BASICS OF METABOLISM

NATURAL LAW: THE WAY GOD USUALLY DOES THINGS

As we begin to plunge into the complicated processes that we collectively call metabolism, it is important to understand some basic truths about nature (I'm defining *natural law* as the way God usually runs the universe). First, matter cannot be created or destroyed, it can only be converted from one form to another (e.g., when matter is converted to energy or energy converted to matter). This description of how nature works is termed the **First Law of Thermodynamics**. Since God created all of nature, He is, of course, not limited or constrained by nature and can interrupt this or that 'Law' if He jolly well pleases. Keep in mind that *natural law* is not an autonomous or independent process that exists apart from God's will. Nature along with all its physical laws are really our verbal and mathematical descriptions of the way God is running or orchestrating His physical universe. The behavior of the universe (from glucose to galaxies) is often predictable and reducible to mathematical formulas because God is a God of order. He is not arbitrary or capricious. Because God runs the universe with wonderful regularity, science is possible. If God was constantly "sticking His oar in" (interrupting how He normally runs the universe) in unpredictable ways, the idea of a scientific method would be useless. In order to do science, we rightly assume that we can trust our senses, that we can think rationally, and that there is a regularity and predictability in the world around us. If a rock falls to the earth at 9.8 m per second squared, but flies upward the next day and sideways or zig-zaggy the day after that, trying to study gravity would be understandably frustrating and futile. On a special occasion when God (maybe in response to our prayers) interrupts nature, we call it a supernatural event or a miracle. That's why they are so special—God rarely does it. For example, when He creates *ex nihilo* (out of nothing) it was definitely not in accord with the First Law.

Another 'Law' is that any system left to itself goes from order to disorder. This refers to the fact that during any energy transfer, like burning gas (chemical energy is converted to light and heat energy plus some combustion products) a higher degree of disorder will result (this measure of disorder is called *entropy*). Also, a certain amount of energy is lost to the surroundings. The term 'lost' means that it is no longer available to do work. This energy is usually in the form of heat. This law is formally called the **Second Law of Thermodynamics**. This law is daily made manifest to us in the general observation that everything (most notably, all our possessions and our bodies), sooner or later wears out, falls apart, or breaks down. A specific example that might shed more light on why entropy (disorder) increases during energy transfers would be a tennis shoe wearing out. As you put the shoe on and walk or run on it, mechanical energy from friction, from stretching due to the movement of your fat foot and the weight of your body distorting the shoe material imperceptibly breaks molecular bonds in the plastic, fabric, rubber, and leather. When these bonds are broken, heat is released to the surroundings, and the shoe material eventually wears out. The heat energy that used to be in the form of chemical bonds (holding the shoe together) is now no longer available to do useful work and is now a miniscule amount of heat energy in the atmosphere.

When chemical reactions occur within our cells they are thermodynamically law abiding. In other words, if one was to measure matter and energy before and after a reaction, the amounts would always balance (unless you were doing an experiment testing the First Law of Thermodynamics during the wedding at Cana or during the feeding of the five thousand). Barring a miracle, no matter or energy would be created or lost. The matter and energy 'checkbook' would always balance.

Now I want to introduce some new terms. If I have two chemicals, say A and B, and I hook them together in a chemical reaction to make C, we call A and B **reactants** and we call C the **product**.

$A + B \rightarrow C$

An example of this would be the reacting of glucose (A) and fructose (B), the reactants, together to make sucrose (C), the product.

Most reactions are reversible in that the products can be converted back into reactants. However, if that happens, then we would call the product a reactant and the reactants, products.

C (reactant) $\rightarrow$ A + B (products)

We also must keep in mind that energy is involved. There are two types of reactions with regard to energy being gained or lost. If the reaction

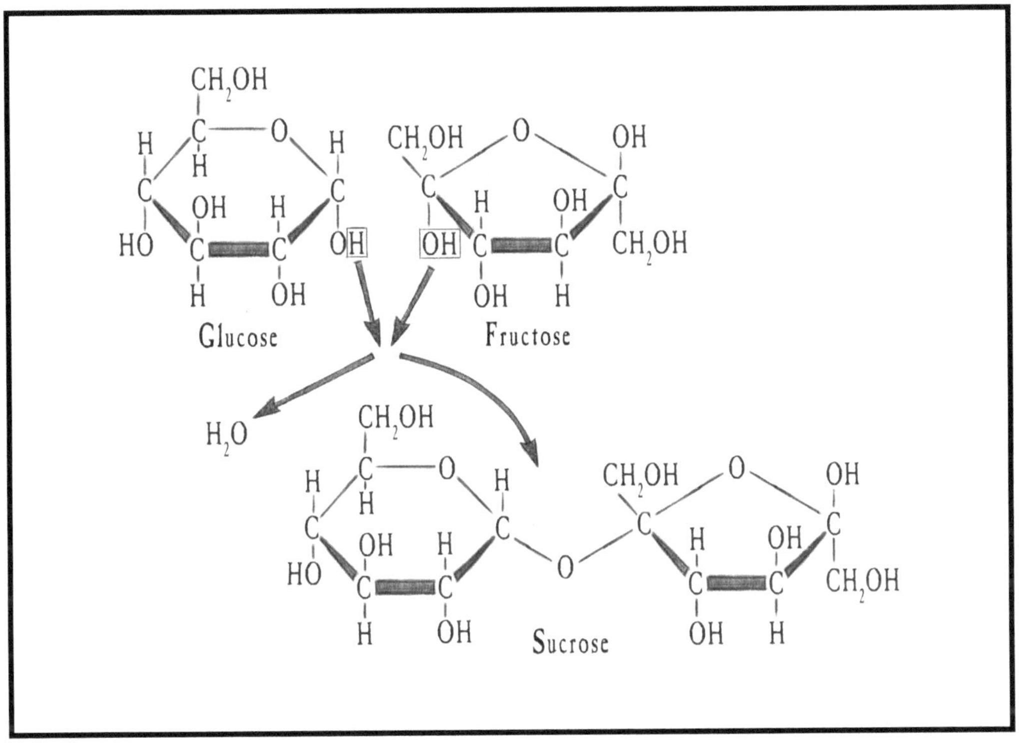

Figure 6.1 Dehydration synthesis

requires an input of energy, it is called an **endergonic** reaction (*enter* has the same Greek root). If energy 'enters' the reaction, it is an input of energy. Let's use a dart gun as an example. The gun and the dart are two different molecules. If we load the dart into the dart gun, it requires an input of energy (not much, but some) and would be an endergonic reaction.

In the carbohydrate example above, an input of energy is required to hook glucose and fructose together, and therefore it is called an endergonic reaction. These types of reactions are often termed *biosynthetic* or *anabolic* reactions because molecules are 'put together' to build bigger molecules.

The opposite reaction is called an **exergonic** reaction. This is when the reactants release energy during the reaction (we get the word exit from the same root). These reactions are also termed *degradative* or *catabolic* reactions because larger molecules are often broken down into smaller molecules. Going back to the loaded dart gun, if we pulled the trigger, the bond is broken and the dart goes flying (a release of energy). This would represent an exergonic reaction. Similarly, if we broke sucrose into glucose and fructose, it would release energy (exergonic), and it would also be a degradative or catabolic reaction in that a molecule was broken down. It is also specifically called a hydrolysis reaction. Another helpful analogy would be building and burning a house. Consider all the building materials as molecules and the nails, bolts, and such as chemical bonds. It takes a lot of energy input to build a house (endergonic) and it goes from smaller molecules (2x4s) to bigger molecules (stud walls) which means that they can be called biosynthetic or anabolic reactions (building up). On the other hand, if we light a match and burn down the house, we have gone from big molecules to very small (ash and charred 2x4s). A lot of energy was given off in the form of a lot of light and heat (exergonic) and it utterly broke the house down (degradative or catabolic reactions).

Metabolism refers to the sum total of all the chemical reactions in cells, tissues, or the entire body. These reactions may require energy (endergonic) and are biosynthetic or anabolic (building up). Or they may release energy (exergonic) and are degradative or catabolic (breaking down). **Energy**, by the way, is the ability to do work and the cells in any creature have plenty of work to do. Here are a few examples of cellular work: active transport, endocytosis, exocytosis, nerve impulses, muscle contraction, and dehydration synthesis reactions. I also mentioned that the vast majority of cellular work requires energy dispensed in a particular form. That particular form is a molecular portable battery called ATP.

ENZYMES

Before we get into the nitty-gritty of metabolism, we need to discuss a famous group of molecules that actually performs most of the metabolic reactions in our cells. If you recall (you'd better) our survey of biomolecules, I mentioned that enzymes belonged to the class of biomolecules called proteins. Remember that proteins are made of building blocks called amino acids that are hooked together in chains. I also proclaimed a trustworthy saying that deserves full acceptance:

"The sequence of amino acids in the chain determines how the protein will fold (loops, hairpins, alpha helix, beta-pleated sheet). The folding pattern of the entire protein determines its overall three dimensional shape and its shape determines its function." More concisely put, 'the amino acid sequence determines its 3D shape and its shape determines its function.' You will do well to remember this! **Enzymes** are those kinds of proteins whose shape and chemical properties bestow upon them the ability to speed up chemical reactions. If you have had a chemistry lab you might recall that heating up the chemicals speed up the Brownian motion of molecules enough to get them to react. However, living cells carry out thousands of chemical reactions quickly and efficiently at relatively low temperatures. We don't need to sit on a Bunsen burner to speed up our metabolic reactions. Instead of adding a lot of heat, we have a multitude of different enzymes that catalyze (speed up) chemical reactions up to millions of times faster than they would otherwise. Enzymes are sort of a heat substitute. Without heat or enzymes, the reactions would simply not proceed fast enough for life to occur. How do enzymes do this? When an enzyme folds up into its proper 3D shape, it usually has an indentation on its surface which has a very specific shape and certain chemical properties. This crevice is called the **active site** and is where reactants temporarily attach to the enzyme and react to form the product. It is then released from the active site. Once the active site is empty, it is free to do the same reaction again and again. Suppose a crescent wrench was an enzyme, then the adjustable cavity that tightens a nut would be the active site. The nut would be the reactant (**substrate**) and its being tightened would be the reaction. A ticket taker at a theatre is another example of an enzyme. His hands are the active site and the ticket is a substrate. When he takes hold of the ticket, it would be like the substrate docking into the active site. The ripping of the ticket would be the reaction and the two halves of the ticket are the product. In enzymatic reactions any reactant is referred to as substrate, so forthwith I will call them substrates. Figure 6.3 is a model of an enzyme molecule (large) and a substrate molecule (small). The cranny in which the small molecule docks is the active site.

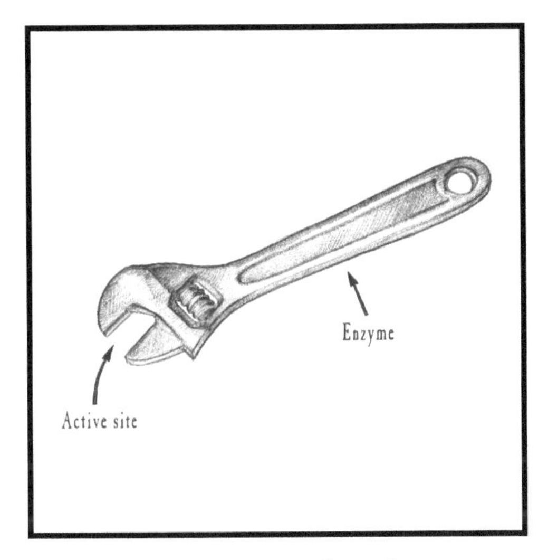

Figure 6.2 Wrench analogy

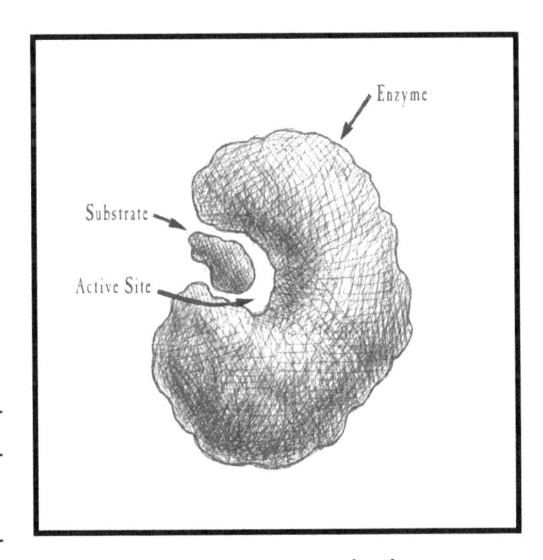

Figure 6.3 Enzyme and substrate

As we learn the basics of metabolism, you will be flabbergasted at all the reactions going on in your cells keeping you alive and healthy at this very moment. Thousands of different kinds of enzymes in each cell are humming away doing their very specialized metabolic jobs, and doing it flawlessly (unless you have a congenital disease of some sort). With that many moving parts, it's a wonder that something doesn't go wrong more often, causing us all to flop over dead.

Our internal environment—namely our body juices within and between our cells—needs to have the correct temperature, pH, tonicity, the right chemical ingredients, and so on. These factors have to be maintained within very narrow limits for our enzymes to work smoothly and according to their designed function. Enzyme activity is temperature sensitive. If our cells are too cold, Brownian motion is slower, which means the molecules won't be diffusing as fast. Consequently molecules won't be bonking into each other as quickly which means substrate molecules won't be docking into the active sites at the normal rate, and reactions will proceed slowly. Each enzyme has an optimal temperature at which it catalyzes its reaction at top speed. However, if the temperature is too hot, the heat energy begins to disrupt and sever hydrogen bonds. This causes the enzyme's amino acid chain to unravel, resulting in the loss of its specific 3D shape. If this happens the enzyme's active site is either deformed or lost altogether and the enzyme can no longer perform its normal reaction. This would be analogous to melting a door knob to the point that the keyhole (active site) is deformed and the key (substrate) will no longer fit. The process of the enzyme losing its proper shape due to heat or some other factor is called **denaturation**. As the temperature increases above the enzyme's optimum temperature, its activity decreases as more and more enzymes are denatured. If a creature heats up to the point that denaturation begins happening to its enzymes, its cells will not be able to carry out necessary life-sustaining reactions and it will ultimately result in death.

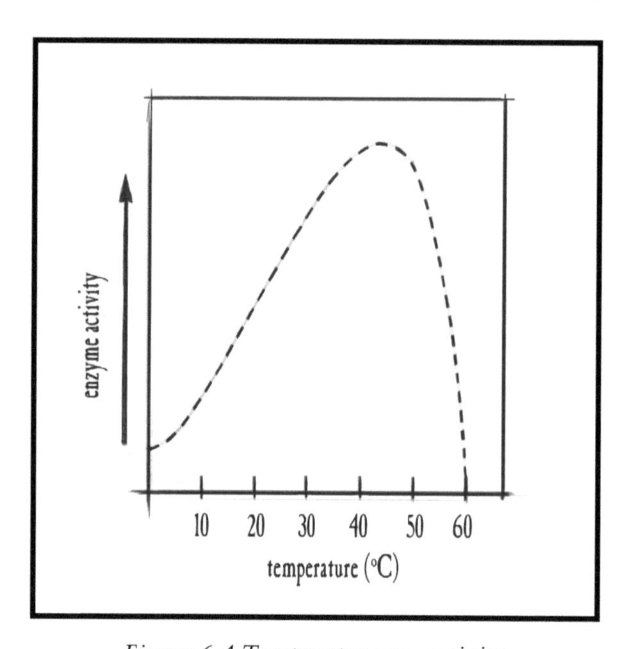

Figure 6.4 Temperature vs. activity

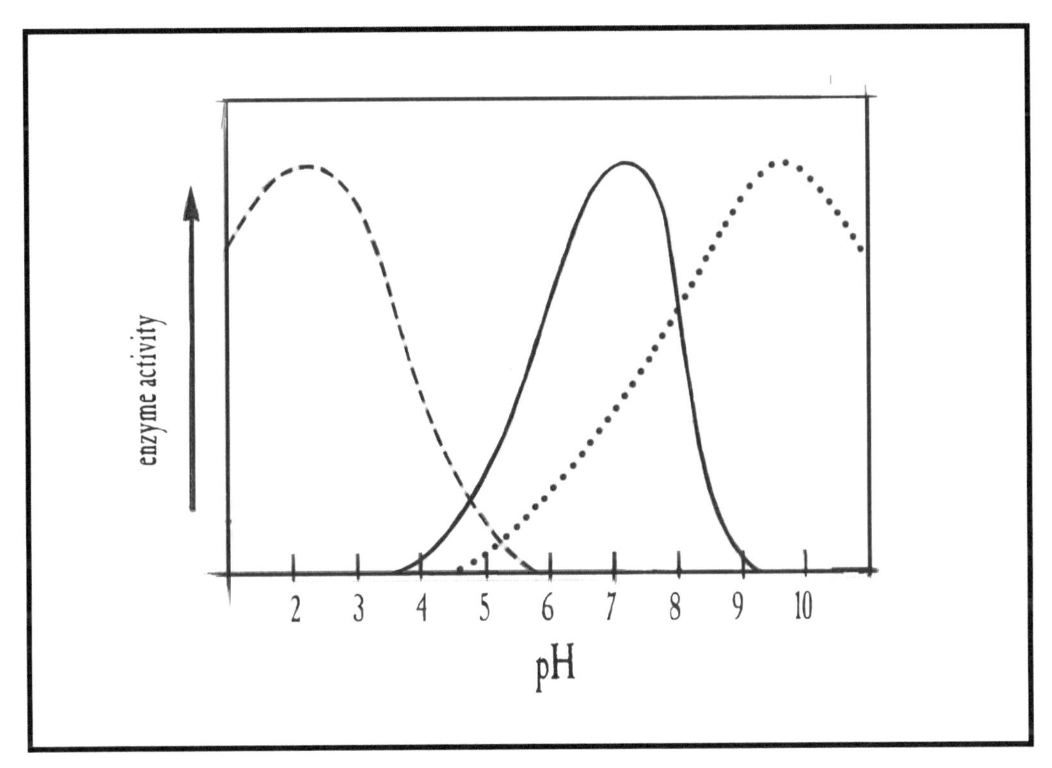

Figure 6.5 pH vs. activity

Many enzymes work together in teams, much like workers in an assembly-line. Enzyme 1 does a reaction, producing a certain product A. Product A is the substrate for enzyme 2 which does the next reaction making product B which is received by enzyme 3 and so on. As in assembly lines, there is a final product which is used by the cell in some way. But the law of supply and demand is true for the cell's economy as it is for business. A healthy cell makes certain products to meet the needs of the cell; it doesn't waste raw materials and energy making things in excess or things it doesn't need. Therefore, the cell also manufactures its own enzymes (factory workers) in the right quantities so that the correct quantities of a certain product are made. If you ran a small fork-lift factory that only needed to make a few hundred fork-lifts per year to supply the market, you would not need to hire thousands of assembly-line workers for such a small demand. This is also true for the cell. If the cell needs more of a certain product, then more of the necessary enzymes are manufactured to meet that demand. This may be an obvious corollary but I'll say it anyway. One way to speed up a reaction would be to make more enzymes. Suppose there is a blockbuster movie showing at the theater and 300 hundred people (you are one of them) purchase their tickets (substrate). The show starts in a few minutes and there is only one ticket taker (enzyme) to rip tickets (do the reaction). If your ticket needs to be ripped to gain entry what would be the best way to get all those tickets ripped before the movie starts? Well, the obvious solution is to get a bunch more ticket takers (enzymes) to rip all those tickets (substrates).

Cells also can gear back on enzyme activity. Enzymes are designed such that if the final product in the enzymatic assembly line is in surplus, some of the surplus product binds to the first assembly line enzyme and shuts it down preventing it from doing the first reaction. This feedback mechanism keeps the cell from overproducing a certain product.

Another factor that affects enzyme activity is pH. Most enzymes work best at neutral pH (7), but if the pH gets too acidic (4-5) or basic (8-9) the enzymes can become denatured causing their activity to come to a grinding halt. Some enzymes are designed to operate at very low pH (stomach enzyme) while other enzymes are at peak performance at pH 10. These oddball enzymes are partially or completely denatured at pH 7.

Many heavy metals also wreak havoc on enzymes causing **allosteric inhibition.** Another crevice or cranny on the enzyme's surface is called an **allosteric site.** Many different types of heavy metals are known to shut down enzyme activity by binding irreversibly to the allosteric site. This indirectly distorts the shape of the active site. Consequently, the substrate can no longer fit into the active site. If the active site is deformed, no reaction. This is called allosteric inhibition. That's why water quality people work hard to keep our drinking water free of heavy metals. Heavy metal poisoning occurs usually by allosteric inhibition.

ENZYME HELPERS

I will introduce a few enzyme helpers presently, but don't expect to fully appreciate or understand them until you see some of the specific jobs that they perform. Right now you will read a boring job description but learning how they are involved in specific reactions is much more interesting . . . but that will come later.

ATP

Many reactions require energy and even if the correct enzyme is present, the reaction won't proceed until an energy boost is delivered to this reaction from our little cellular battery, **ATP.** The enzyme is often needed to hydrolyze the ATP to release the stored energy as well as convert the substrate to the product.

Coenzymes

Many enzymes require assistance from another non-protein molecule to carry out their reactions, much like superheroes need sidekicks to do their job efficiently and effectively.

NADH and **$FADH_2$** are **coenzymes**, working in concert with enzymes, that swipe electron pairs from certain molecules and transfer them to other molecules. The reason for this will become evident when you see the 'big picture' of photosynthesis (how plant cells make sugar from CO_2 and water using light energy) and cellular respiration (how the cell generates ATP by burning food molecules). For now, suffice it to say that NADH and $FADH_2$ are electron shuttles. When we discussed covalent bonding we found that electron pairs are the 'glue' or bond that holds the adjacent atoms together. If electrons are swiped by NAD+ or FAD, it doesn't take too much imagination to predict that the molecules 'robbed of electrons' might fall apart. Think of electrons as the little sticks holding Tinker Toys together or nails holding boards together. If we take them away, the structures fall apart.

NADPH is another electron shuttle service that works and looks much like NADH, except that it does its job in the context of photosynthesis rather than cellular respiration.

CHAPTER 6: REVIEW QUESTIONS

1. The law that states that matter cannot be created or destroyed but can be converted from one form to another is the ______.

2. Contrast biosynthetic or anabolic with degradative or catabolic reactions. Which ones are endergonic and which ones are exergonic? Using A, B, and C show both reactions in a simplified form.

3. Proteins that speed up chemical reactions millions of times faster are called ______.

4. Name three things that affect enzyme activity.

5. Using simple shapes draw an enzyme with its active site bound to a substrate. Label the enzyme, active site, and substrate.

6. Enzymes convert substrates into ______ using their active sites.

7. The sum total of all the chemical reactions in cells, tissues, or the entire body is called ______.

8. Heavy metals can act as poisons by binding to the enzyme's ______ site. This deforms the active site which destroys enzyme function.

CHAPTER 7

PHOTOSYNTHESIS

BUILDING PLANTS OUT OF THIN AIR

I've already given a brief overview of photosynthesis when we looked at the function of chloroplasts. The general equation of this amazing reaction is:

$$6\ CO_2 + 6\ H_2O \rightarrow C_6H_{12}O_6 + 6\ O_2$$

The magic of photosynthesis, as I said before, is that the chloroplasts take the two ingredients of thin air (CO_2 and H_2O) and build glucose ($C_6H_{12}O_6$) from them. From this basic building block most of the fabric of the plant can be constructed. Yes, a lot of biochemical pathways and enzymes are required to transform glucose into a myriad of different biomolecules, but it can be done by the plant's many enzymes. What I want to do now is get into the nitty-gritty of photosynthesis so that you can see in a simplified way how the chloroplast does this amazing transformation. First, we must set the stage and zoom down from what you can see to what you can't see. Photosynthesis can occur in many parts of the plant, but the major sites are the leaves.

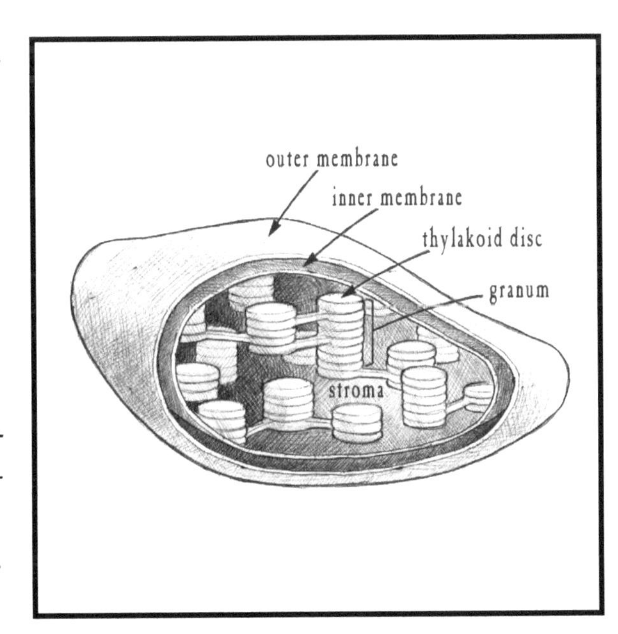

Figure 7.1 Chloroplast

The upper layer of cells on a leaf is called the **upper epidermis** (this layer has no chloroplasts). The lower layer is called the **lower epidermis**. The only cells that have green chloroplasts in the lower epidermis are guard cells. An exception is in lily pads where guard cells are in the upper epidermis because air openings need to be on the atmosphere side. These wiener-shaped guard cells form little pores called **stomates** to let outside air into the interior of the leaf (there are a lot of air spaces between the cells). The interior of the leaf, which is usually about ten to twenty cells thick, is composed of plant cells jam-packed with chloroplasts. This photosynthetic tissue is called **mesophyll** which means 'middle leaf' (Figure 7.2).

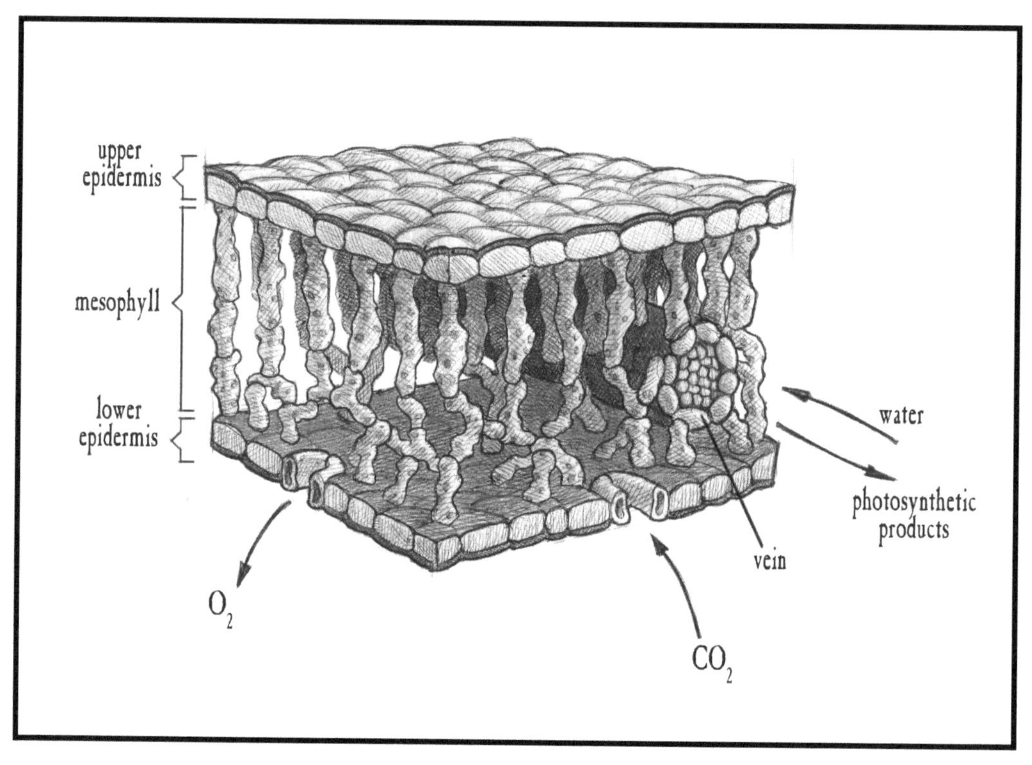

Figure 7.2 Section of a leaf

The incoming air has one of the ingredients for photosynthesis: **carbon dioxide (CO_2)**. The other ingredient is **water (H_2O)**, which comes from the roots via the plant's veins. The CO_2 diffuses from the tiny air spaces into the cytoplasm of the mesophyll cells. CO_2 is now dissolved in a fluid medium and diffuses into the chloroplasts (the organelles of photosynthesis). The chloroplast boundary is composed of two membranes—an **outer** and an **inner membrane**—both of which are phospholipid bilayers. The chloroplast's interior fluid is called the **stroma** and suspended therein are stacks of membranous disc-like compartments called **thylakoids**. A whole stack of thylakoids is called a **granum**. The fluid-filled space inside a thylakoid disc is the **lumen**.

As I describe the construction site, the workers, and the tools they employ, always keep in mind the overall goal: to build the molecule glucose from CO_2 and water. Even though I am simplifying it considerably, pay close attention, because it is quite an involved process. There are two main processes going on at the same time but I will describe them separately. The first occurs in the membranes of the thylakoids and is called the **Light Dependent Reactions**, simply because they are dependent on light. The bottom-line of the Light Dependent Reactions is to build up a good supply of ATP (which is used as an energy source in the construction of glucose) and NADPH (which is an electron carrier). Remember, electrons are the stuff of covalent bonds, so you can think of electrons as nails and NADPH as a loaded nail gun. Of course, analogies are never perfect but they help get the main idea across. Consider glucose as a simple backyard fort made of 2x4s. The 2x4s are the CO_2, the nails hooking all the 2x4s together are the electrons, and the power to drive the nails is in the ATP.

So how does the thylakoid make NADPH and ATP? You have probably heard of the green pigment, chlorophyll. This pigment is embedded in the thylakoid membrane and surrounded with other types of 'antenna' pigments, namely carotenoids (which are in the yellow and orange range) and phycobilins (red and blue range). These pigment clusters are called **photosystems.** Thylakoid membranes are loaded with these photosystems (predominantly chlorophyll). All this chlorophyll makes photosynthetic tissue green. The other color pigments are always there but their presence is masked by the abundance of chlorophyll. Not only do antenna pigments bestow a variety of beautiful colors to plants, they also play an essential role in catching various wavelengths of light energy that the chlorophylls are not designed to catch. When light energy directly strikes chlorophyll (in photosystem II) certain electrons in the main chlorophyll (P680) get excited and jump to a higher energy level. Additional light energy absorbed by the surrounding 'antenna' pigments is transferred to the chlorophyll molecule. All this incoming light energy causes the chlorophyll to get so excited that the molecule fumbles its electrons. A loose analogy is when a running back (when unduly excited) carries the football at arm's length and fumbles the ball when slightly jostled. These fumbled electrons are recovered and passed speedily through the **electron transport system (ETS**; see Figure 7.3). This system is an 'electron bucket brigade' composed of various molecules embedded in the thylakoid membranes. They mindlessly pass electrons (fumbled by the chlorophyll) at lightening speed. The electrons (nails) are ultimately passed to NADP+ (empty nail gun). When the electrons are dumped onto NADP+ it then becomes NADPH (loaded nail gun).

When and where is the water needed since it is, after all, a necessary ingredient of photosynthesis? In short, water is the ultimate supplier of electrons (nails). A chlorophyll molecule only has enough electrons to load one empty NADP+ nail gun. When chlorophyll loses its original electrons to the electron transport system, it needs to be reimbursed with more electrons. Reimbursement electrons are supplied by water. An enzyme in the thylakoid membrane (a water-splitting enzyme) yanks electrons from two water molecules and reimburses the chlorophyll molecule with them. This causes the water molecules to fall apart, resulting in O_2 (remember that this is a waste product of photosynthesis) and four H+ ions (when one pries nails from an object it often falls apart). Once chlorophyll is resupplied with electrons it promptly gets excited (again) by the steady stream of light energy and loses them (again) to the electron transport system. Midway through the ETS there is another photosystem (photosystem I), whose main chlorophyll (P700) also gets excited by light and loses its electrons in the same fasion as P680 in photosystem II. It gets reimbursed by the electrons flowing through the ETS from photosystem II. Ultimately the electrons flow from water, through photosystem II, through the ETS, then photosystem I, then more ETS, and finally is deposited on NADP+ (see figure 7.3)..

Why all this rigmarole? Why flow electrons through this light-powered ETS roller coaster? Couldn't God just design an enzyme that could yank

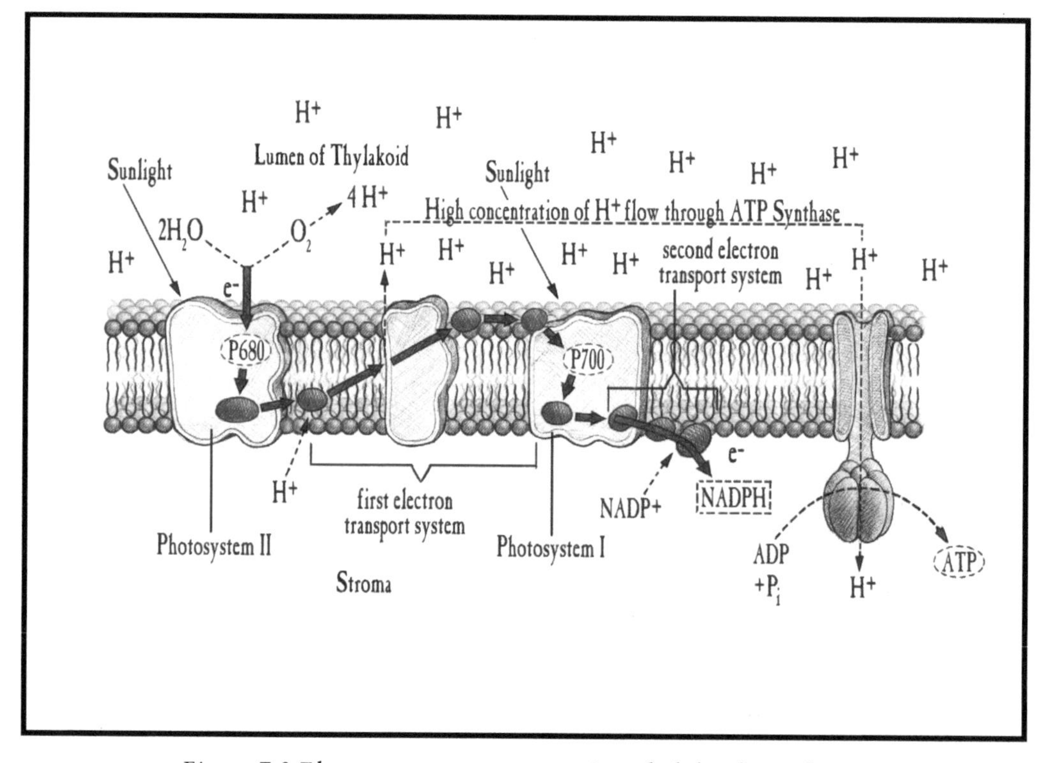

Figure 7.3 Electron transport system in a thylakoid membrane

electrons right off water and directly load NADP+ with them? Maybe so, but the ETS rigmarole isn't there just to make biology more difficult. It is needed to make ATP. How? These electrons flowing through the ETS from water to NADP+ are quite literally an electric current and we all know that electric currents can do useful work.

This current basically runs an electric pump. As electrons are flowing through the ETS, H+ ions are pumped from the stroma through one of the electron transporters and into the lumen of the thylakoid disc. Also, when water is split to reimburse the P680 chlorophyll with electrons, H+ ions are given off by the split (photolysis) and are released into the thylakoid lumen. The end result is that lots of H+ ions accumulate inside the lumens of the thylakoid discs. As long as the sun is shining, the ETS will chug away, which will keep generating a high H+ ion concentration (low pH) in the lumen and a lot of NADPH in the stroma. So how can this high concentration of H+ ions be used to make ATP? Before I tell you what happens, I will prime the pump with another analogy (Figure 7.4). One of the ways we generate electric energy is to harness water flow. Engineers have designed and built hydroelectric dams on many rivers with the simple idea that if water flows downhill (from high elevation to low elevation) they could capture that mechanical energy and convert it into electrical energy. Dams are constructed

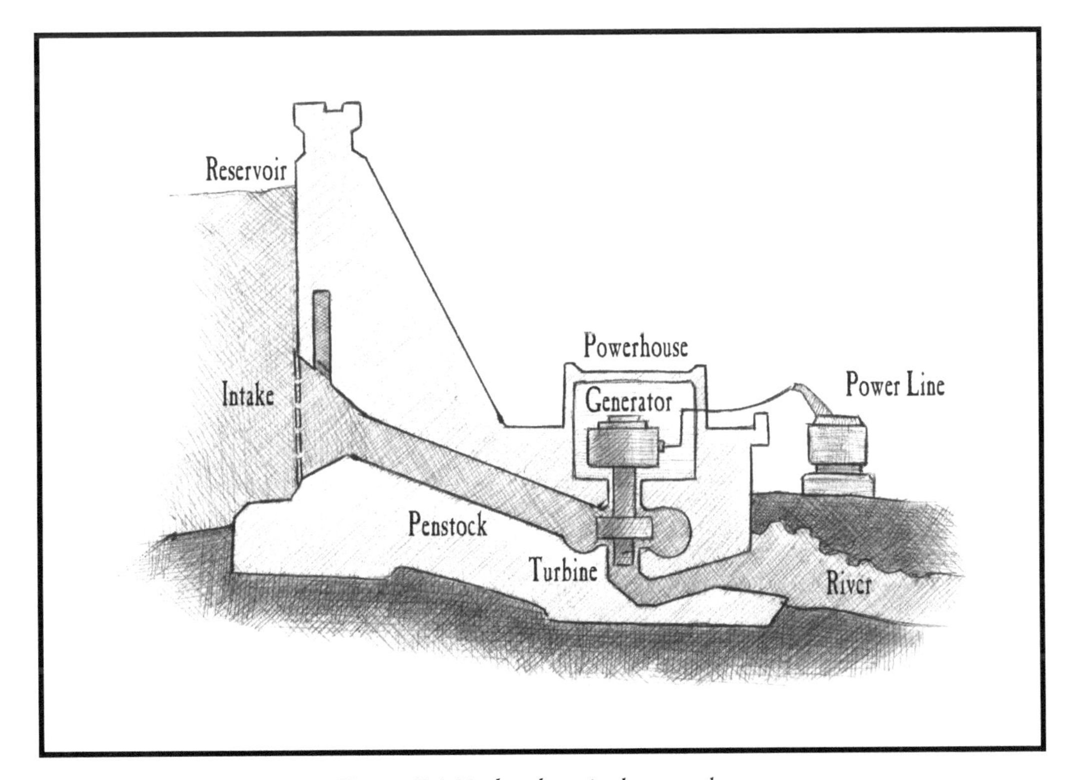

Figure 7.4 Hydroelectric dam analogy

so that water flows through a penstock and then through a turbine in its descent through the dam. The water flow turns the turbine (mechanical energy) which is promptly turned into electrical energy by the generator.

The electricity can be distributed through power lines to where it is needed. A similar principle applies in the chloroplast when making ATP. We all know that water flows through a dam from high to low elevation if given an opening. In the same way, since the thylakoid lumens have a high concentration of H+ ions, they would naturally flow from high to low concentration through the thylakoid membrane if given an opening. God has designed just such an opening. It is an uber-cool enzyme/channel protein which is located in the thylakoid's membrane: it is called **ATP synthase** and is analogous to the turbine/generator of a dam. This wonderful enzyme/channel protein allows the accumulated H+ ions to flow (by diffusion) from the lumen to the stroma (passive transport). This enzyme is designed such that ADP and P (substrates) bind into an active site which converts them to ATP (product) which is released in turn when H+ flows through. This process is called **phosphorylation.** It is a very sophisticated enzyme and a complicated process. Figuring out the mechanisms therein has occupied very bright biochemists for many years. For our purposes, know what happens, not how it happens.

A quick summary for the light dependent reactions is that light energy gets the electrons (nails) flowing from water to NADP+ converting it to NADPH. When water loses its electrons it falls apart into oxygen and H+ ions. To add to the H+ ions generated by water splitting, electron flow through the ETS pumps H+ ions into the lumen of the thylakoid. High H+ ion concentration in the lumen results in H+ ions flowing through the ATP synthase to produce ATP in the same way that high water flows through a turbine/generator in a dam to produce hydroelectricity. Bottom line: Light dependent reactions produce ATP (energy to power the nail gun) and NADPH (the loaded nail gun). These two products will be used to build glucose (a backyard fort) from CO_2 (2x4s).

The other main process is called the **Light Independent Reactions**, simply because it is not directly dependent on light. In other words, light is not directly needed to drive the process. There are two ingredients (NADPH and ATP) from the light dependent reactions that are necessary for this process which occurs in the stroma. Conveniently, both NADPH and ATP are produced in the stroma on the surface of the thylakoid discs. This is where the CO_2 will be transformed into glucose. It's not simple, so I will simplify it so you can get the main gist. Obviously six CO_2 can't be stuck together to make glucose. That would make C_6O_{12} which is not glucose. No, it is much more roundabout than that. First, CO_2 molecules diffuse into the leaf through the stomates from the atmosphere. From there the six CO_2 diffuse into the mesophyll cells and into the stroma of their chloroplasts. Why six? This number is simply for accounting purposes because we need six carbon atoms to make one glucose molecule. Actually thousands at a time are coming into a single chloroplast. Here a biochemical pathway called the **Calvin-Benson Cycle** occurs. The first biochemical reaction that takes place is the incorporation of six CO_2 into six RuBP (ribulose 1, 5 bisphosphate—RuBPs are 5-carbon sugar molecules). So each 5-carbon sugar gets a 1-carbon CO_2 hooked to it by a specific enzyme. (Five plus one equals six.) So the resulting six molecules are six carbons long (Figure 7.5 on the next page).

The six 6-carbon long intermediates (which are very unstable) immediately split in two (they are so short-lived that they don't have a name). There are now twelve 3-carbon long PGAs (phosphoglycerates). This is where the NADPHs and ATPs are utilized. Suffice it to say that when the twelve PGAs receive electrons from NADPH and energy from ATP, they now all have more "nails" and energy, and are therefore primed to make bonds with each other. Once NADPH dumps its electrons on PGA, it becomes NADP+ (empty nail gun) and has to go back to the thylakoid membranes to get reloaded by the light dependent reactions. The ATP, after delivering energy to the PGAs, also needs to go back to the thylakoid membrane to be re-energized by the ATP synthase in the light dependent reactions. When a molecule or atom receives electrons it is **reduced**. If they lose electrons, they are **oxidized**. So after all twelve PGAs get reduced (i.e. receive electrons or "nails") by NADPHs and are energized by ATP, each one is now called PGAL (phosphoglyceraldehyde). Of these twelve PGALs, two of them are whisked away to make glucose. In other words, two 3-carbon PGALs undergo several enzymatic steps to become a 6-carbon glucose (this also occurs in the stroma). The remaining ten 3-carbon PGALs (10 x 3-carbon molecules = 30 carbon atoms) go through a series of involved reactions (every reaction requires a different enzyme) in which they are rearranged into six 5-carbon RuBPs (6 x 5-carbon molecules = 30 carbon atoms) which is what we started with. So we've now gone full circle and are back at the beginning with six RuBPs ready to receive another six CO_2. With each turn of the cycle, another glucose molecule is made. Of course, this doesn't happen in a circle. In reality, thousands of CO_2 molecules are being processed into glucose at any given instant. Realistically, there is a pool of all the necessary enzymes and when CO_2, PGA, PGAL, or whatever attaches to

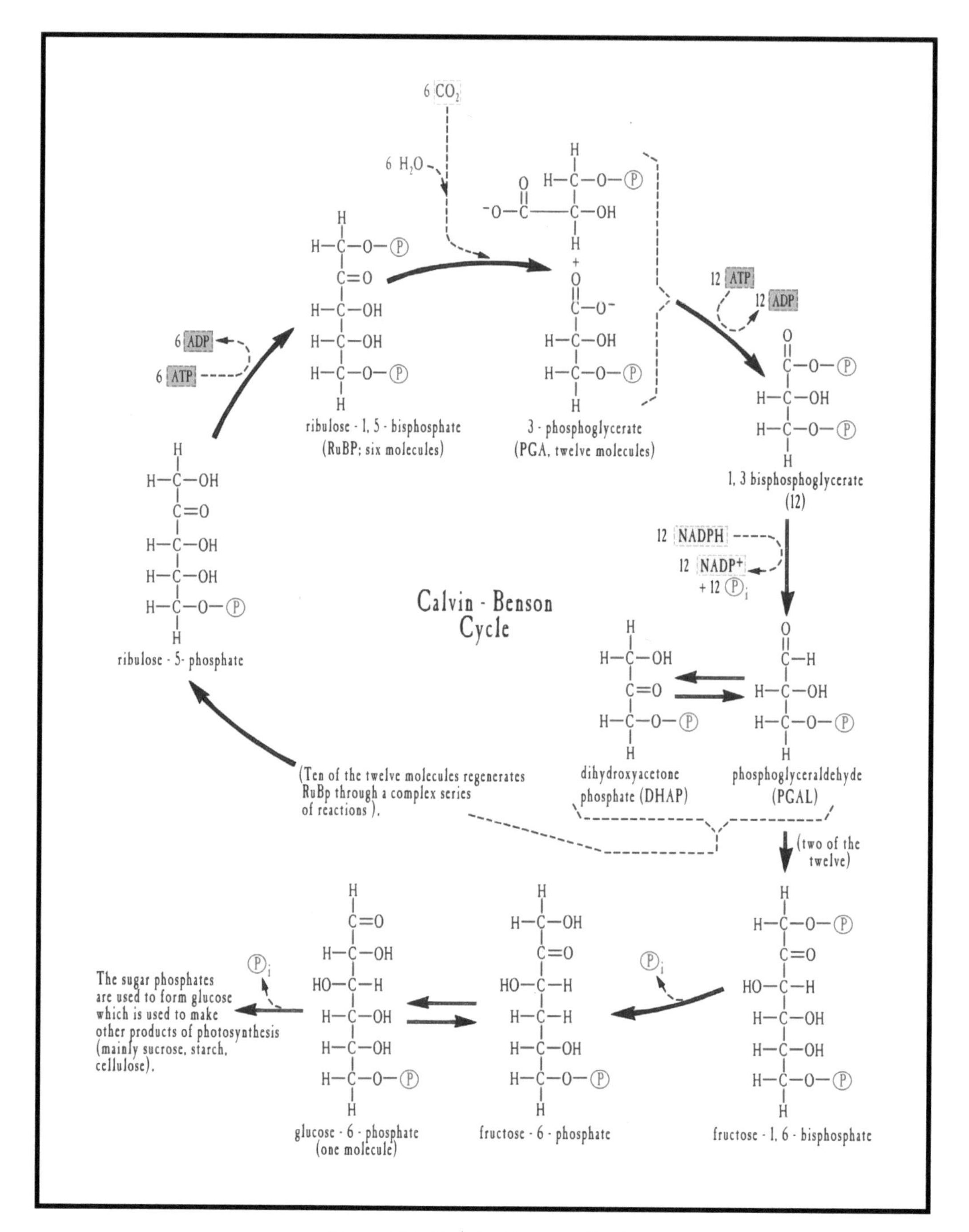

Figure 7.5 Calvin-Benson Cycle

its appropriate enzyme, the reaction occurs and the product is spit out and grabbed by another enzyme which does the next reaction, and so on.

We just draw it in a nice tidy circle so that we can systematically see what's going on. When glucose is made in the chloroplast, it may temporarily be stored there (usually as starch). Eventually it is transported out of the chloroplast and used as is or biochemically modified into many different biomolecules which build or run the plant body. For instance, glucose can be chained together (dehydration synthesis) to form either starch or cellulose. The former is used for storage for later utilization and the latter is used to make the bulk of plant cell walls. Some glucose is converted into different monosaccharides to make a variety of disaccharides, primarily sucrose (which we extract from sugarcane and sugar beets for our sugar industry). Photosynthates (products of photosynthesis) are often transported as disaccharides (often sucrose) throughout the plant body in cellular pipes in the veins called **phloem**.

Glucose can be broken down and reconfigured to make glycerol and fatty acids which can then be used to make mono-, di-, and triglycerides (vegetable oil). Of course, the plant needs to make its own membranes for cells and organelles, so each cell has enzymes that can, with some added ingredients, even make phospholipids from glucose.

Lastly, using other enzymatic pathways, the 'all purpose' glucose molecule can even be used to make the carbon-based portions of amino acids which in turn are used to make protein.

Think about it—photosynthesis makes glucose from CO_2 and water using the energy from light. By using their biochemical 'bag of tricks,' plants transform glucose into the vast majority of biomolecules needed to build the plant body as it grows. And if all kinds of plants are considered, they produce for us countless varieties of food, medicine, clothing, and lumber . . . and almost all of it comes from thin air.

CHAPTER 7: REVIEW QUESTIONS

1. What is the general equation of photosynthesis?

2. The photosynthetic pigments are in clusters called ______ and ______. These, along with the electron transport chain, move electrons from ______ (the ultimate electron source) to ______.

3. What accumulates inside the thylakoid discs when they are receiving light?

4. Phosphorylation of ADP occurs when ______ ions flow through a channel protein/enzyme called ______.

5. What are the two important products of the Light Dependent Reactions?

6. The cycle that produces glucose from CO_2 is called the ______ cycle.

7. The Light Dependent Reactions occur in the ______ membrane but the Light Independent Reactions (Calvin-Benson cycle) occurs in the ______.

8. The major pigment that captures light energy and drives the electron transport system in the chloroplasts is ______.

9. Other pigments that capture a wider range of wavelengths of light and transfer that energy to chlorophyll are the ______ pigments.

CHAPTER 8

CELLULAR RESPIRATION

MAKING FOOD INTO THIN AIR

Earlier on in the book, I gave a brief overview of the function of mitochondria. It is commonly referred to as the power plant of the cell and is the organelle where most of cellular respiration occurs. Cellular respiration is a fancy way of saying 'burning food at the cellular level'. When I discussed mitochondria during the survey of organelles, I said that mitochondria 'burn' the sugars and lipids into biological exhaust, which are CO_2 and H_2O. I also compared mitochondria to power plants making electricity.

Power plant: coal + oxygen → smoke and ash + energy (electricity)
Mitochondrion: food + oxygen → CO_2 + H_2O + energy (ATP)

We have just slogged through photosynthesis and you may have noticed that chloroplasts do essentially the opposite of what mitochondria do.

Photosynthesis: $6\ CO_2 + 6\ H_2O \rightarrow \text{Light} \rightarrow C_6H_{12}O_6 + 6\ O_2$
Cellular respiration: $C_6H_{12}O_6 + 6\ O_2 \rightarrow 6\ CO_2 + 6\ H_2O + 38\ \text{ATP}$

Photosynthesis makes glucose from CO_2 and H_2O and requires an input of energy (light) whereas cellular respiration burns glucose into CO_2 and H_2O and gives off energy (ATP). It's wonderful that the waste products of cellular respiration (CO_2 and H_2O) are the essential ingredients of photosynthesis. Cellular respiration involves several different processes and occurs in two different areas in the cell.

GLYCOLYSIS

The first process occurs in the cytoplasm and is called **glycolysis** (glyco = sweet; lysis = loosen) which has come to mean 'to split sugar'. When **glucose** comes into the cell by passive transport, it encounters a battery of enzymes that eventually split glucose (through a series of enzymatic reactions) into two 3-carbon molecules called **pyruvate**. Think of glucose as an uncut piece

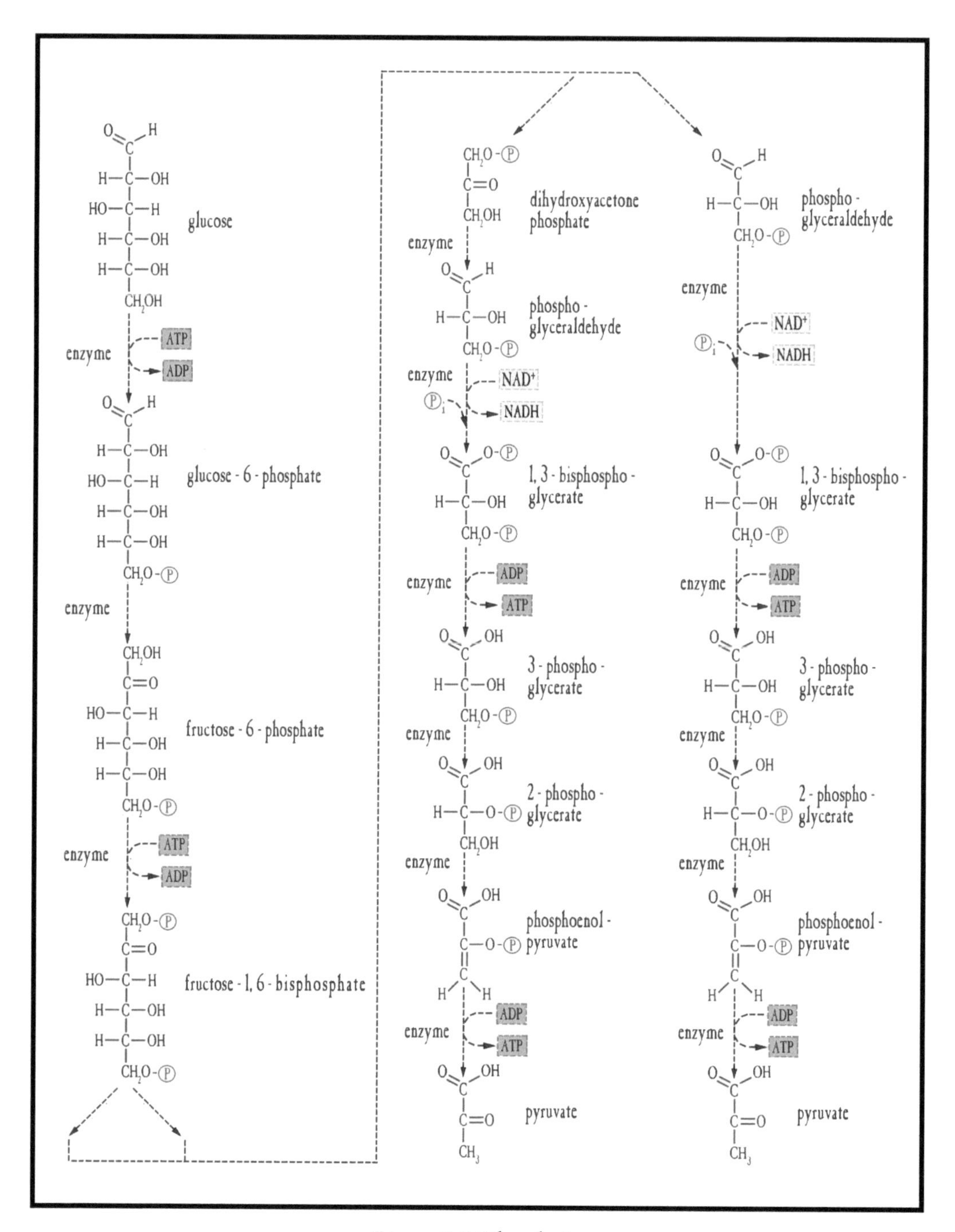

Figure 8.1 Glycolysis

of firewood. Splitting it in two would be glycolysis and the two half logs would be pyruvate. The two half logs then go into a wood-burning steam generator (mitochondrion) which generates heat but is converted to electrical energy (ATP). The waste is smoke and ash (CO_2 and H_2O). I'm keeping it simple, but there are several details of glycolysis that you need to know.

One is that two ATPs need to be invested to accomplish the split. In the same way, some energy is expended to split the log. Also two NAD+ come along and swipe electrons (pry some nails) from one of the intermediates of glycolysis. This stealing of electrons by NAD+ reduces it into NADH. Note that this is very similar to the NADP+ → NADPH conversion. The difference is where the electrons are coming from. In glycolysis, the electrons are being stripped from glucose (a food molecule) and loaded on to NAD+ which becomes NADH (reduced). In photosynthesis, the electrons were stripped from water. Remember, that stripping electrons is like prying off nails. Whatever is stripped of nails often falls apart. Near the end of glycolysis, four ATP are produced. Two are used near the beginning and four are produced near the end, which makes the net yield of glycolysis two ATP.

Bottom line for glycolysis: 2 ATP (net), 2 NADH, and 2 pyruvate. The pyruvate can then enter the mitochondrion to be further burned (oxidized).

IN THE MITOCHONDRION

Before I get into the reactions inside the **mitochondrion,** I want to name the stage and the more important props involved in this tiny molecular drama. The mitochondrion has two membranes: the **inner** and **outer membranes.** The inner membrane is highly folded and wrinkled and is termed **cristae.** The space between the outer and inner membranes is called the **intermembrane space** and the space inside the cristae is called the **matrix.** These terms will be periodically used when discussing the goings-on within the mitochondrion.

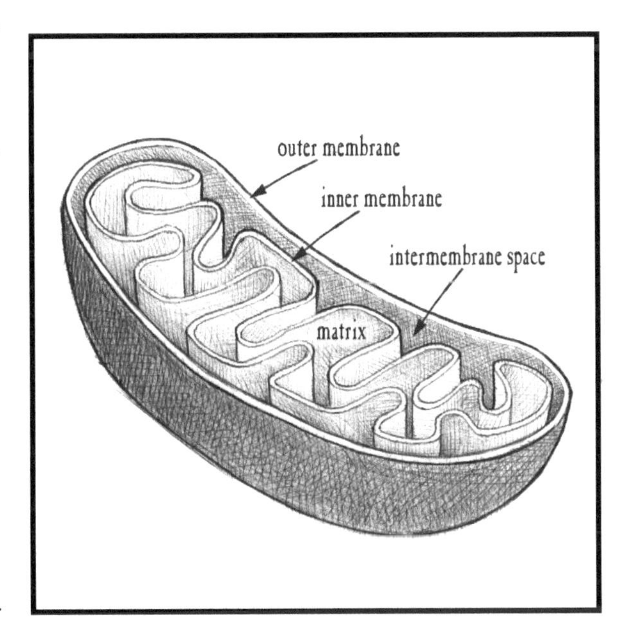

Figure 8.2 Mitochondrion

Although there are two pyruvates from glycolysis, I will describe what happens to one of them. Whatever is produced in the burning of one pyruvate, keep in mind that the same fate awaits the other. So this means that you multiply whatever one pyruvate produces by two.

The first reaction in the mitochondrion is the oxidation (removal of electrons) of pyruvate by NAD+ becoming NADH. In this reaction CO_2 is snipped off of pyruvate. This CO_2 leaves the mitochondrion (and cell) as waste. Consequently, the remaining molecule is two carbons long (it is called an **acetyl group**). The acetyl group is attached to **coenzyme A** to form a molecule called **acetyl-CoA**. The 2-carbon acetyl group then enters a famous cycle called the **Krebs Cycle** within the matrix of the mitochondrion (it is also called the Citric Acid Cycle).

The first step in this cycle is the acetyl group being transferred to a 4-carbon molecule (oxaloacetate) to make a 6-carbon molecule. This 6-carbon molecule (citrate) is rearranged into a similar 6-carbon molecule (isocitrate) to prepare it for another attack by NAD+. NAD+ steals electrons becoming NADH and another CO_2 is wacked off. This dismemberment results in a 5-carbon molecule (α-ketoglutarate). Another attack from NAD+ pries off some more electrons, resulting in yet another NADH with another CO_2 being lopped off. Coenzyme A also gets involved in this reaction so at the end of it we are down to a 4-carbon molecule with a CoA attached (succinyl-CoA). In the next reaction CoA is chopped off which releases enough energy to produce one ATP. The product from this reaction is also a 4-carbon molecule (succinate). The next reaction involves a compound similar to NAD+ and does essentially the same thing—steal electrons. It is called FAD and it steals electrons from succinate, becoming $FADH_2$. The 4-carbon molecule is now called fumarate. Fumarate is converted to another 4-carbon molecule called malate. Lastly, malate is stripped of more electrons by another hit-and-run by NAD+. This of course makes another NADH and malate is now the 4- carbon molecule oxaloacetate, which is what we started with at the beginning of the Krebs cycle. It's important to realize that each reaction in the Krebs cycle is done by a specific enzyme.

Let's bottom-line the products (and wastes) of running both pyruvates into the mitochondrion and through the Krebs cycle. (Note: "x 2" means that we double what we produced from one pyruvate because we are burning two pyruvates, not just one.)

4 NADHs (1 right before the Krebs cycle; 3 during the Krebs cycle) x 2 = 8 NADH

1 $FADH_2$ during the Krebs cycle x 2 = 2 $FADH_2$

3 CO_2 (waste) (1 right before the Krebs cycle; 2 during the Krebs cycle) x 2 = 6 CO_2

*3 carbons enter the cycle (as pyruvate) and 3 carbons leave the cycle as 3 CO_2

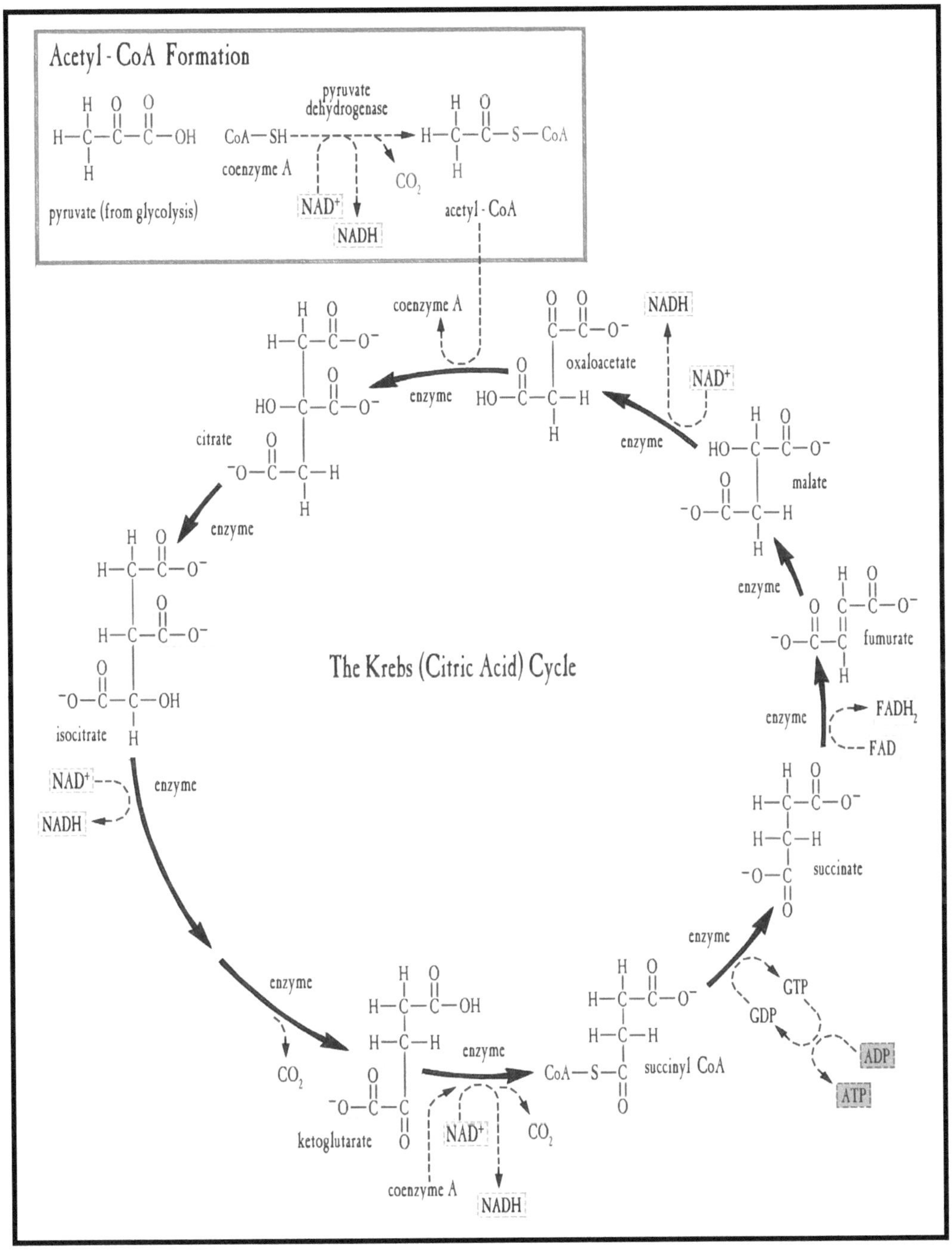

Figure 8.3 Krebs Cycle

The whole goal in cellular respiration is to generate a lot of ATP to supply the energy needs of the cell. So far, only four ATP have been generated: two ATP (net) from glycolysis plus two directly from the Krebs cycle. You might remember only one was made in the Krebs cycle but recall we multiply by two since there are two pyruvates that are burned down to CO_2. Four ATP isn't much of a return from one glucose molecule. However, we're not finished. We have generated 2 NADH from glycolysis, eight NADH and 2 $FADH_2$ from the Krebs cycle and the reaction preceding it. These electron carrying molecules can indirectly be used to produce a hydrogen ion gradient very similar to the one generated during the light dependent reactions of photosynthesis. The electrons on NADH and $FADH_2$ are dumped on to an electron transport system in the inner membrane (cristae) of the mitochondrion. The electrons are relayed through the chain in bucket brigade fashion. This electric current drives an ion pump that pumps H+ ions from the matrix into the intermembrane space. This generates a H+ ion gradient (high H+ concentration in the intermembrane space vs. a low H+ ion concentration in the matrix). At this point, ATP is made in the same way that the thylakoid membrane makes it. The inner membrane has many ATP synthase proteins. The H+ ion flow through this membrane channel/enzyme generates ATP for the cell. So what's the exchange rate? Each NADH that dumps its electrons onto the ETS pumps enough H+ ions out so that when they flow back through the ATP synthase, 3 ATPs are produced.

1 NADH → 3 ATP

Each $FADH_2$ dumps its electrons onto a different electron transporter in the ETS and consequently misses one of the H+ ion pumps. The $FADH_2$ electrons running through the ETS result in fewer H+ ions being pumped out, so that when they flow back through the ATP synthase, only 2 ATP are produced.

1 $FADH_2$ → 2 ATP

Let's tally the grand total ATP molecules generated in the complete 'burn' or oxidation (or removal of electrons) of one glucose molecule.

Glycolysis (cytoplasm)	
2 NADH x 3 =	6 ATP
Directly made →	2 ATP (net)
Mitochondrion	
8 NADH x 3 =	24 ATP
2 $FADH_2$ x 2 =	4 ATP
Directly made →	2 ATP
Grand Total **=**	**38 ATP per glucose**

How is the oxygen involved? Let's look at the general equation.

$C_6H_{12}O_6 + 6\ O_2 \rightarrow 6\ CO_2 + 6\ H_2O + 38\ ATP$

So far we've burned glucose down into CO_2 by pulling electrons off in a sequential manner. These electrons were ferried over to the ETS by NADH and $FADH_2$ so that a H+ ion gradient could be produced by electron flow. Then ATP synthase produced 38 ATP by the passive transport flow of H+ ions. So where does the oxygen come in? Oxygen is the final electron acceptor at the end of the ETS. When oxygen receives electrons, it is enzymatically converted into water (H_2O).

$C_6H_{12}O_6 + 6\ O_2 \rightarrow 6\ CO_2 + 6\ H_2O + 38\ ATP$

That's why we and most living creatures need oxygen to live. If oxygen intake ceases via a number of unpleasant scenarios, there is an electron traffic jam in the ETS in all your trillions of mitochondria. If the last electron carrier has no place to dump its electrons, then it can't receive electrons from the previous carrier and so on. Thus ETS grinds to a sickening halt. When electron flow ceases, H+ ion pumping ceases. When H+ ion pumping ceases, the H+ ion gradient can't be maintained. No H+ ion gradient, no H+ ion flow through ATP synthase. No H+ ion flow, no ATP production.

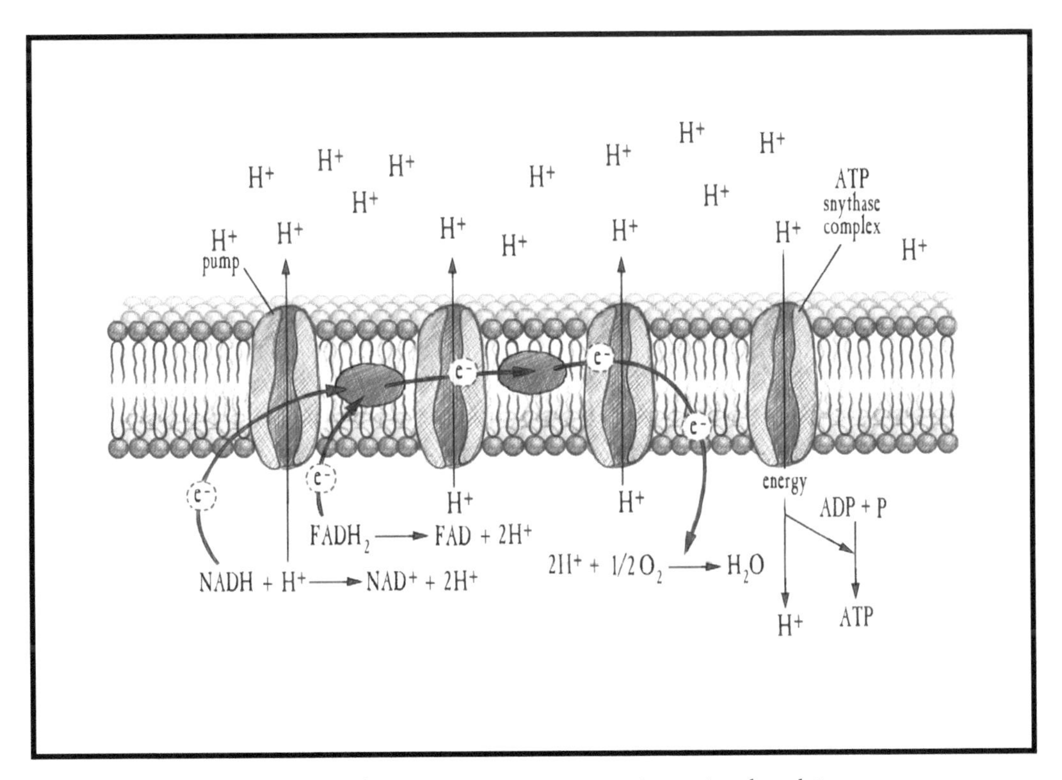

Figure 8.4 Electron transport system in a mitochondrion

No ATP production, you're toast because all life processes cease. So thank God for your ETS and oxygen!

If you are clever, you might have wondered how we burn other food molecules to get energy. So far we've only considered glucose as an energy source . . . but we all know that we eat more than glucose to get energy. We consume fats and oils and yes, we generate energy from them . . . but how? Fats and oils are made of glycerol and fatty acids. With just a few chemical reactions we can prepare these molecules for either the Krebs cycle or both glycolysis and the Krebs cycle. Glycerol is a 3-carbon molecule that can be slightly modified into one of the intermediates about halfway through glycolysis. It then is metabolized into pyruvate . . . and you know the rest of the story. What about fatty acids, those variably long chains of carbon atoms saturated with hydrogens? Fatty acids are enzymatically chopped up into 2-carbon lengths which are made into acetyl groups. These, if you recall, are attached to Coenzyme A and enter the Krebs cycle as acetyl-CoA.

There you have it. Most cells are fairly versatile in terms of the fuel they burn. They can burn both sugar molecules and glycerides to generate lots and lots of ATP molecules.

These last three chapters have discussed energy, some laws governing matter and energy, enzymes, and two of the most fundamental biochemical processes that occur in living cells: photosynthesis (plants, blue-green algae, and algae) and cellular respiration (most living creatures). These amazing processes have been discussed in a very simplified manner but I hope you are starting to grasp life's mind-boggling complexity, and are beginning to appreciate the transcendent intelligence of God who designed and created these processes. We are indeed fearfully and wonderfully made.

CHAPTER 8: REVIEW QUESTIONS

1. The *net* production of ATP in glycolysis only is ______.

2. The ______ cycle generates the most NADH.

3. In glycolysis, glucose is ultimately split (by oxidation) into two ______.

4. In cellular respiration the electron transport chain occurs in the ______ membrane of the ______ (organelle).

5. In the mitochondria what two molecules release ("dump") their electrons onto the electron transport system?

6. What is pumped out into the intermembrane space of the mitochondrion as electrons zip through the electron transport system?

7. Phosphorylation of ADP occurs when ______ ions flow through a channel protein/enzyme called ______.

8. How many NADHs are produced (total) when burning one molecule of glucose?

9. In cellular respiration what important molecule from the air does all aerobic life need, that accepts electrons (and hydrogen) at the end of the electron transport system?

10. What happens to ATP production if 'the answer to number 9' is withheld?

11. What is the grand total ATP yield from burning one molecule of glucose into $6CO_2$ and $6H_2O$?

CHAPTER 9

THE CENTRAL DOGMA: DNA

AND HOW IT CODES FOR PROTEINS

A BRIEF HISTORY

The story of how the three dimensional structure of DNA was discovered is filled with drama. Science does not progress in an impersonal objective search for truth by noble-minded scientists. Rather, it is filled with talented people with fears, insecurities, academic deficiencies, selfish ambition, personality conflicts, and very different approaches to scientific inquiry.

I couldn't do the story justice in this textbook, so I won't try. I will, however, recommend James D. Watson's *The Double Helix* as a good, straightforward account of the behind-the-scenes intrigue of this great discovery. For now, I will present the essential historical facts.

In the early 1950s, a precocious young American named **James Watson** and an Englishman named **Francis Crick** met at Cambridge University. Their mutual interest in the big questions and their agreement that DNA was the genetic material motivated them to put their minds together to decipher the 3D structure of the DNA molecule using data not from their own experimental work (for they didn't have much of any) but from that of **Rosalind Franklin** and **Maurice Wilkins** at Kings College in London, as well as certain pertinent facts from the work of other scientists. Watson and Crick published their proposed model of DNA in the prestigious journal *Nature* in 1953. It was one of the most important scientific discoveries of the twentieth century, for it laid the foundation for our understanding of how the blueprints of life are copied, read, and translated into all the cellular components that carry out all of life's myriad processes. Watson, Crick, and Wilkins won the Nobel Prize for their discovery in 1962. Rosalind Franklin died before the prize was awarded, so she couldn't be honored.

DNA'S STRUCTURE

As mentioned earlier in the section discussing all the various biomolecules, DNA is a double helix (a twisted ladder) composed of repeating units (or monomers) called nucleotides. Nucleotides are themselves composed of yet other molecules: a sugar (a five-carbon monosaccharide called deoxyribose), a phosphate, and a nitrogenous base.

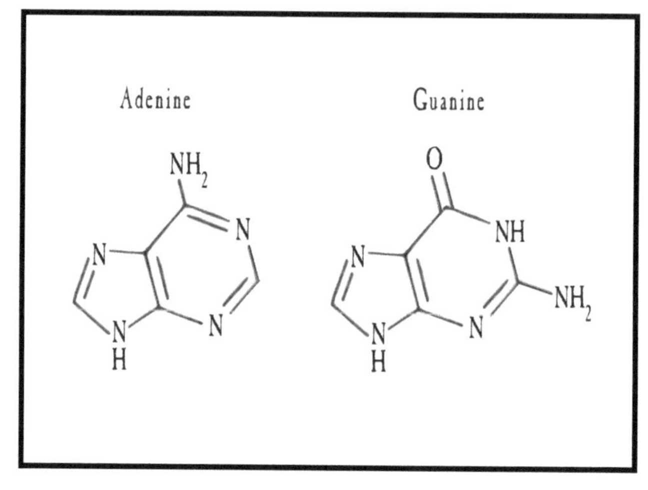

Figure 9.1 Purines

These are hooked together such that the "poles" of this twisted ladder are composed of the sugar and phosphates alternating with each other. Each "rung" of this ladder is composed of two nitrogenous bases—either adenine and thymine or guanine and cytosine. **Adenine** and **guanine** are two-ringed bases called **purines. Cytosine** and **thymine** are single-ringed bases called **pyrimidines.**

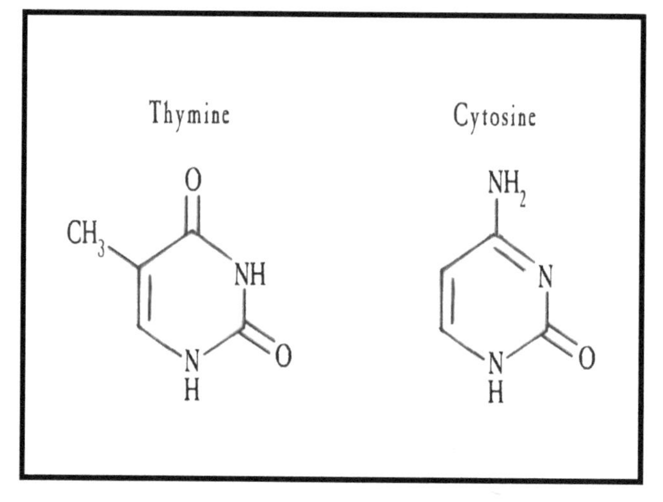

Figure 9.2 Pyrimidines

A silly (but helpful) way to remember that adenine and guanine are purines, is to remember that many kinds of *ag*ricultural livestock feed (*ag* in *ag*ricultural stands for *a*denine and *g*uanine) is made by *Purina.* Also, cytosine and thymine both contain the letter *y* in them, and so does the word pyrimidine, to which group they belong.

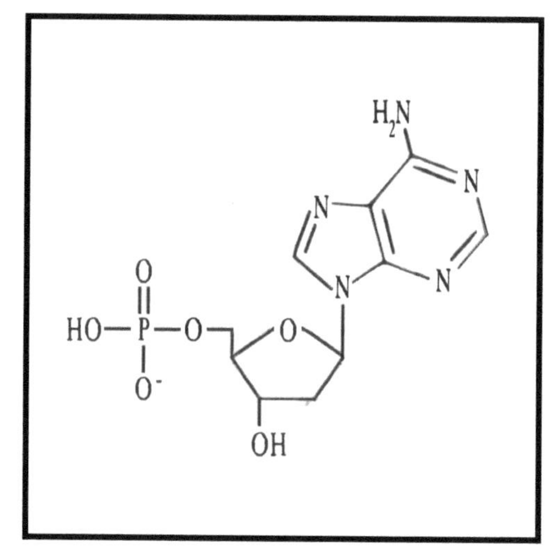

Figure 9.3
Deoxyadenosine monophosphate

When these nitrogenous bases are hooked to their sugar and phosphate it constitutes a nucleotide. Consider the nucleotides in figures 9.4 and 9.5: Thc first is dcoxyadenosine monophosphate (deoxyadenosine = adenine + deoxyribose) and the second is deoxyguanosine monophosphate.

The arrangement of nucleotides to form the double helix is said to be antiparallel. This means that one strand is upside down relative to the other. The rungs are always composed of an adenine base-pairing with a thymine or a guanine with a cytosine. In either case it is a purine base-pairing with a pyrimidine. This insures that the rungs are uniform in length; i.e., three rings long.

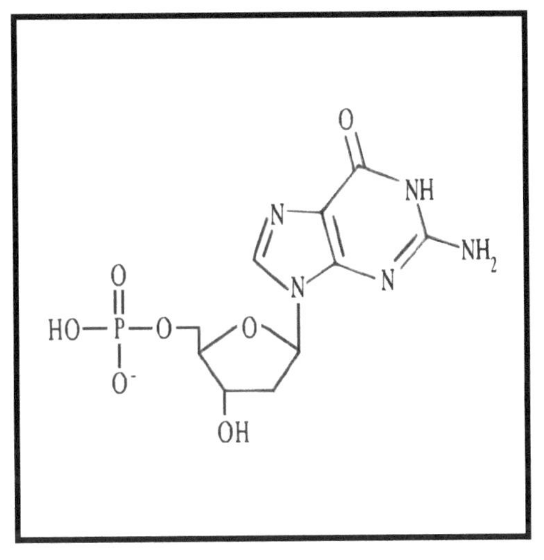

Figure 9.4
Deoxyguanosine monophosphate

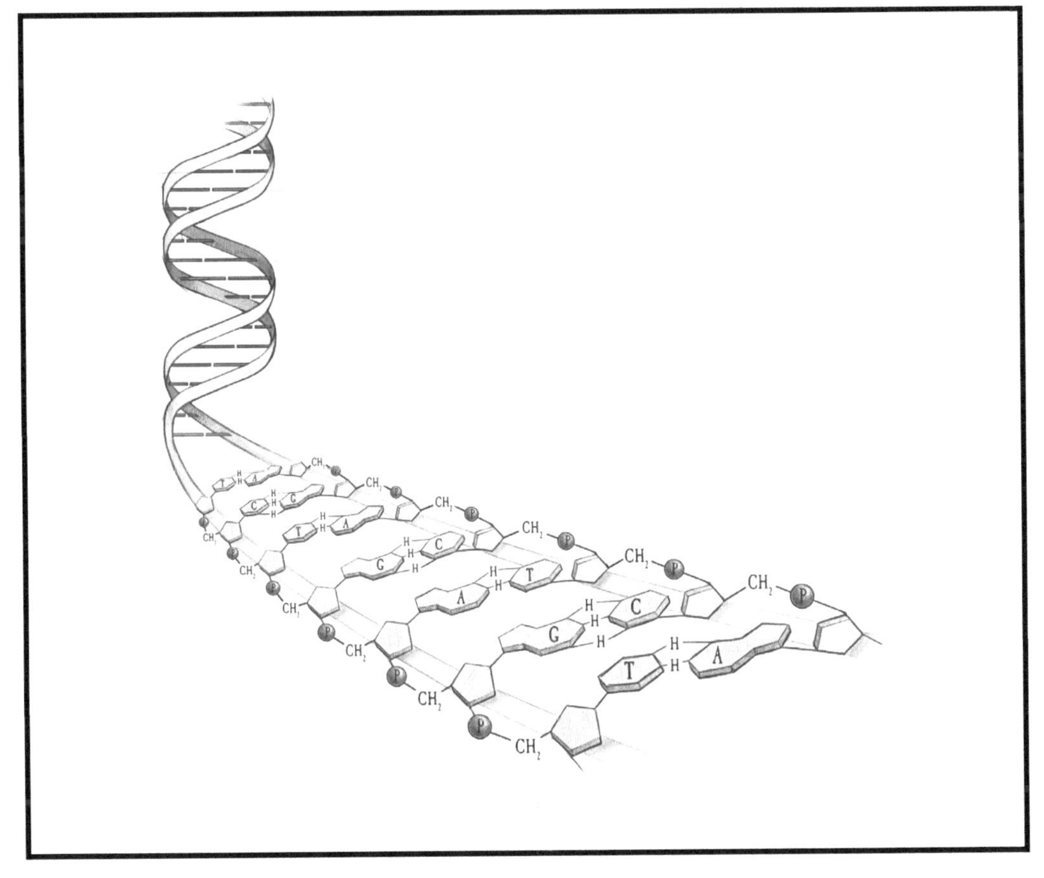

Figure 9.5 Nucleotides in DNA

The ladder poles on the outside of the molecule are formed by alternating sugars and phosphates. These are conveniently called the sugar-phosphate backbones. Figure 9.5 shows the arrangement of nucleotides in the DNA molecule.

Note that the thymine is base-pairing with the adenine with two hydrogen bonds and guanine is base-pairing with cytosine with three hydrogen bonds.

CHROMOSOME STRUCTURE

Like *DNA,* the term **chromosome** has become a household word. Although most people have a vague notion that both terms have to do with genetics, they are often foggy about the relationship between DNA and chromosomes. Well, we are all familiar with knitting skeins, right? A skein is a bundle made from an orderly arranged length of yarn. So, a chromosome is essentially a skein of DNA.

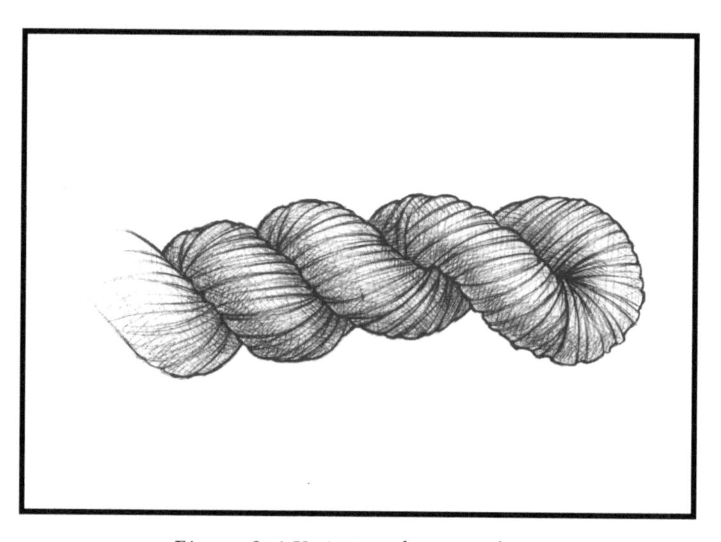

Figure 9.6 Knitting skein analogy

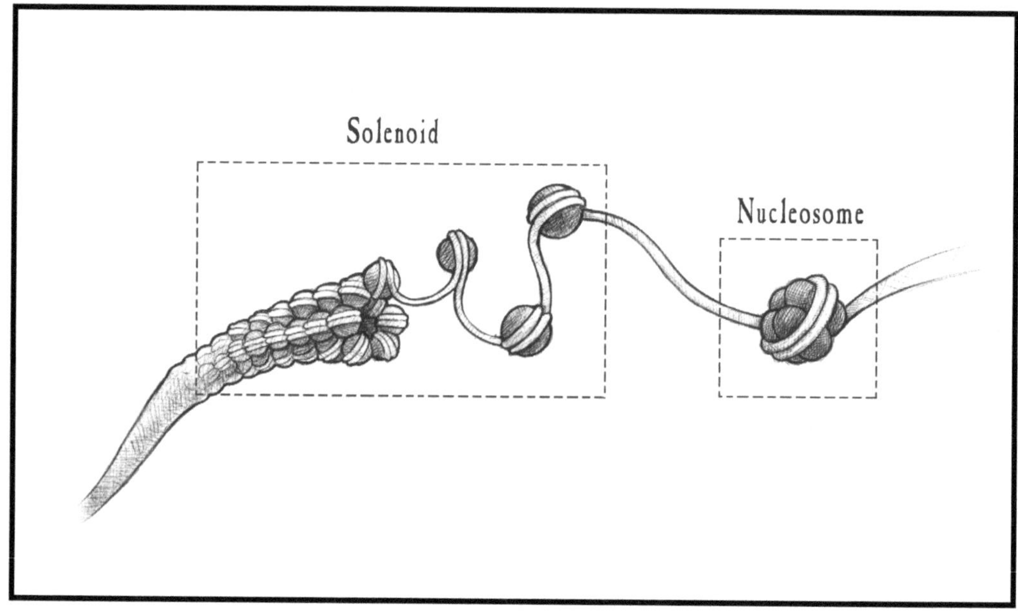

Figure 9.7 Smallest coils within a chromosome

There are, of course, differences in how the DNA is coiled compared to how yarn is coiled, but the idea is the same. For the sake of showing you how fearfully and wonderfully all living creatures are made, I want you to see the coiling pattern of DNA within a chromosome.

First the double helix is wrapped twice around groups of spool-like proteins called **histones**. This small spool is called a **nucleosome**. Adjacent nucleosomes are separated by short lengths of DNA. Many nucleosomes are then arranged into larger coils called **solenoids** (Figure 9.7).

Solenoids are coiled into still larger coils, which are coiled into even larger coils (Figure 9.8).

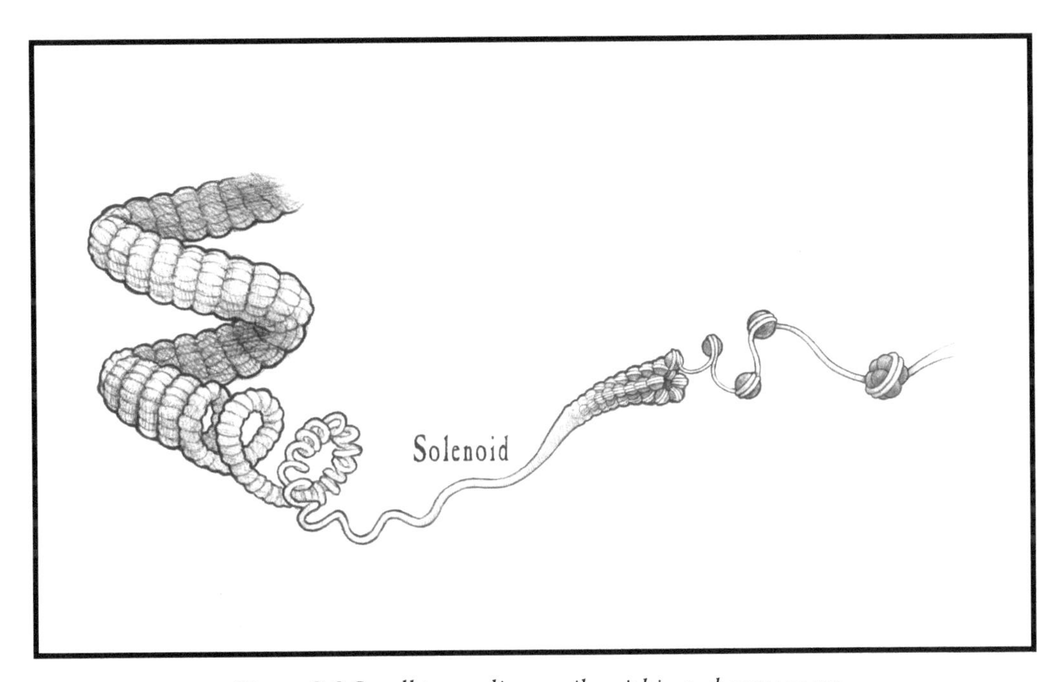

Figure 9.8 Small to medium coils within a chromosome

Finally these larger coils are wound into the largest coils, which form the arms of a chromosome, which are visible under normal light microscopy. Figure 9.9 on the next page shows all the different levels of coiling.

Now that you have a general idea of the intricate coiling of DNA in chromosomes, we can consider its genetic function, which is storing and expressing its genetic information.

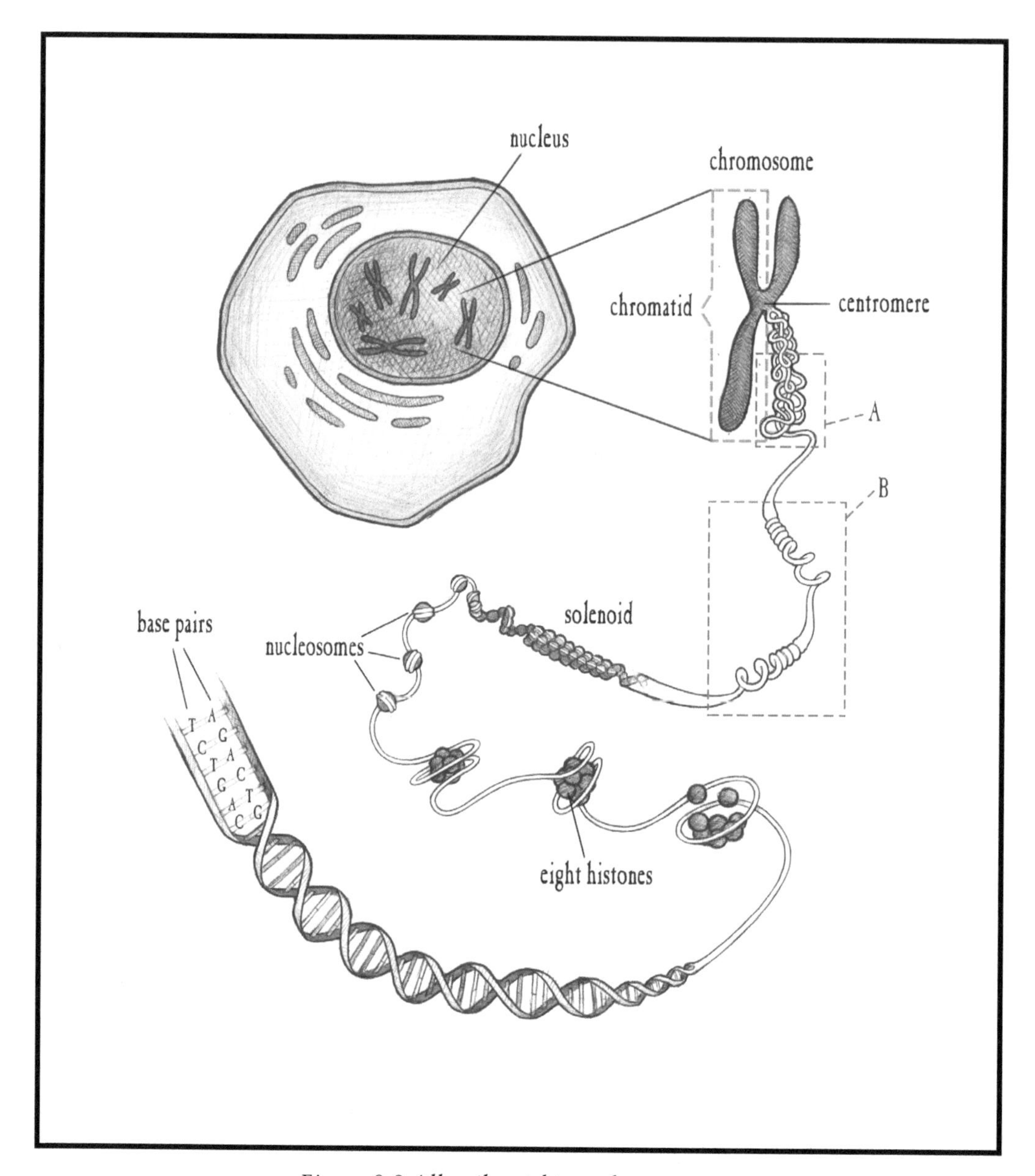

Figure 9.9 All coils within a chromosome

THE CENTRAL DOGMA

In the next several decades after the discovery of DNA's 3-D structure, many different molecular biologists around the world were on a quest to figure out how a gene on a chromosome dictated whether a protein was made, what type of protein was made, and when it was made. This research ultimately led to the discovery of several processes collectively called the central dogma. The **central dogma** can be summarized as the flow of cellular information from DNA to DNA, DNA to RNA (it may stop at RNA),

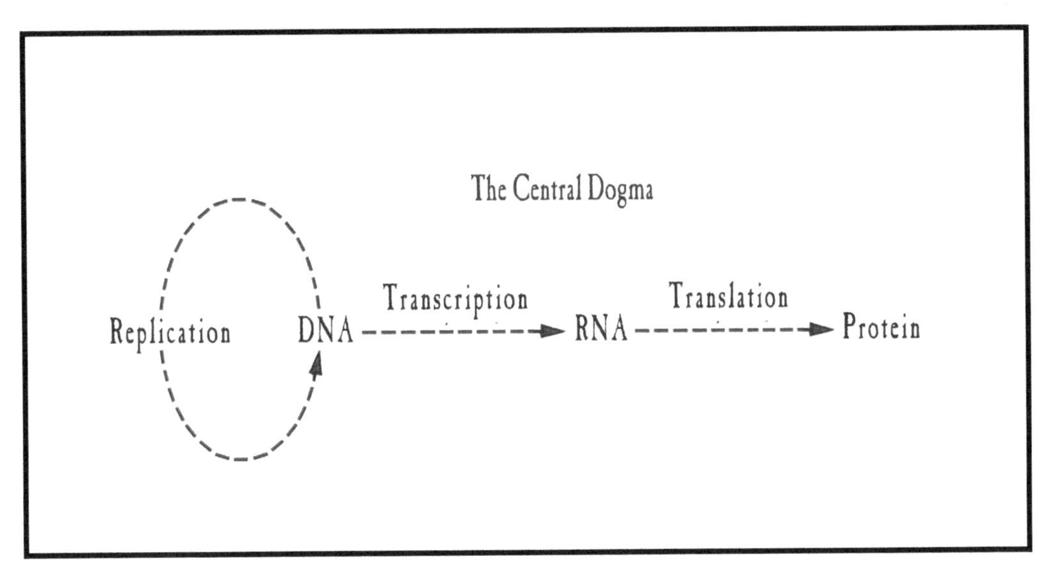

Figure 9.10 The Central Dogma of Molecular Biology

or DNA to RNA to protein (certain viruses like HIV and Hepatitis B are exceptions to the central dogma).

This is a good time to define "gene." A **gene** is a segment of DNA that either codes for a specific protein or for a specific RNA.

I will discuss the three major processes included in the central dogma. The first is **DNA replication** (or **replication**). This is when DNA is used as a template (pattern) to copy itself. The second is **RNA transcription** (or **transcription**). This is the process by which a segment of DNA (a gene) is used as a template to make a copy of RNA. If RNA is the end product, it is deployed in various ways in the cell. If it is a protein-coding gene, the RNA is fed through a ribosome to make protein. This third process is called **protein translation** (or **translation**).

Since discussing the details of DNA replication is best considered while laying the groundwork of mitosis and cell division, I am not going to discuss it in this chapter. However, I will pick it up again at the beginning of Chapter Twelve. Above is a diagram of the central dogma.

RNA TRANSCRIPTION

As mentioned before in the biomolecules chapter, RNA is a similar molecule to DNA with a few notable differences. First, RNA generally exists as a

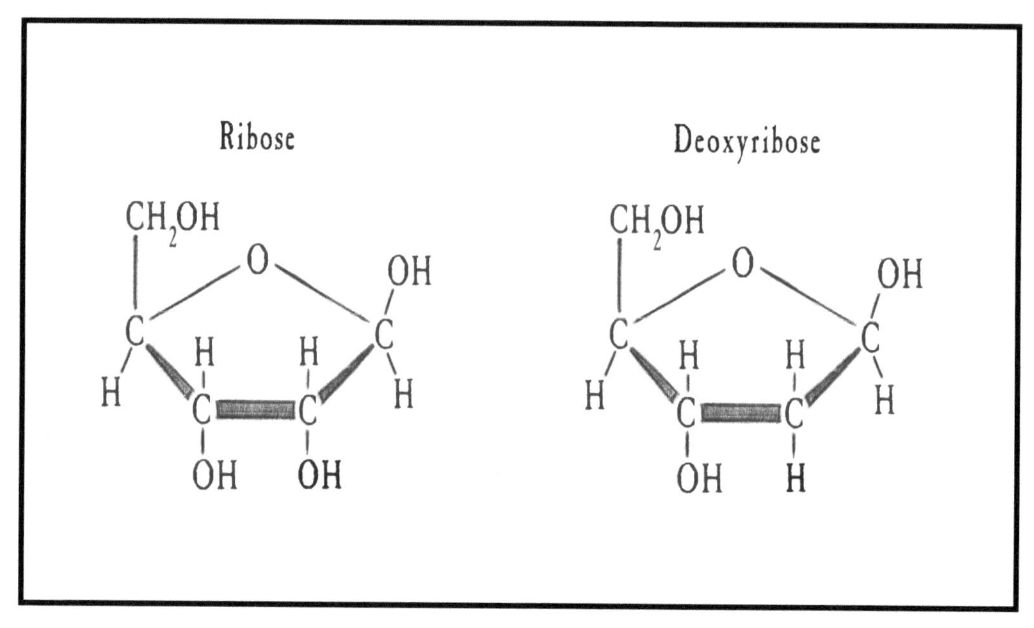

Figure 9.11 Ribose and Deoxyribose

single-stranded molecule. Second, RNA nucleotides have the monosaccharide ribose, not deoxyribose. The difference is slight: ribose has an -OH and deoxyribose has an -H on the #2 carbon.

The last significant difference is in the nitrogenous bases. DNA has adenine (A), guanine (G), cytosine (C), and thymine (T). RNA has the first three but does not have thymine. Substituting for thymine is another similar pyrimidine called uracil (U).

The process of transcription is a mind-blowing process when we consider the speed, scale, and fidelity at which it occurs. The goal of transcription is to provide a disposable copy of the original blueprints of a gene to be used by ribosomes in the manufacture of proteins. The gene, as already stated, is a section of DNA that codes for a single protein or RNA. We also know that the DNA resides and stays in the nucleus of the cell. Proteins, however, are manufactured out in the cytoplasm on ribosomes. So how do we xerox a disposable copy of the original blueprints of DNA? RNA transcription is just such a process.

THE PROCESS OF RNA TRANSCRIPTION

An incredible enzyme called **RNA polymerase** binds to an area called a **promoter.** The enzyme has the ability to temporarily unzip the double helix so as to read one of the DNA strands and enzymatically construct an RNA strand by base-pairing RNA nucleotides with the exposed DNA bases. For example, if the first DNA nucleotide had a T (thymine), then RNA polymerase would stick in an A (adenine) RNA nucleotide to pair with it. If the next DNA base was an A, then the RNA polymerase would stick in a U for uracil. (Remember that RNA doesn't have thymine. Other than that, base-pairing is the same.) In this fashion RNA polymerase works down one strand of the DNA like a train cruising along on one rail building the other rail. Transcription occurs at about thirty nucleotides per second! As the RNA strand is made, it quickly peels away from the DNA strand and the two DNA strands zip back up into a double helix. If the following DNA strand was transcribed by RNA polymerase, the complementary RNA strand below would be produced.

DNA	TAC/AAG/CGA/TCG/ACC/GAA/TCG/TCG/GTT/CGA
RNA	AUG/UUC/GCU/AGC/UGG/CUU/AGC/AGC/CAA/GCU

TYPES OF RNA

There are three types of RNA that are manufactured in this way. The type that contains the information encoding a protein is called **mRNA** (for messenger RNA). It contains the message for building a protein. Another type of RNA is the **rRNA** (for ribosomal RNA). It is woven together with certain proteins to form the highly complex fabric of the ribosome. Lastly, the **tRNA** (transfer RNA) performs the task of capturing specific amino acids and delivering them to the ribosome for assembly into proteins as specified by the mRNA. When we discuss protein translation, we will get a little glimpse of the incredible complexity involved in putting together amino acids in a highly specific sequence.

Suppose an RNA transcript which has been manufactured during RNA transcription is mRNA (i.e. it contains the information to construct a protein). Does anything happen to the newly transcribed RNA before it is translated into an amino acid sequence?

Why yes, something does.

EDITING THE TRANSCRIPT

In eukaryotic organisms, the mRNA freshly transcribed from the DNA is not ready to be translated into protein at the ribosome. It first must undergo some editing. Certain enzymes snip out segments called *introns* from the RNA which are not destined to be translated. After the introns are cut out the remaining portions (called exons) are spliced together by other enzymes.

This whole process is analogous to the way film editing cuts out unnecessary footage from a movie and splices together the parts of the film to be kept.

PROTEIN TRANSLATION

For a little preview, it is good to recall an important truth about proteins: **The amino acid sequence determines its 3D shape, and its shape determines its function.** So let's take this back a couple steps further. What determines the amino acid sequence? Answer: The base sequence in the RNA. And what determines the base sequence in the RNA? Answer: The base sequence in the DNA. Another key fact to know ahead of time is that groups of three bases code for one amino acid. That is why I have inserted slashes between groups of three bases:

AUG/UUC/GCU/AGC/UGG/CUU/AGC/AGC/CAA/GCU

These groups of three are called **codons**. Each codon codes for one amino acid. The strand of thirty bases (nucleotides) will code for a polypeptide chain of ten amino acids.

Look at the table on the other page: it's the genetic code in table form. The genetic code was discovered in the 1960s and appears to be nearly universal for all creatures studied from *E. coli* to elephants. There appears to be very few exceptions, and even the exceptions are minor differences.

Let's return to the RNA sequence from before:

AUG/UUC/GCU/AGC/UGG/CUU/AGC/AGC/CAA/GCU

In the genetic code table on the facing page, the first bases are listed in the far left column, second bases are on the top, and third bases are in the far right column. The first codon in our sequence is AUG. To determine which amino acid AUG codes for, you pick the row of the first base, A (third row down). The second base, U, is the first column. Now look in the box where the third row and first column intersect. You have now narrowed the field down to one box where isoleucine (Ile) is listed three times and methionine (met) is listed once. The third base, G, tells you which of the four you select in that box. Since G is the bottom base listed in the third row of the far left column, you know that methionine is the amino acid coded for by AUG.

FIRST BASE	SECOND BASE				THIRD BASE
	U	C	A	G	
U	Phe	Ser	Tyr	Cys	U
	Phe	Ser	Tyr	Cys	C
	Leu	Ser	STOP	STOP	A
	Leu	Ser	STOP	Trp	G
C	Leu	Pro	His	Arg	U
	Leu	Pro	His	Arg	C
	Leu	Pro	Gln	Arg	A
	Leu	Pro	Gln	Arg	G
A	Ile	Thr	Asn	Ser	U
	Ile	Thr	Asn	Ser	C
	Ile	Thr	Lys	Arg	A
	Met	Thr	Lys	Arg	G
G	Val	Ala	Asp	Gly	U
	Val	Ala	Asp	Gly	C
	Val	Ala	Glu	Gly	A
	Val	Ala	Glu	Gly	G

Using the genetic code (and probably some scrap paper), figure out the sequence of amino acids from the nine remaining codons. See if your sequence matches the correct one below. If you messed up, make sure you see where you went wrong.

This is the rest of the sequence.

Phe – Ala – Ser – Trp – Leu – Ser – Ser – Gln – Ala

If given a sequence of DNA bases, you should be able to transcribe it into RNA, group the bases into codons, and then translate the codons into an amino acid chain.

Now that you have an idea how to derive the amino acid sequence from a DNA sequence symbolically, let's look at the process in more detail.

Once the editing is finished, the mature mRNA moves out of the nucleus where transcription occurred, through a nuclear pore and to a ribosome. The mRNA binds to the smaller subunit of the ribosome. Then the larger subunit of the ribosome attaches such that the bases of the first two codons are positioned next to two molecular 'parking spaces'; the first codon is right in front of the first parking space called the **P site** and the second codon is right in front of the second parking space called the **A site** (see Figure 9.12). The P and A sites are tRNA parking spaces. The tRNAs are nifty little RNA molecules that fold up on themselves forming several hairpin turns where bases in the same molecule base pair with each other. In tRNA, on the cul-de-sac of the middle hairpin turn are three loose bases sticking out. These three bases form the **anticodon** which is designed to base-pair with the codons of the mRNA. Since the codon AUG codes for methionine, the tRNA whose anticodon is UAC is designed to fetch methionine. It is important to remember that the codon is used to determine the amino acid, not the anticodon. Even though the tRNA with the UAC anticodon retrieves methionine, the codon AUG codes for methionine.

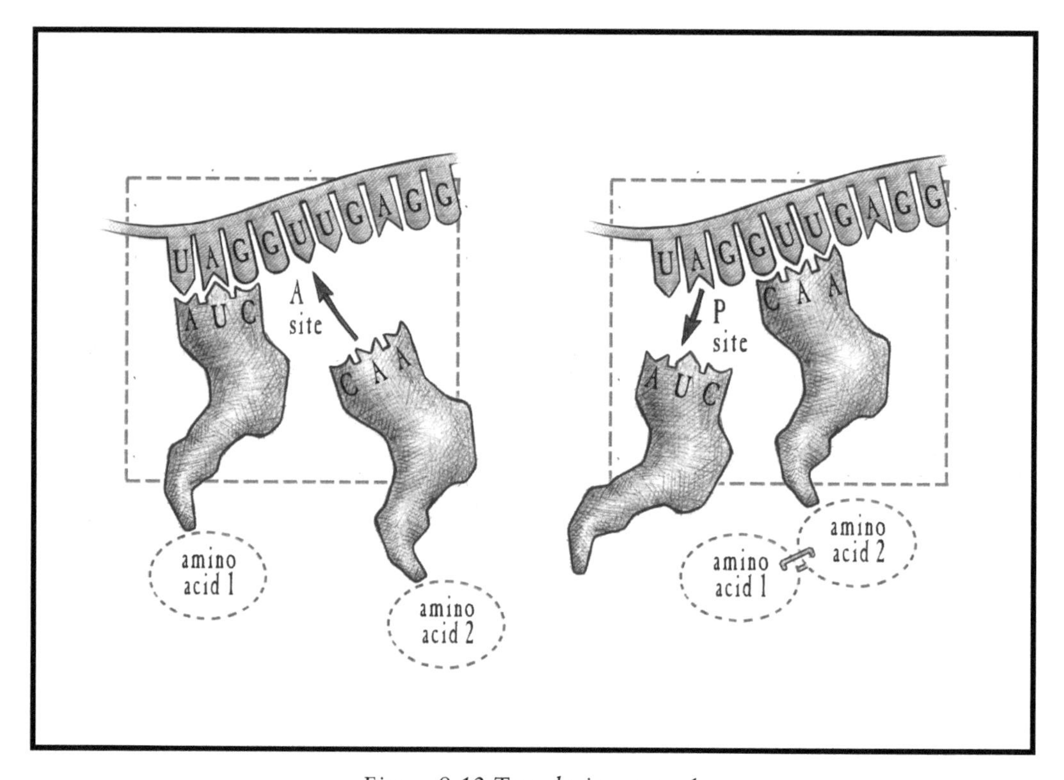

Figure 9.12 Translation, part 1

If a tRNA has an anticodon which is complementary to the mRNA codon, it parks on the P site. Recall that tRNAs are designed to fetch amino acids, so on the opposite end of the tRNA is an amino acid. It is of paramount importance to know that a particular tRNA (with a particular anticodon) can only fetch one type of amino acid, period. This insures that a given codon will specify a given amino acid and no other. Another tRNA whose anticodon matches the second codon will park in the A site, its anticodon bound to the second codon.

Now there are two tRNAs parked next to each other with their particular amino acids hitched on their rear ends. This places the amino acids next to each other (almost like it was planned...). Then another enzyme does a dehydration synthesis reaction forming a peptide bond between the two. The ribosome then shifts position so that the first tRNA falls off leaving its amino acid peptide bonded to the amino acid of the second tRNA. The second tRNA is now in the P site. This shift opens up the A site so that the third tRNA (which matches the third codon) parks there along with its amino acid hitched on its rear (see Figure 9.13).

Now a peptide bond forms between the second and third amino acid, the ribosome shifts, the second tRNA falls off, leaving the three conjoined amino acids hooked to the third tRNA which is now positioned in the P site. Now the A site is open for the forth tRNA along with its corresponding amino acid. This cycle keeps on happening until a **stop codon** is encountered such as UAA (see the genetic code on pg. 125). When a stop codon is lined up with the A site, no tRNA parks there; rather a **release factor** parks which causes the mRNA, tRNA, and the newly translated protein to fall off the ribosome. This newly minted protein, as mentioned in the organelle chapter, may undergo several make-overs in the rough and/or smooth ER and/or Golgi body before it is ready for action in the cell.

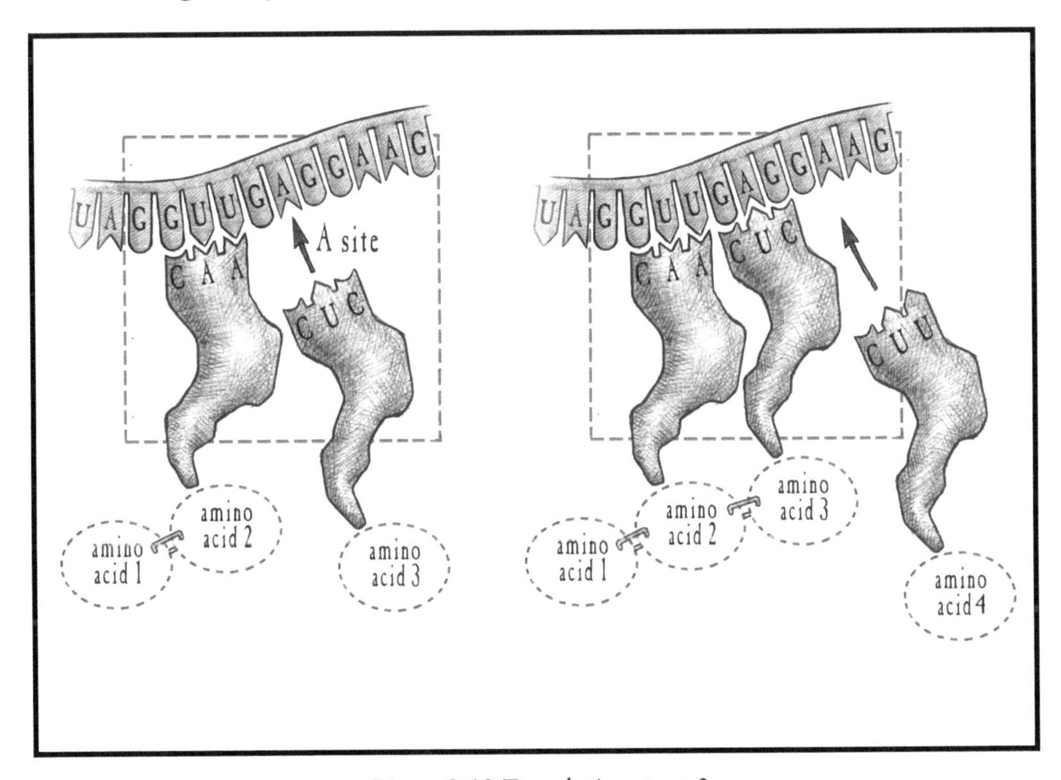

Figure 9.13 Translation, part 2

THE BIG PICTURE

Ponder a moment about the significance of transcription and translation. Proteins essentially run the cell and every single protein is made at ribosomes. The enzymes (which are proteins) do thousands of chemical reactions whether it be building molecules for the cell or burning food molecules for the energy needs of the cell. Consider all the proteins for membrane transport and all the enzymes that carry out transcription and translation; they are all translated at the ribosomes after their genes were transcribed from the DNA. This may provoke the question, "If enzymes are necessary to make enzymes, how did the first enzymes arise? Where did the first enzymes necessary to orchestrate the very first transcription come from? They couldn't have been made through transcription and translation because they would need to exist in order to bring about their own existence. Hmmmmm?

CHAPTER 9: REVIEW QUESTIONS

1. Who were the two main discoverers of the structure of DNA?
2. Who also won the Nobel Prize with them?
3. The data most valuable to this discovery was generated by two scientists named ______ and ______.
4. What are the three parts to a nucleotide?
5. What are the four different nitrogenous bases?
6. The double helix can be likened to a twisted ladder. The 'ladder sides' are called the ______ backbones and the "rungs" are the base-pairs.
7. In a chromosome, DNA is neatly wrapped around proteins called histones forming little repeating spools called ______.
8. The enzyme that unzips the two parental strands of DNA apart and constructs a complementary strand of RNA is called ______.
9. Name three structural differences between RNA and DNA nucleotides.
10. If a DNA strand is T-A-C-G-C-G-C-T-T-G-A-T-T-T-A, what is the mRNA sequence? (Put a slash between codons.)

11. What is the amino acid sequence? (Use the three letter abbreviations for the amino acids; refer to the genetic code below.)

FIRST BASE	SECOND BASE				THIRD BASE
	U	C	A	G	
U	Phe	Ser	Tyr	Cys	U
	Phe	Ser	Tyr	Cys	C
	Leu	Ser	STOP	STOP	A
	Leu	Ser	STOP	Trp	G
C	Leu	Pro	His	Arg	U
	Leu	Pro	His	Arg	C
	Leu	Pro	Gln	Arg	A
	Leu	Pro	Gln	Arg	G
A	Ile	Thr	Asn	Ser	U
	Ile	Thr	Asn	Ser	C
	Ile	Thr	Lys	Arg	A
	Met	Thr	Lys	Arg	G
G	Val	Ala	Asp	Gly	U
	Val	Ala	Asp	Gly	C
	Val	Ala	Glu	Gly	A
	Val	Ala	Glu	Gly	G

12. When protein is made from an mRNA transcript, the process is called ______.

13. What molecule contains the anticodon and retrieves the appropriate amino acid?

14. True or False. Portions of RNA are snipped out (i.e., edited out) and the remaining pieces are spliced together before translation occurs.

CHAPTER 10

THE LAC OPERON

HOW GENES ARE TURNED OFF AND ON

When we speak of genes being turned on, it means that a particular gene is transcribed, and then translated. In other words, the cell is going to make a protein from a particular gene. Every cell in our body has all the genes for every human protein. In other words, every cell has all the genetic instructions. However, a particular cell obviously doesn't make all the proteins it's capable of. For instance, our liver cells have the genes to code for hair protein (keratin) but no liver cell worth its bile would transcribe and translate the human hair gene. None of us would do well with a hairy liver. No. The hair genes are thankfully turned off in the liver and the liver enzyme genes are turned off in our hair follicle cells. Only the genes necessary for a particular cell's job are turned on. We don't think about it, but the body has many ways to turn on and off our genes. Back in the 1960s Jacque Monod and Francois Jacob, two French Jedi knights of molecular biology discovered the first mechanism of how genes are turned on or off.

The organism that they studied and discovered the first instance of gene regulation was *E. coli,* the bacterial 'lab rat'. The word **operon** was coined for any gene or set of genes that is turned on or off as a single unit. The specific operon they studied was called the **Lac Operon** because it was a set of genes in *E. coli* which was turned on if the disaccharide, lactose, was available as a food source. If lactose was absent in the food supply then the genes were turned off. This was a tremendous breakthrough because it showed how an organism, in principle, could regulate genes analogous to how a thermostat regulates heat production. In the same way that a thermostat keeps the furnace off if it is warm enough, the cell doesn't make a particular protein unless it is needed by the cell.

The structure of the lac operon involves several regions on the DNA. First, the cell makes a continual supply of a **repressor protein** so that it is always on hand. Downstream on the DNA is a promoter (where the RNA polymerase attaches to transcribe the gene or genes). Right next to the

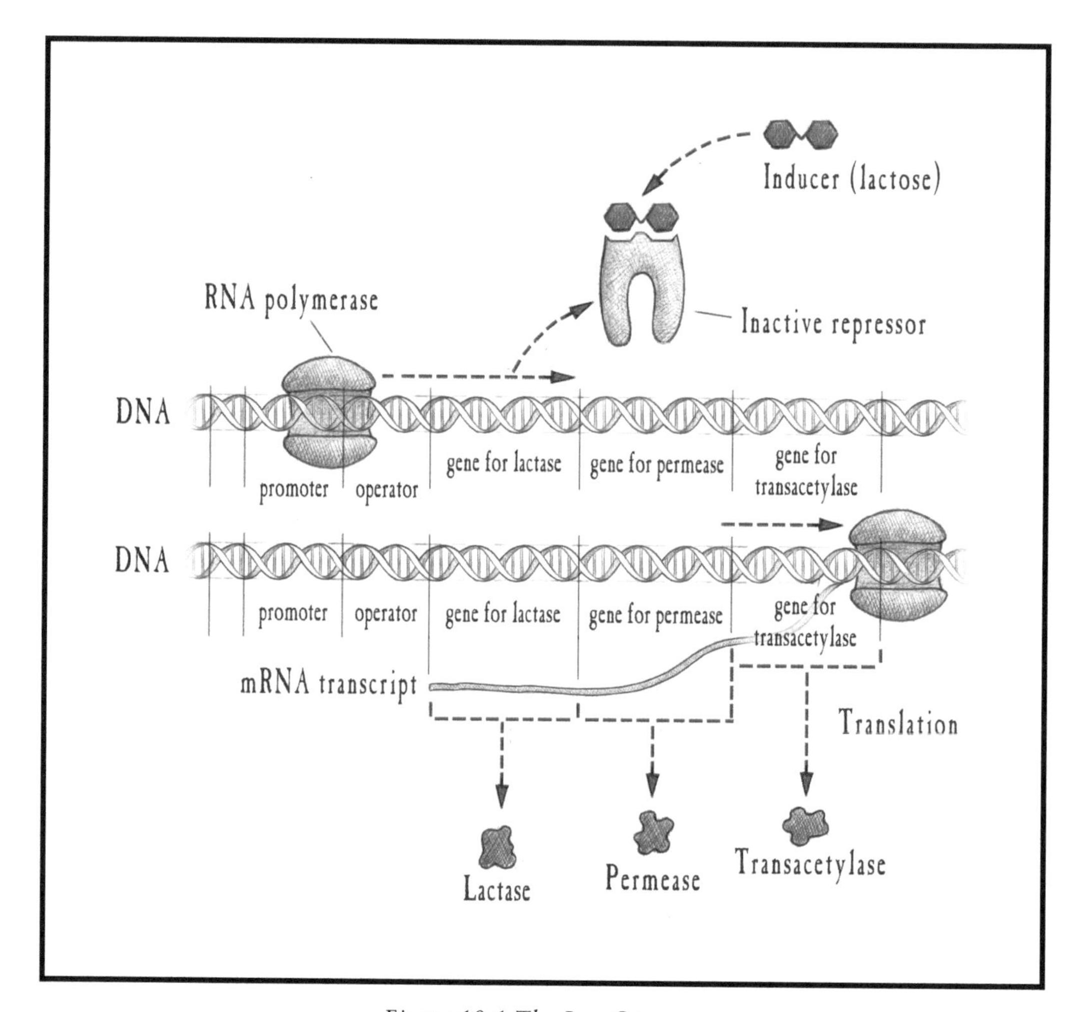

Figure 10.1 The Lac Operon

promoter just downstream is another region of the DNA called an **operator.** This is where the repressor protein binds. If it does, it literally acts like a roadblock for the RNA polymerase. In fact, the RNA polymerase can't even attach to the DNA if the repressor is bound to the operator. So what can't the RNA polymerase transcribe due to the repressor's blockade? The genes that are being blocked are the gene for lactase (also called β-galactosidase, an enzyme that hydrolyzes lactose), the gene for permease (a membrane protein that pumps lactose into the cell), and transacetylase (don't worry about this).

If lactose is unavailable to the cell there is no point in making proteins necessary for lactose metabolism. Consequently the lac *repressor* binds to the *operator* and effectively blocks the transcription of these genes responsible for lactose metabolism. On the other hand, sometimes lactose is available or is the only food source for the bacterium, so when this happens lactose enters the cell. At this point no enzyme is being made that can hydrolyze lactose. Lactose acts as an inducer in that it binds to the repressor causing it to fall off the operator.

When this occurs the RNA polymerase is free to bind to the promoter and can happily transcribe the genes in the operon. The RNA made is then translated at the ribosome. The first two proteins made, fold up into their 3D structure. The first, the enzyme lactase, chops lactose in two so the two resulting monosaccharides can be 'burned' in cellular respiration. The second, permease, becomes a membrane protein designed to pump lactose into the cell so that the bacterium can metabolize it. This whole process eventually can shut itself down. Once the lactose is consumed, lactose is no longer available to act as an inducer. When there is no more lactose hogtying the repressor, the repressor is able bind to the operator which once again effectively shuts down the transcription of the genes involved in lactose metabolism.

CHAPTER 10: REVIEW QUESTIONS

1. What protein attaches to the operator to prevent certain genes from being transcribed in the lac operon?
2. What is the place on DNA to which RNA polymerase attaches at the beginning of transcription?
3. A gene or a set of genes that are turned on or off by a single switch is called a(n) ______.
4. In the lac operon, lactose binds to the ______ which causes it to fall off the operator.
5. If this binding occurs, name the first enzyme that is made (translated)?
6. What does this enzyme do?

CHAPTER 11

RECOMBINANT DNA TECHNOLOGY

AND GENETIC MODIFICATION

It wasn't long after these great biomolecular breakthroughs were discovered (the structure of DNA by Watson and Crick, the central dogma, the lac operon by Monod and Jacob, etc.) that practical applications were being researched and put to use. Several researchers (Daniel Nathans, Werner Arber, and Hamilton Smith) in the late 60s and early 70s discovered several enzymes that actually cut DNA at specific sequences. They were awarded the Nobel Prize in 1978. These enzymes were dubbed **restriction enzymes** because they restricted foreign DNA from successfully invading the cell. They served as a molecular DNA 'shredder'. Foreign DNA, say from a virus, would be chopped up into harmless fragments so the virus couldn't do its mischief in the cell it was trying to invade. Dozens of different restriction enzymes have been discovered and named since then. Each enzyme's **restriction site** (the DNA sequence it specifically binds to and cuts) has also been determined. One famous and frequently used restriction enzyme is *Eco*R1 (isolated from *E. coli*). Its restriction site is

```
----GAATTC---------
----CTTAAG---------
```

This kind of cut produces overhanging 'sticky ends.'

```
----G        AATTC---------
----CTTAA        G---------
```

If a segment of DNA is cut out of a genome (a **genome** is the entire hereditary information of an organism) using a particular restriction enzyme and the very same enzyme is used to cut another piece of DNA, the two fragments could be spliced together since they would have identical sticky ends. But this is hard to do without the aid of an enzyme designed to splice sticky ends together. Fortunately, just such an enzyme was discovered in a virus at about the same time. It was dubbed **DNA ligase**. This enzyme was opposite in function to the restriction enzymes in that its job is to splice any matching sticky ends together. Other key players essential for recombinant DNA technology were small hoops of DNA found in bacteria called **plasmids.**

Certain laboratory techniques were worked out so that plasmids or any other DNA could be separated from the rest of the cell and purified. Once purified and placed in test tubes, a **gene of interest** from a certain organism could be cut out and spliced into a plasmid using a restriction enzyme and DNA ligase. The plasmid would serve as a vector (vehicle) to introduce the gene of interest into a recipient cell. Once a DNA fragment has been spliced into a plasmid (recombinant DNA) within a test tube, the next challenge is to successfully insert it into a recipient cell. This is called **transformation** and is defined as the uptake of DNA into a cell such that the cell actually transcribes and translates (expresses) it. One way this can be done is to use chemicals and heat to make the recipient cell wall and membrane leaky enough for external DNA to slip through it. **Transduction** is another type of transformation that uses virus particles as a vector to insert foreign DNA into a cell.

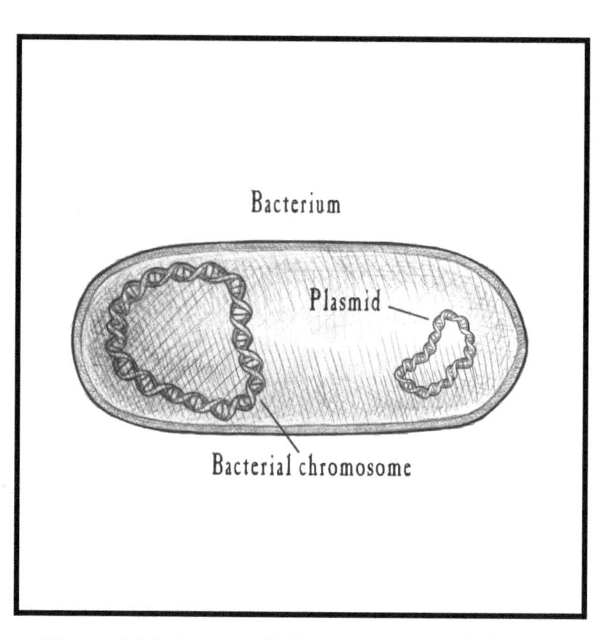

Figure 11.1 Bacterial chromosome and plasmid

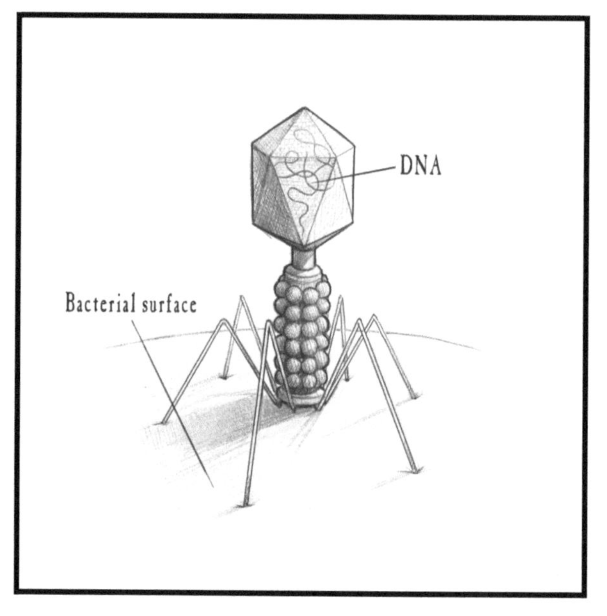

Figure 11.2 Transduction

Conjugation is the introduction of DNA into a bacterial cell through a **pilus.** A pilus is a tiny tube constructed by the bacteria that can temporarily link two cells together. Replicated DNA can travel through the tube from the donor cell into the recipient cell. This natural process can be harnessed by man to introduce recombinant DNA from one bacterial cell into another.

Gene guns (bioballistics) literally shoot DNA-coated microscopic metal particles into the cell.

Whether artificial or natural, transformation is the use of these techniques to introduce DNA into a recipient cell.

The basic steps in recombinant DNA technology:

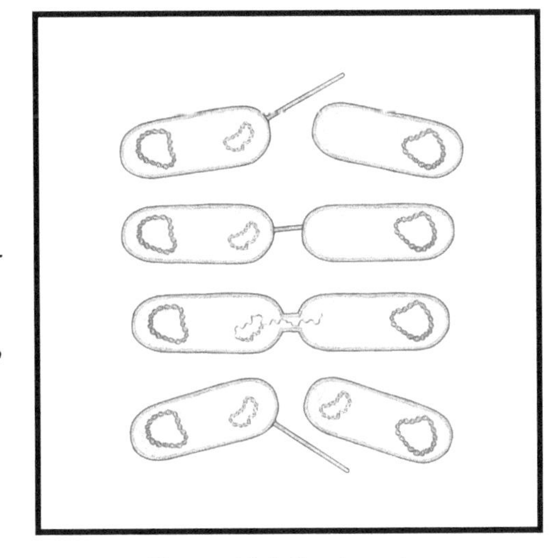

Figure 11.3 Conjugation

- Purify DNA containing *gene of interest*
- Cut out *gene of interest* with appropriate restriction enzyme(s)
- Separate *gene of interest* from DNA it was cut from
- Open up purified plasmid with same restriction enzyme
- Add *gene of interest* to opened up plasmid
- Splice *gene of interest* into plasmid using DNA ligase thus creating recombinant DNA
- Transformation of recipient cell with recombinant DNA (plasmid)

In order to determine which cells successfully received the plasmid, the plasmid needs to have an antibiotic resistance gene on it. After transformation has been performed (this is done to millions or billions of cells and only a tiny fraction of the total actually take up the plasmid) the cells are spread out on a Petri-dish containing the antibiotic. The antibiotic used in the Petri-dish needs to be the kind with the recombinant plasmid that has a gene that confers resistance. In other words, if it's ampicillin in the Petri-dish, the plasmid must have a gene that is resistant to ampicillin. So the only cells that survive and reproduce are the ones that were transformed by the plasmid. The cells that didn't take up the plasmid die from the ampicillin.

A FEW APPLICATIONS

Making Insulin for Type I Diabetics

This disease afflicts thousands of people and is lethal if the victim is not treated with insulin. In this disease the pancreas has lost the ability to produce its own insulin. Insulin is the protein hormone that enables body cells to take up glucose from the blood stream and without it our cells die because they can't get enough glucose as fuel to make ATP. The glucose is plentiful in the blood but it can't be brought into our cells without insulin. Type 1 diabetics, prior to recombinant DNA technology, had to rely on insulin derived from cattle or pigs. This was expensive and risky because animal insulin isn't quite the same and would sometimes trigger dangerous

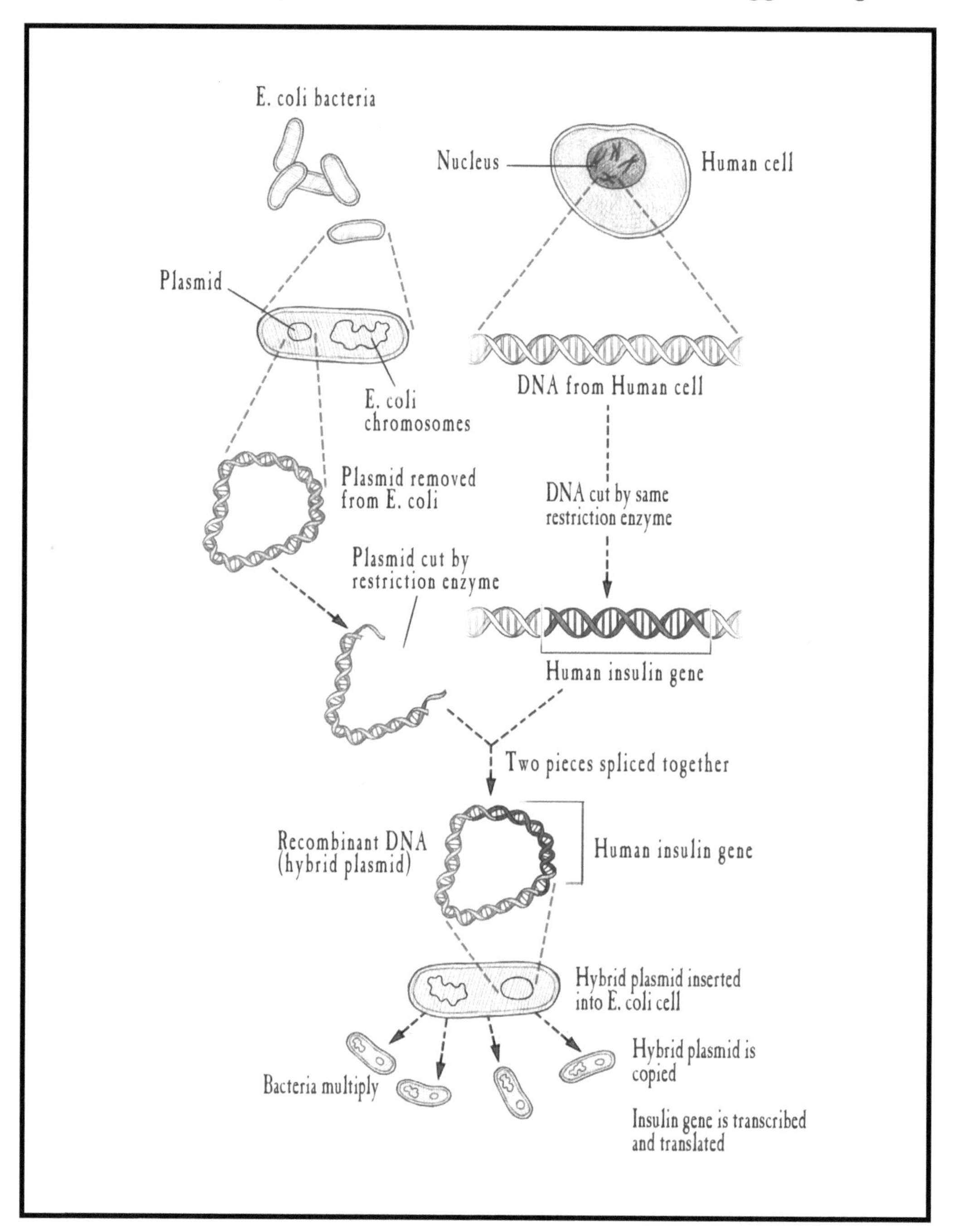

Figure 11.4 E. coli making human insulin

allergic reactions in the patient receiving it. Recombinant DNA technology was a Godsend. In 1978, Herb Boyer successfully produced a synthetic human insulin gene (there was a moratorium on recombinant DNA experiments at the time, but it didn't apply to synthetic genes). He cut open a purified *E. coli* plasmid (vector) and spliced the synthetic insulin gene into the plasmid using DNA ligase. This was then followed by the transformation of *E. coli*. The plasmid would be inserted into living *E. coli* cells. Thanks to this technology, human insulin can now be produced by these tranformed bacteria in great quantities for patients with Type 1 diabetes.

Gene Therapy for SCIDS (Severe Combined Immunodeficiency Syndrome)
This tragic congenital disease results in an immune system that is extremely crippled. There are several forms of SCID which arise from a few different mutations but they all result in the bone marrow making extremely defective B and T cells (lymphocytes). B and T cells play an essential role in the adaptive immune response. This condition has been called the "Bubble boy" disease because victims must be kept in a sterile bubble if they are to be protected from a whole host of pathogens (disease-causing germs) that surround all of us daily. For SCID patients contracting the mildest 'bug' is life threatening. Though early attempts at gene therapy (treatment using recombinant DNA technology) occasionally resulted in tragedy, it has enjoyed recent success and holds much promise for the future. One form of SCID is due to a defective ADA (adenosine deaminase) gene. Molecular biologists have been able to cut normal ADA genes from the human genome using a particular restriction enzyme. Normal ADA genes are then spliced into bacterial plasmids and inserted into bacteria via transformation. Through another method, the ADA genes are inserted into viral vectors (these viruses have been made harmless). Defective T cells are taken from the SCID patient, cultured outside the body, and infected with harmless viruses containing normal ADA genes (viruses have 'tricks' that enable them to insert their DNA into the genome of the host cell they enter). In this way normal ADA genes are incorporated into the defective T cells so that they get 'fixed'. These genetically modified T cells are cultured to make sure they can indeed make ADA. If so, the healthy T cells are reintroduced into the bone marrow of the SCID patient. Recent successes using gene therapy have cured SCID victims and have enabled them to live normal lives outside the bubble.

Genetically Modified Crops

Recombinant DNA technology can also be employed with plants, particularly crops. There is a soil-inhabiting bacterium called *Agrobacterium tumefaciens* which commonly infects a wide array of broadleaf plants and gives them the disease called crown-gall.

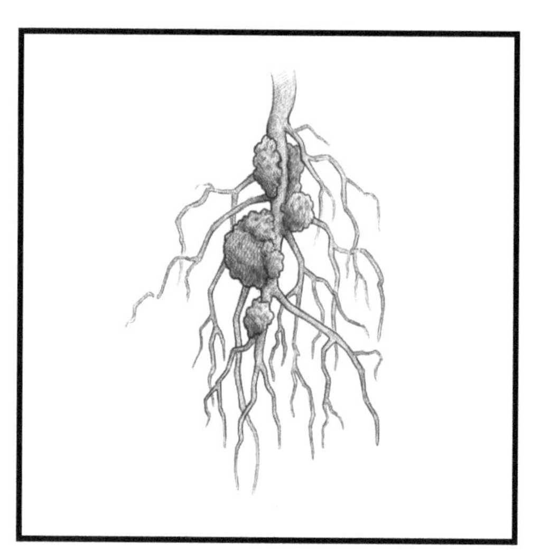

Figure 11.5 Crown gall

This bacterium is a natural genetic engineer thanks to its T*i* plasmid. This plasmid has a number of tumor-inducing genes as well as a *vir* region which enables the bacterium to insert its tumor-inducing genes into the plant genome. After it enters through a plant wound it does just that. The genes code for enzymes that manufacture plant hormones at levels that throw off normal plant development. The end result is a nasty warty-looking tumor in which the bacteria happily reside. How can this be used for good? First, through recombinant

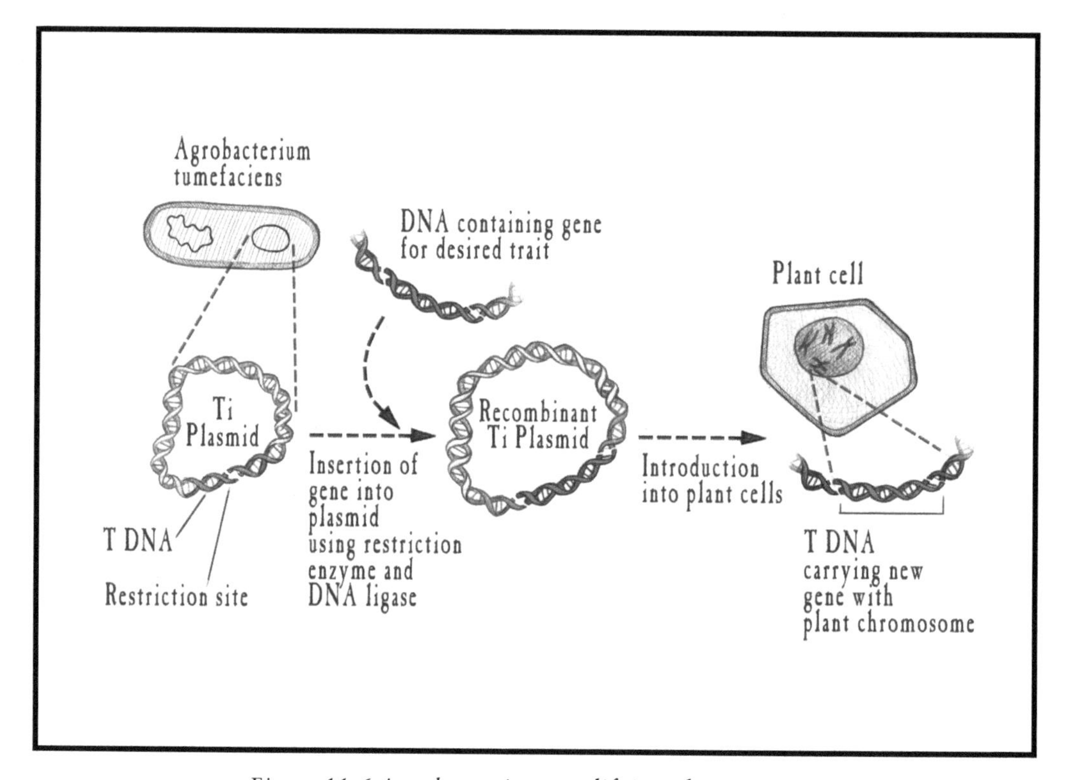

Figure 11.6 Agrobacterium modifying plant genome

DNA technology, the T*i* plasmid is genetically modified by cutting out the tumor-inducing genes using a restriction enzyme and then splicing it back together again using DNA ligase (nothing inserted). Another recombinant plasmid (containing the tumor-inducing genes) is cut open using restriction enzymes. This cut interrupts the tumor-inducing genes. Then a foreign fragment of DNA (presumably some *useful gene* with the appropriate sticky ends) is spliced into the recombinant plasmid. This plasmid is inserted into *Agrobacterium* having a harmless T*i* plasmid. Some target crop plant is then infected with this bacterium. Since it has a T*i* plasmid with the *vir* region, it can successfully insert this *useful gene* into the plant genome. However, since the tumor-inducing genes were removed, the plant doesn't get the disease. It can now express this new gene. Here are some examples of how *Agrobacterium* has delivered beneficial abilities to crop plants. Using this method they have modified certain crops with a gene that codes for a toxin (BT toxin) that kills caterpillars (harmless to humans). The crop is essentially the same, except when caterpillars start munching on the plant, they die. They have also modified crops with a gene that makes them resistant to the herbicide, Roundup (which normally kills broadleaf plants and grasses). As a result, weeds of all kinds (grass and broadleaf weeds) can be eliminated without harming the crop plants.

CHAPTER 11:REVIEW QUESTIONS

1. Enzymes used to cut DNA at specific sequences are called ______ enzymes.
2. The enzyme used to splice DNA fragments together is called ______.
3. Overhanging ends of single-stranded DNA which facilitate the splicing process are called ______.
4. After a *gene of interest* is spliced into a plasmid, what must be done next in order to put the gene to work?
5. What mode of DNA acquisition involves the uptake of 'foreign DNA'?
6. What mode of DNA acquisition involves a virus as a vehicle to inject DNA into the cell?
7. What mode of DNA acquisition is from a bacterium to another bacterium through pilus?
8. List the seven basic steps in recombinant DNA technology.

CHAPTER 12

MITOSIS AND CELL DIVISION

It's very important to lay conceptual groundwork before plunging into mitosis and cell division. Too often students memorize this process but do not know a stitch about the purposeful and logical progression of the events that happen. Knowing *why* it's happening the way it does makes it much easier to memorize *what's* happening. Memorizing a ballad in English is a lot easier than memorizing it in a foreign language of which you know nothing. Why? It's because you understand the story in English. Consequently, memorizing the specific word order is easy because you know the progression of events in the story. Many biology students memorize biological processes the way they would memorize a ballad in Chinese: brute memorization of weird-sounding syllables in a certain order that mean nothing. Let's try to make it easier than that and learn it like you would learn a story.

DNA REPLICATION

I put off telling you about one process in the central dogma (DNA replication) because it is a great prelude to understanding why chromosomes look like skinny Xs. And in order to understand mitosis (the division of the nucleus) it really helps to understand why the chromosomes look like Xs.

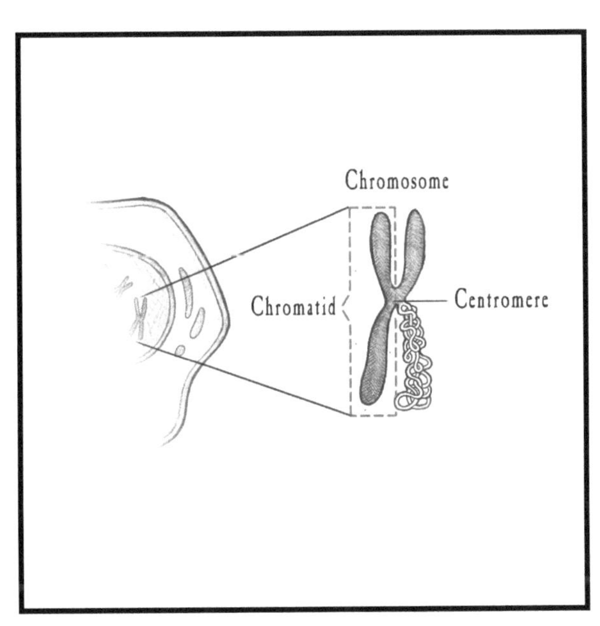

Figure 12.1 Chromosome

Before mitosis occurs, the DNA in the nucleus needs to

replicate itself. The DNA of one nucleus is not one long strand that coils up into one big chromosome. Rather, all the genetic material is contained on different pieces of DNA (when the DNA is in its uncoiled state it is called **chromatin**). Each species has a certain number of chromosomes per nucleus. In bats the chromosome number is 44. In camels, the chromosome number is 70. In humans, it's 46, and in mosquitoes, it's 6. The number of separate pieces of DNA is the number of chromosomes.

Now why does each chromosome (after the DNA coils up) look like an X? The answer is that the right half is an identical copy of the left half. Each half is called a **sister chromatid** but to avoid confusion I like to call them one-copy chromosomes. When they are together, as in Figure 12.2, I call them two-copy chromosomes. This is very important to understand so that you won't get confused later. Two-copy chromosomes are like receipts in duplicate. When the cashier prints it out (both copies) you can legitimately call it one receipt. When she gives you one copy, did you get a half of a receipt? No! You got a whole receipt (one copy) and she got a whole receipt (one copy). It is the same with chromosomes. A sister chromatid isn't half a chromosome. It is one copy from the duplicated chromosome.

THE PROCESS OF DNA REPLICATION

In order for a long strand of DNA to be replicated, it must first be unzipped. This is accomplished when the DNA is not all coiled up into a skein-like chromosome. Rather, it is unwound in its chromatin state. An enzyme called **Helicase** unzips the double helix into two single strands. As it is unzipping another important enzyme called **DNA polymerase** grabs the single stranded DNA and, in a manner very similar to RNA, polymerase 'reads' the exposed bases and snatches DNA nucleotides from the nucleotide stockpile in the nucleoplasm. The main difference is that it is not reading one to a few genes: it is replicating the entire piece of DNA. One old strand is receiving a new complementary strand and the other old strand is receiving a new complementary strand. When this is finished, the *one copy chromosome* is now a *two-copy chromosome*, i.e. it looks like an X when it coils up (Figure 12.2).

So, why should the cell make each of its one-copy chromosomes into a two-copy chromosome? When the nucleus divides in two, each new nucleus receives one complete chromosome of each kind. For example, mosquitoes have six chromosomes. When a mosquito cell divides into two daughter cells, those daughter cells both need a nucleus with six chromosomes. That is why DNA replication needs to occur before the nucleus and cell divide.

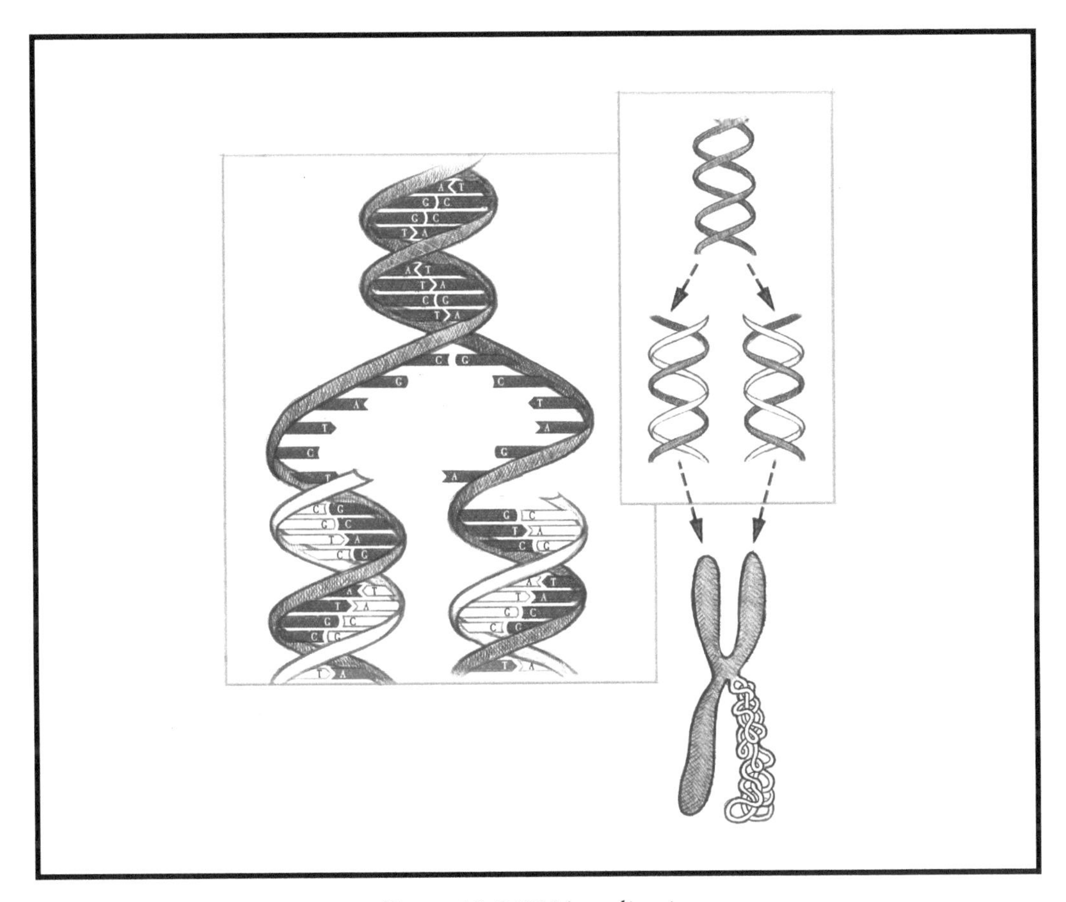

Figure 12.2 DNA replication

In summary, all the genetic information in a cell needs to be duplicated so that when the nucleus divides, each new daughter cell receives a complete set of genetic information.

Secondly, since the DNA needs to be divided equally between two cells, the DNA pieces need to be coiled up into chromosomes. Similarly, when getting ready to move your belongings to a different house, you usually pack it up in boxes. It makes the move easier and more orderly. However, prior to coiling up, DNA replication must occur so that all the chromosomes are two-copy. Replication can't occur when the DNA is all coiled up into the dense chromosomes.

INTERPHASE: THE NORMAL LIFE OF THE CELL

This period of time is the majority of the cell's existence. This is when cells live and carry out their normal daily activities. The DNA is all uncoiled so that under the microscope you would not observe discrete skein-like chromosomes, just a grayish haze (chromatin). This is when DNA replication, RNA transcription, normal cellular activity, and growth occur. **Interphase** is usually divided up into three phases.

- **G1** (gap 1): normal cell growth and activity
- **S** (synthesis): DNA replication (so all one-copy chromosomes become two-copy)
- **G2** (gap 2): cell growth, synthesis of proteins particularly important in mitosis

Interphase can be a permanent state for certain cells, but for cells destined to divide the cell transitions into mitosis: the process in which one nucleus divides into two nuclei. This is normally accompanied by the whole cell dividing where each new daughter cell receives one nucleus, but it can occur without cellular division.

MITOSIS: THE DIVISION OF THE NUCLEUS

Prophase, Metaphase, Anaphase, and Telophase (PMAT)

Prophase

Rather than rattle off all the events of **prophase**, I want to tell you why each event occurs along with what occurs. (See Figure 12.3 on page 149 for a drawing of the whole process.) It is of paramount importance that as cells divide to grow into multicellular creatures, each cell gets a complete set of genetic information. As I have said, the S phase in interphase accomplished *DNA replication* so that each daughter cell can receive one copy of each chromosome. To keep things from looking too complicated, we will consider mosquito cell division. Recall that mosquitoes have six chromosomes per cell. As a mosquito cell enters mitosis, its DNA must coil up into (six) two-copy chromosomes. Why coil up? If you are going to move across town, the most sensible thing to do is pack up your belongings so that they are consolidated into discrete boxes that can be moved easily and efficiently. Similarly the DNA can be easily divvied up into separate cells if it is coiled up into compact, tidy chromosomes. If the DNA remained uncoiled during division it would be like trying to tease apart one colander full of ultra-long spaghetti noodles onto two separate plates without breaking any noodles. That would not likely be a successful operation. Rather (at the risk of running with this analogy too far), it would be good if each noodle coiled itself into something like a package of Ramen (just out of the bag). That way the noodles could be separated without tangling and breaking.

Another event that happens simultaneously with DNA coiling is the disintegration of the nuclear envelope. Although this doesn't happen when folks move to another house, wouldn't it be great if all the barriers like the interior walls and walls of the house automatically disassembled during the move so that all the boxes and furniture could be moved into the moving van with ease? Then after the move, the walls would automatically erect themselves back to their original structural soundness (work with me . . . it's just an analogy).

When moving it is also essential to have people, either professional movers or friends help you move the stuff into the moving vans or trucks. So what is the cellular equivalent of movers? The microtubules, previously mentioned in the chapter on cellular organelles, are one of the cytoskeletal elements of the cell. These form cellular 'gondola cables' upon which various motor proteins ratchet along carrying some type of cargo. In mitosis, a whole mess of microtubules assemble and span the cell in such an orientation that when the chromosomes attach to them, a motor protein (on the chromosome) can actually haul them along the microtubule. These points of attachment between the chromosomes and the spindle microtubules are called **kinetochores**. They are protein assemblages that pinch the two-copy chromosomes together like a rubber band holding two skeins of yarn together. The kinetochore also contains a little ATP-driven motor protein that literally chews its way along the microtubule. The specialized assemblage of microtubules upon which the chromosomes haul themselves along is called the **mitotic spindle**. Also during prophase, each chromosome attaches to the mitotic spindle by its corset-like kinetochore, and then each chromosome is 'jockeyed around' towards the plane of division (plane . . . not 'line of division' because cells are three dimensional). This plane of division, also called the **spindle equator**, is usually located in the middle of the cell. This plane will be where the cell actually divides. Because there are lots of things going on in prophase, it is the longest phase of mitosis. See Figure 12.3 for the picture.

Metaphase

This is very a short and sweet phase. When the (six) two-copy chromosomes are neatly aligned along this spindle equator, with the identical copies of each chromosome facing towards opposite sides of the cell, then this arrangement constitutes **metaphase**. That's it.

Anaphase

In metaphase, the (six) two-copy chromosomes are lined up and are ready to be 'drawn and quartered'. The kinetochore, as mentioned, is designed to chew its way along the microtubule such that the tubulin subunits are released from the cylindrical microtubule. In **anaphase**, the two copies of each chromosome separate from each other due to their respective kinetochores munching their way in opposite directions along a microtubule. One copy of each chromosome moves toward one side of the cell and its identical sister chromatid moves to the other side of the cell. We started with six two-copy chromosomes in the middle, and end up with six one-copy chromosomes on opposite sides.

Telophase

The last of the four phases begins when the one-copy chromosomes arrive at the opposite poles of the cell. To recap, the mother cell had six two-copy chromosomes, so now there are six one-copy chromosomes on opposite ends of the cell. **Telophase** is essentially the opposite of prophase. Use the simple logic of moving to predict what must happen. After you move to your new location, your futuristic self-assembling house erects itself around your belongings. With regard to telophase, a new nuclear envelope forms around the two clusters of one-copy chromosomes. Also, once you've finished moving you can send the movers away (after you've fed them pizza). In the same way, the microtubules which provided transport cables for chromosome movement are no longer needed in this abundance or arrangement, so much of the spindle disintegrates. Of course, some microtubules hang around to provide normal transportation cables in the cell. What else happens after your move? You unpack your belongings so that they can be used in your new abode. Similarly, the chromosomes uncoil so that the cell has access to the genetic information during the subsequent interphase, i.e. RNA transcription (G_1 or G_2) or DNA replication (S phase).

Cytokinesis

Cytokinesis is the actual dividing of the original cytoplasm into two separate compartments. This splitting occurs at the same time as telophase and happens at the plane of division, right where the chromosomes were all lined up in the middle of the cell during metaphase. The two separate compartments contain one nucleus each from the recent nuclear division. The organelles of the mother cell are divvied up equably, although not necessarily in perfectly equal portions. When cytokinesis is finished we finally

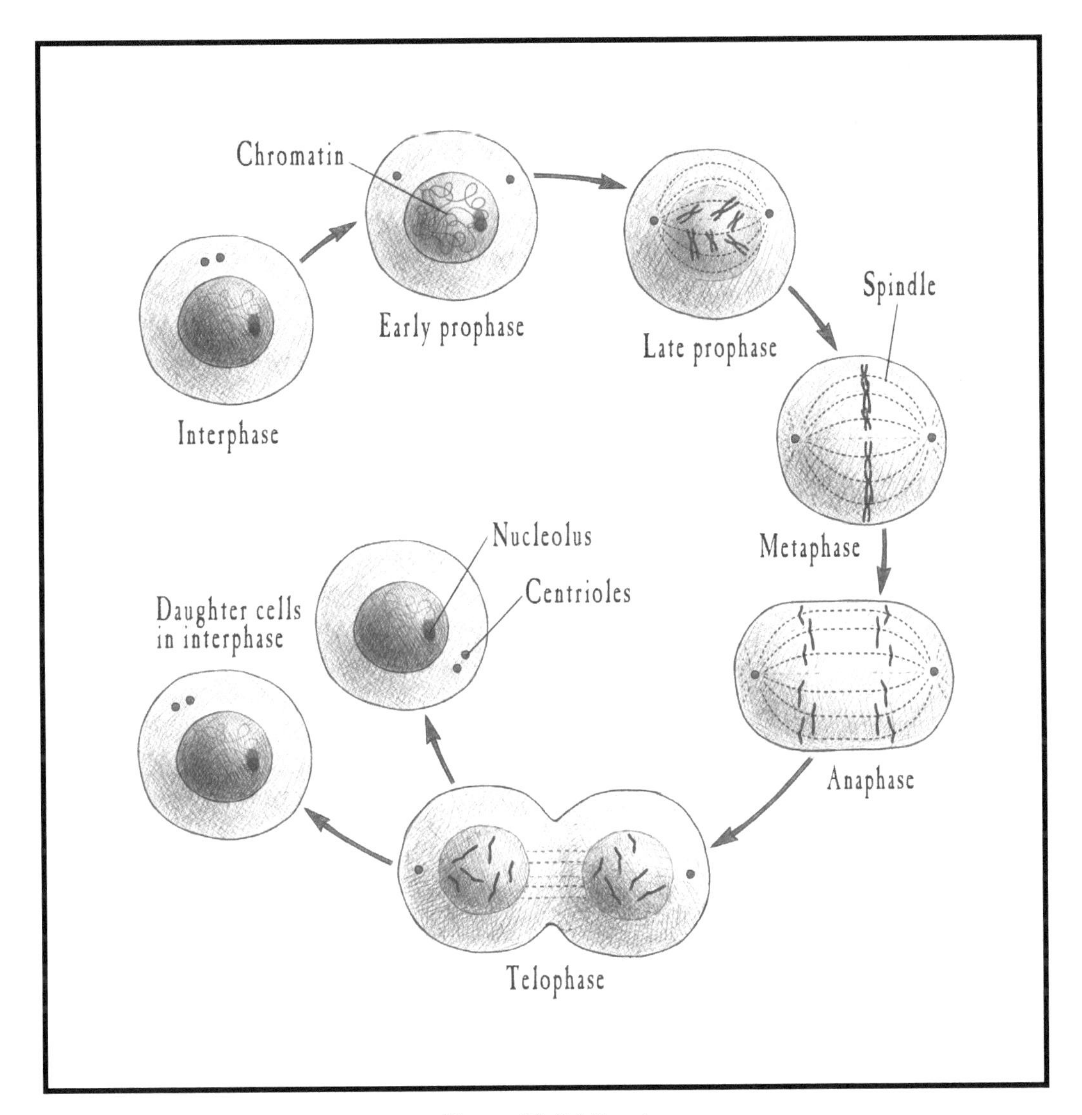

Figure 12.3 Mitosis

have two new cells that enter the normal cellular life of interphase. These daughter cells, depending on the type of organism and where the cells are located in the organism, may or may not undergo another mitotic division. If the cells remain unspecialized (undifferentiated) then they often retain the ability to undergo more mitosis. However, if they become specialized (differentiated) then they usually forfeit the ability to do mitosis.

There are two basic versions of cytokinesis that occur during telophase of mitosis. In human and animal cells, various cytoskeletal elements form an apparatus that cinches up the membrane surrounding the plane of division like a drawstring (although the cinching is internally exerted). The cell splits in two compartments similar to a balloon sculptor twisting a balloon into two segments. This is called **cleavage furrowing.**

In plant cells, the splitting occurs through a very different process. It is called **cell plate formation.** Since plants have cell walls, cleavage furrowing is not practicable. Instead, plant cell Golgi bodies were designed to manufacture and pinch off lots of little cellulose vesicles which congregate along the plane of division. These vesicles begin fusing to form a cell plate

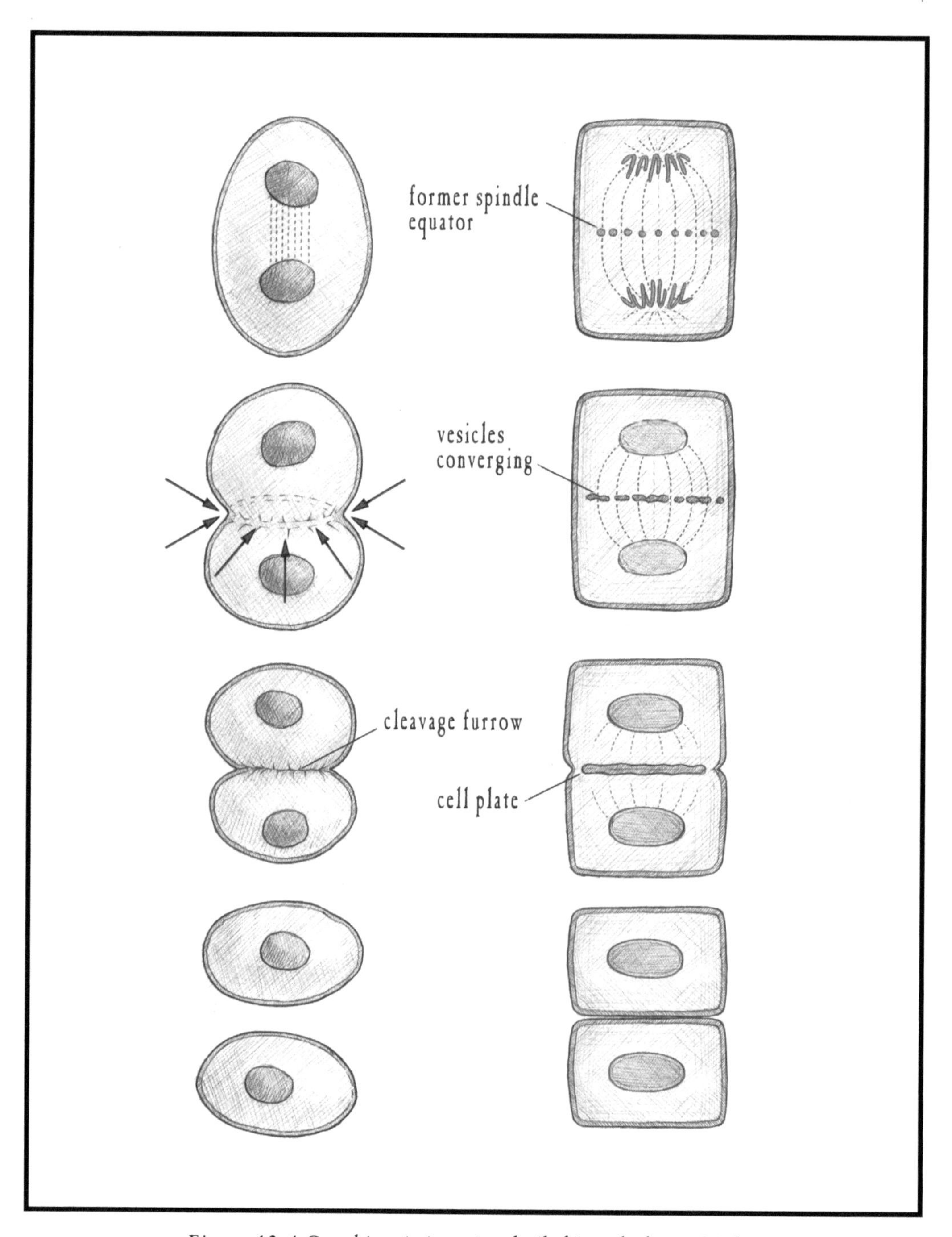

Figure 12.4 Cytokinesis in animals (left) and plants (right)

like a cubical partition partially separating two office spaces. The cell plate continues to expand as more cellulose vesicles are added. Eventually the cell plate connects to the cell wall surrounding the plane of division so that now there are two separate cells.

CHAPTER 12: REVIEW QUESTIONS

1. What process in the central dogma needs to occur for mitosis to occur?
2. This above process occurs during ______ phase of interphase.
3. The enzyme that produces daughter strands of DNA by placing complementary nucleotides along each parental strand is called ______.
4. Why does this need to occur before mitosis?
5. A skein of DNA and proteins is called a ______.
6. Chromosomes are lined up at the spindle equator during ______.
7. DNA coils up into chromosomes, the spindle forms, and the nuclear envelope breaks up during ______.
8. Plant cytokinesis is accomplished through the formation of a ______ at the spindle equator.
9. Sister chromatids (one-copy chromosomes) migrate to opposite poles of the cell during ______ of mitosis.
10. When the spindle disappears, the chromosomes unravel, and the nuclear envelope reforms around each nucleus, the cell is in what phase of mitosis?______.

CHAPTER 13

MEIOSIS

Meiosis, though having a lot in common with mitosis, is a bit of a bear to teach without it looking mighty complicated. Before you read on, make sure that you understand the steps and logic of mitosis. As before, it is paramount to lay some groundwork before we plunge in head first.

Why meiosis? In sexual reproduction (in humans and animals) certain cells called sperm and egg unite to form a fertilized egg called a **zygote**. The zygote then divides by mitosis to eventually form the adult. As we learned in the last chapter, humans have 46 chromosomes per cell. If we produced sperm and egg by mitosis, then each sperm cell would have 46 chromosomes and so would each egg. If fertilization occurred in this unfortunate arrangement we would have a serious problem. 46 plus 46 equals 92 chromosomes in the zygote, which would be lethal. With each generation the chromosome number would double. Thankfully human zygotes don't have 92 chromosomes: they only have 46. This means that a sperm and egg must have 23 chromosomes each. This insures that when they come together they will yield the normal chromosome number of 46. Meiosis is that special kind of nuclear division that insures that the resulting cells have half the original number.

HOMOLOGOUS CHROMOSOMES

I now need to explain something that wasn't necessary to broach when discussing mitosis. Chromosomes are like shoes—they come in pairs (this has nothing to do with "two-copy" chromosomes, which we'll discuss in a bit). When I mentioned different chromosome numbers in different creatures (i.e., humans have 46 or mosquitoes have 6), those numbers represent a double set (2N, where N is a complete set of chromosomes). In other words, human cells have 46 chromosomes or 23 pairs of homologous chromosomes. **Homologous chromosomes** are very similar to each other in size, shape, and the genes they carry. Let's get personal. Each one of your cells has 46 chromosomes. This is because you started out as one cell, a zygote. You, the zygote, had 46 chromosomes. Now you are composed of roughly 35 to 40 trillion cells (if you're an average size person) and every one of them has 46 chromosomes because mitosis has always maintained the same number of chromosomes per cell through all those rounds of mitosis you've undergone. So why do you have 46 chromosomes per cell? Because 23 chromosomes from your mom was in the egg and 23 chromosomes from your dad was in the sperm at your conception. When the sperm fertilized the egg, two complete sets of human chromosomes merged together to yield a zygote with 46 (1N=23, 2N=46). Having one complete set of chromosomes (**1N**) is also called **haploid**. Having two complete sets (**2N**) is called **diploid**. There are 23 kinds of chromosomes in humans, and all normal humans have two of each kind. Suppose the two chromosomes in Figure 13.1 are a homologous pair of chromosomes.

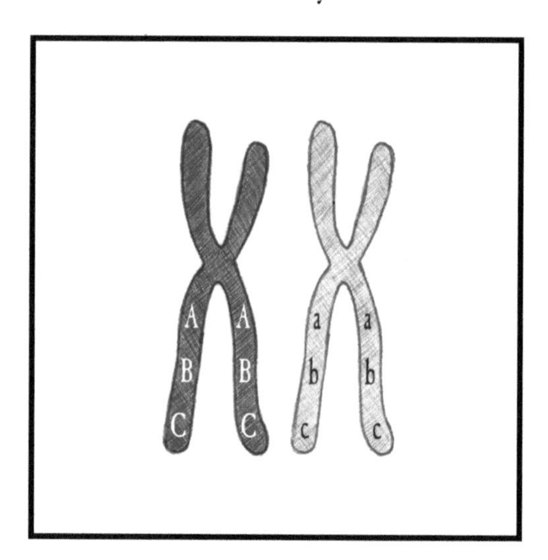

Figure 13.1 Homologous chromosomes

The darker one represents the one donated from your father; the lighter one, from your mother. Note that they are the same shape and size, and both have genes a, b, and c. Having the same genes mean that each codes for the same protein (whose effect may produce a visible trait). Having the same genes doesn't mean identical: they can be different versions of the same genes. These different versions of the same genes are called **alleles**. Of course, the two big A's within one two-copy chromosome are identical genes because the two sister chromatids are identical (recall that these separate in anaphase of mitosis).

There would be hundreds of other genes on the same chromosomes, but labeling them all would make the diagram too confusing. Suppose gene A (from your father) is a developmental gene that is a recipe for a big, bulbous nose. The corresponding gene on the maternal homologous chromosome (a) is a gene that is a recipe for a cute pug nose. The B allele (dad) is a recipe for brown eyes and the b allele (mom) is a recipe for blue. The C allele (dad) is a recipe for curly hair and the c allele (mom) is for straight hair. I am not necessarily implying that the genes coding for these three traits of nose shape, eye color, and hair texture are all found on the same chromosome. I'm just illustrating the concept of homologous chromosomes. Below is a **karyotype**, which is all the homologous chromosomes labeled numerically from 1 to 22 (the 23rd pair are the sex chromosomes). Each homologous chromosome is two-copy. This is what confuses many students. It is easy to think that having two-copy chromosomes has something to do with being diploid (2N) and having one-copy chromosomes has something to do with being haploid (1N). No! No! No! A thousand times *no!*

If the chromosomes in the karyotype below underwent mitosis, each daughter cell would receive a one-copy chromosome from all 46 two-copy chromosomes. That means that the daughter cells after telophase would still receive one maternal and one paternal chromosome from each homologous

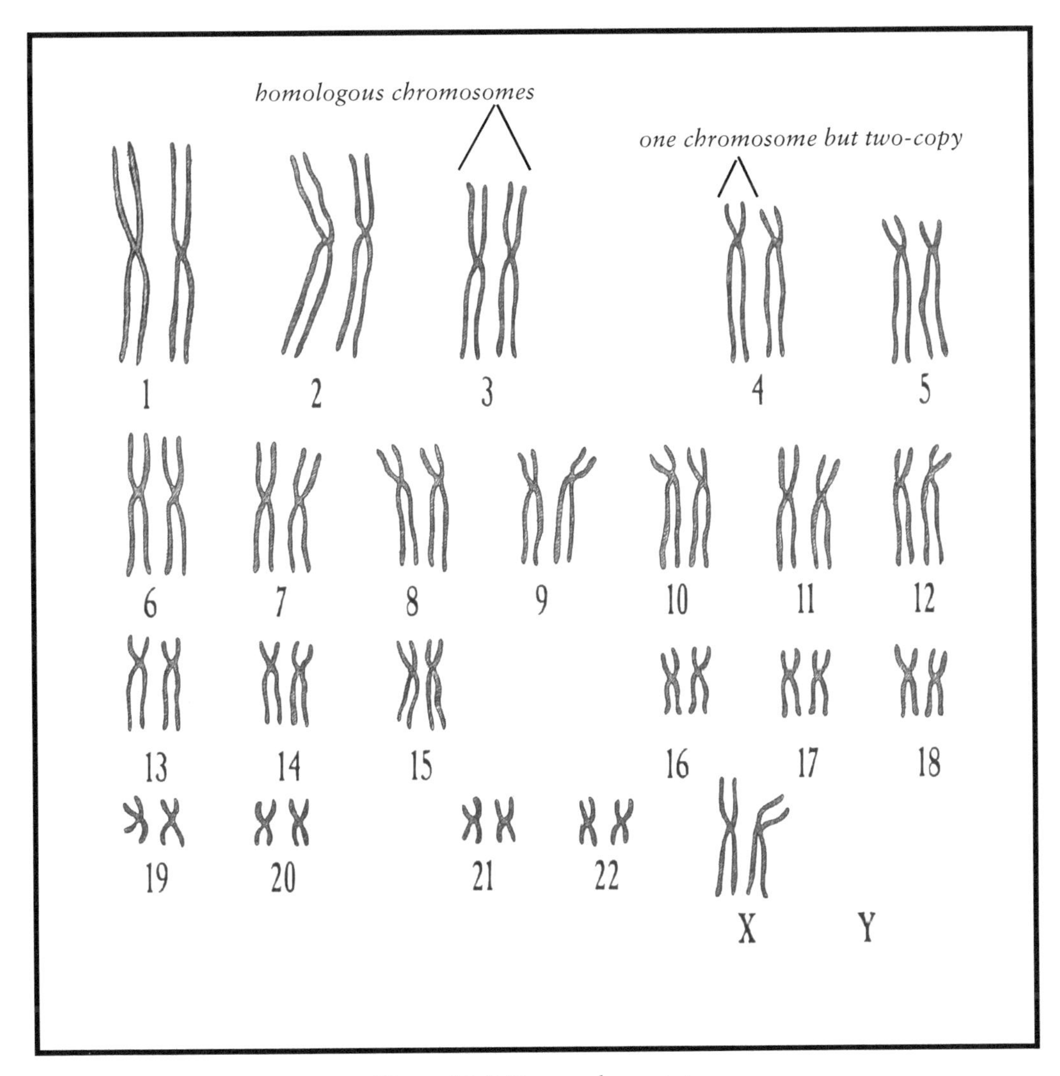

Figure 13.2 Human karyotype

pair and therefore would still be 100% 2N (diploid). The only difference is that all of the chromosomes would be one-copy. Each homologous pair still remains paired. Homologous pair #1 still has one from mom and one from dad. Homologous pair #2 still has one from mom and one from dad. Homologous pair #3 still has one from mom and one from dad, and so on. Homologous chromosomes do not pay attention to each other during mitosis. That's why I never mentioned them before. In mitosis all 46 two-copy chromosomes line up on the plane of division during metaphase and their copies separate in anaphase. Consequently, for all 23 kinds of chromosomes, the daughter cells get two of each.

Where Does Meiosis Occur?

Since meiosis is responsible for making gametes (sperm and eggs) in animals and humans, meiosis occurs to special cells in the gonads (testes and ovaries). In plants, meiosis makes spores rather than gametes. In flowering plants, meiosis occurs in the ovary (which becomes the fruit) of the flower and in the anther (which produces the pollen). In mosses and ferns, meiosis occurs within sporangia.

MEIOSIS: THE PROCESS

If we are to think through this logically, as I am fond of doing, it would make sense to look at the goal. The goal of meiosis is to have each of the daughter cells have only a single set (1N) rather than a double set (2N) of chromosomes. Remember that 1N varies from organism to organism. For humans, that number is 23 (2N=46). How would you line up the 46 chromosomes so that each daughter cell receives only one complete set of chromosomes (23) rather than two? Well the only way to do it would be to pair up all the homologous chromosomes so that during metaphase, 23 homologous pairs are lined up in the plane of division rather that 46 (two-copy) chromosomes. And that is just what happens (see Figure 13.4 for a drawing of the whole process).

Interphase

This phase is the same in all cells, but I want to remind you that all the chromosomes have been replicated (S phase) so that each is two-copy.

Meiosis I

There are two divisions in meiosis resulting in 4 cells. The first is **meiosis I** and the second, **meiosis II** (I hope you're with me so far). The phases are named as in mitosis followed by the number of the division such as prophase I (this means that it is prophase of meiosis I) or telophase II (telophase of mciosis II).

Prophase I

This occurs in much the same way as prophase in mitosis with two major differences. The similarities are that 1) the DNA coils up into discrete chromosomes (remember that you pack up before you move), 2) the nuclear envelop breaks down (easier to move if the walls got out of the way), 3) the meiotic spindle (made of microtubules) begins to form (movers come to move your belongings) and attach to the **centromeres** of the chromosomes. The chromosomes are jockeyed around and eventually move toward the plane of division. One major difference I have already alluded to: The chromosomes pair up as homologous couples. Another interesting complexity and difference is that the homologous pairs swap equivalent pieces of their chromosomes. This maneuver is called **crossing over** and is akin to shuffling or cutting a deck of cards.

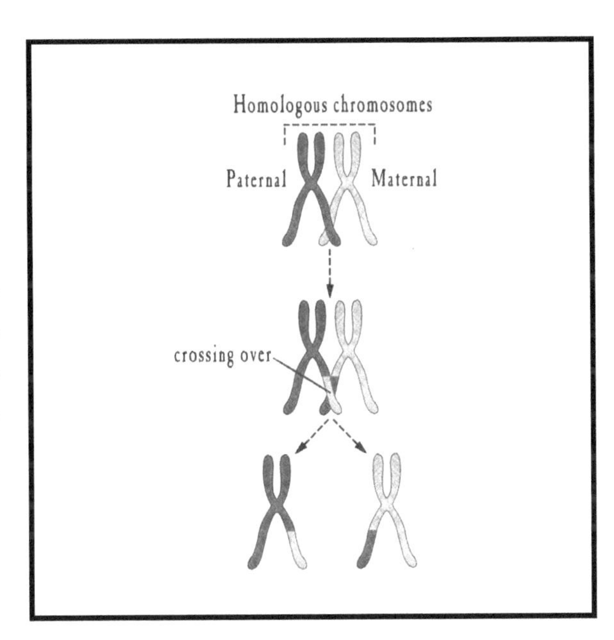

Figure 13.3 Crossing over

To fully appreciate this you need a lesson or two in basic genetics and heredity, which I don't want to get into right now. Suffice it to say that, as these chromosomes are divvied up into sperm or eggs, crossing over increases the possible number of genetic combinations (see next chapter for more details).

Metaphase I

Meiosis I is called the **reduction division** because this is when a reduction in ploidy occurs (this phrase simply means that the cell goes from 2N to 1N or diploid to haploid). Ploidy refers to how many sets of chromosomes a cell has (1N and 2N are two different types of ploidy). Metaphase I begins when the chromosomes are lined up in the plane of division, but instead of lining up so that the sister chromatids separate, they line up as homologous pairs. This arrangement allows the homologous pairs to separate; one chromosome from each pair to be moved to opposite sides.

For simplicity, the meiosis illustrated in Figure 13.4 (which I refer to for the rest of this chapter) has a mosquito number of chromosomes (1N=3, 2N=6). Note that there are only three pairs of homologous chromosomes rather than twenty-three.

Anaphase I

This phase simply consists of the homologous pairs separating and migrating to opposite sides of the cell. Note that only the haploid number (N=3) is on each side. Also note that all the chromosomes are still two-copy. If this were human anaphase I, just visualize 23 pairs separating rather than three pairs.

Telophase I

Telophase I is much like telophase in mitosis. The chromosomes unwind, the spindle begins to disintegrate, and the nuclear envelop reforms. Cytokinesis occurs so that the cell splits into two, resulting in two haploid cells. If this were human telophase I, just visualize each daughter cell having 23 two-copy chromosomes in its nucleus (one chromosome from each pair). I know I'm repeating things a lot but if I don't, utter confusion will be crouching at the door. Telophase I is also a transition into prophase II.

Meiosis II

Now that the essential reduction division has occurred, which changed the ploidy from 2N to 1N, meiosis II multiplies the possible number of gametes by going through a round of division which is essentially the same as mitosis. It may seem like meiosis II will just clone the two existing gametes, making more of the same since the sister chromatids are identical. Ah . . . but they aren't identical! Remember, homologous chromosomes are different from each other. Also, the *crossing over* of homologous chromosomes during *prophase I* involved the swapping of equivalent pieces of chromosome from the two chromatids facing each other.

After crossing over occurs, the chromatids within a two-copy chromosome are different. So if these separate into different cells in meiosis II, it will result in a greater variety of sperm or eggs.

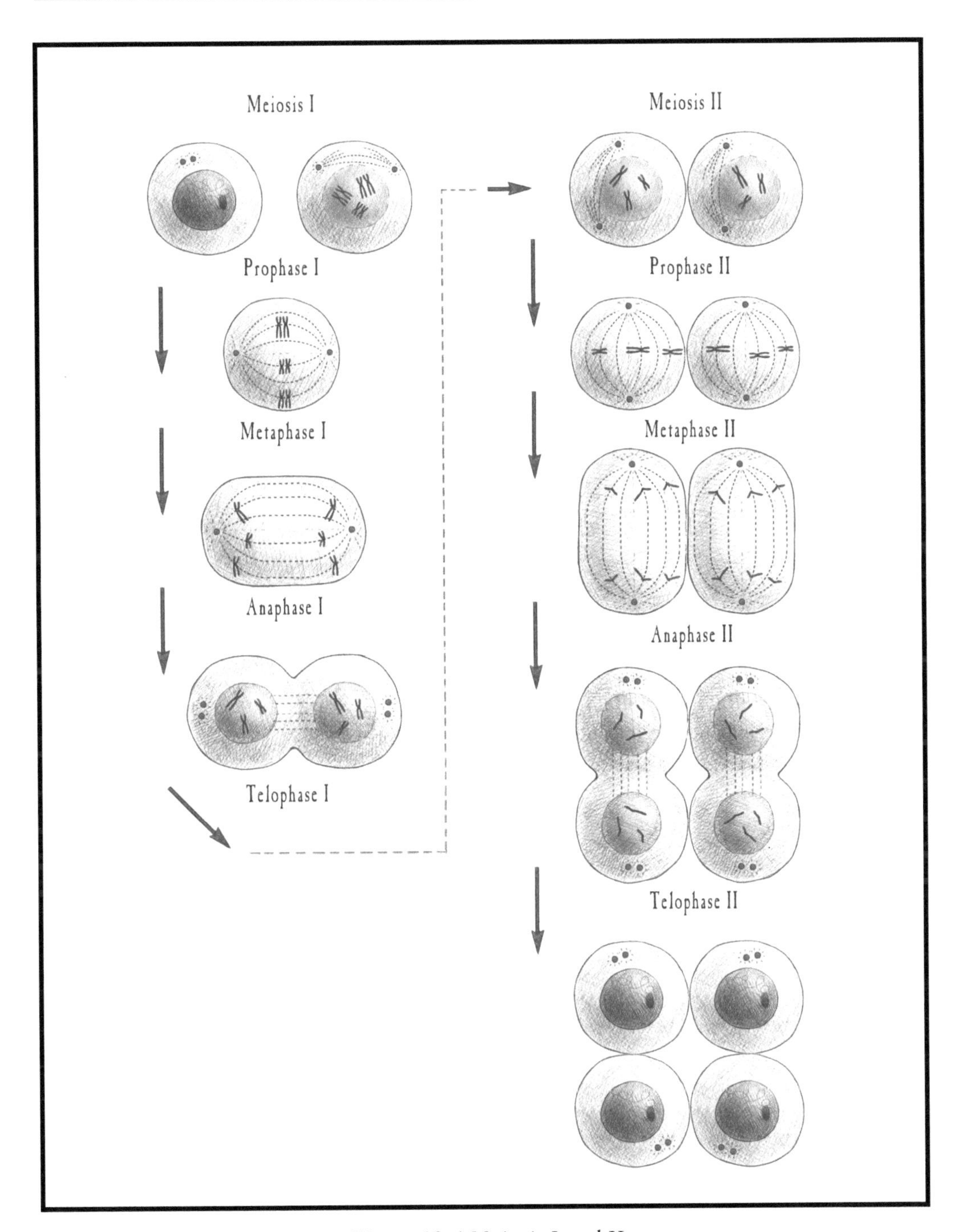

Figure 13.4 Meiosis I and II

Prophase II

The nuclear envelopes disintegrate and newly oriented sets of meiotic spindles form. The chromosomes coil back up and their centromeres hook onto the spindles. They are then jockeyed toward the plane of division in the two cells (which is at right angles to the first plane of division of meiosis I).

Metaphase II

Once the two chromosomes are lined up at the plane of division, we have metaphase II. This is just like mitosis. The two copies are fixin' to separate in both cells.

Anaphase II

You guessed it. The sister chromatids (one-copy chromosomes) separate as each kinetochore munches along its spindle fiber (microtubule). The one-copy chromosomes move toward opposite poles of the two cells.

Telophase II

Finally, nuclear envelopes form around the groups of one-copy chromosomes at each end of the two cells. The chromosomes unwind and the spindle begins to disintegrate. As this occurs, cytokinesis splits the two cells into four haploid gametes. In male testes these four cells eventually develop into torpedo-like flagellated sperm. In female ovaries three of the four cells disintegrate and one develops into an egg or ovum.

CHAPTER 13: REVIEW QUESTIONS

1. Homologous chromosomes separate during ______.
    a. Anaphase of mitosis
    b. Anaphase I
    c. Anaphase II
2. The reduction division occurs during ______.
    a. Mitosis
    b. Meiosis I
    c. Meiosis II
3. Sister chromatids separate during ______.
    a. Anaphase I
    b. Anaphase II
4. Pairs of chromosomes that resemble each other in size, shape, and the genes they carry are called ______.
5. Crossing over occurs during ______.
6. What does crossing over accomplish in terms of offspring?

7. What is the big difference between metaphase of mitosis and metaphase I of meiosis?

8. Reduction division is when the cell changes in ploidy from ______ to ______.

9. Where does meiosis occur in animals and humans? In males? In females?

10. What does meiosis produce in animals and humans?

11. What does meiosis produce in plants?

12. When a cell has two complete sets of genetic information it is said to be ______ or ______.

13. When a cell has one complete set of genetic information it is said to be ______ or ______.

CHAPTER 14

THE BASICS OF MENDELIAN GENETICS

Since meiosis is fresh in your mind, we will look at how genes on chromosomes are passed from generation to generation. Genetics can be studied in any form of life: bacteria, protists, plants, fungi, animals, or humans. For thousands of years breeders of crops and domestic animals have been in the business of identifying favorable traits they want and selecting those individuals to breed, while at the same time eliminating (or at least not breeding) those individuals with undesirable traits. However, this was different than trying to understand scientifically and quantitatively what was going on and trying to identify the principles (if any) that were at work in governing the inheritance of certain traits.

In the mid-nineteenth century (1800s), a humble monk from the present day Czech Republic was the first to actually figure out some of these inheritance patterns in pea plants. **Gregor Mendel** grew up on a farm and was experienced in gardening and bee-keeping. He was educated in philosophy and physics at the University of Olomouc. He entered the Department of Natural History and Agriculture and studied under several professors who did research of inherited traits of agricultural plants and animals. He also was trained as a Catholic priest and became an Augustinian monk in his early twenties.

GREGOR MENDEL

Inspired by both his professors and fellow monks, he continued his extensive pea breeding experiments at the monastery. He recorded his results and analyzed them thoroughly. He also continued research in astronomy and meteorology and kept quite active in bee-keeping. But due to a paper published on his pea experiments he is now known as the father of modern genetics. At the time of publication its significance was hardly noticed. It wasn't until the turn of the century, after his death, that its implications were realized. To summarize his work, he studied the inheritance of seven different traits in pea plants, two of which we will discuss. After inbreeding pea plants over several generations he was able to establish a strain of purebred pea plants which were all tall. Similarly, he was also able to establish a strain of purebred pea plants which were all short. These were the **parental generation** for his subsequent experiments. He crossed the tall pea plants with the short pea plants and collected and planted the seeds (plant embryos) from the cross (**F1 generation**). When they grew he found that they were all tall. What happened to the short trait? Was it lost forever? When Mendel crossed two plants of the F1 generation he again collected the seeds (the **F2 generation**), planted them, and observed their traits when they matured. Three quarters of the F2 generation were tall and one quarter was short. In thinking about these results, Mendel inferred that the factor responsible for the short trait was somehow masked in the F1 generation and reappeared in the F2 but never was lost or destroyed. Mendel knew nothing of DNA, chromosomes, genes, or meiosis. Compared to our current knowledge of these things, he was 'working in the dark'.

Figure 14.1 Gregor Mendel

Nevertheless, like many science pioneers he had great reasoning skills and inferred that these inherited factors were **segregated** in the process of making the reproductive cells (sperm and eggs) of the pea plants. The egg is contained in the ovule (immature seed) of the flower's female parts. The sperm is contained in the pollen grains. Our understanding of DNA, chromosomes, genes, the central dogma, and the process of meiosis sheds a lot of light on what Mendel was discovering. In the case of pea plant height, there were two versions of the same gene governing plant height. As you might remember, modern geneticists call these alternative versions **alleles**. These alleles can be symbolized using letters. Uppercase T symbolizes the allele that codes for **tall** pea plants and the lowercase t symbolizes the allele for **short** pea plants (T = tall; t = short). Each plant carries two alleles for each trait. The tall parent plant (purebred) had two T alleles (TT) and the short parent plant (also purebred) had two t alleles (tt). Another term for

purebred is **homozygous** and another term for **hybrid** is **heterozygous**. The combination of alleles for any given trait or traits is called the **genotype**. For example, TT and tt are the two parent genotypes. TT is homozygous tall, tt is homozygous short, and Tt is heterozygous tall. The outward expression of the genotype (tall plant or short plant) is its **phenotype**.

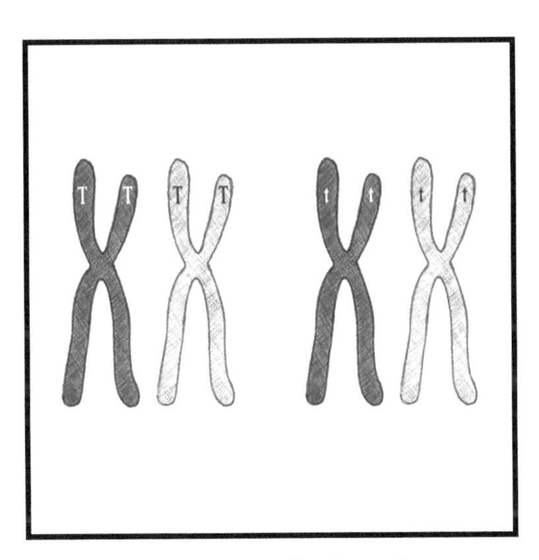

Figure 14.2 TT and tt homologous chromosomes

In Mendel's experiment, when the pea plants made their sperm and eggs, these alleles were segregated into separate gametes. But since the tall parent was homozygous (TT), the only gametes it could produce were T gametes. Likewise, the short parent with a homozygous genotype of tt could only produce t gametes. When we recall that meiosis makes gametes (or spores that will eventually produce gametes), segregation is simply a homologous pair of chromosomes separating during Anaphase I. For example, the TT parents had homologous chromosomes with the same allele for plant height. The tt parents had homologous chromosomes with the same allele for short plant height. From these observations, Mendel proposed the **Law of Segregation** which holds that when an organism produces gametes, the two alleles (versions of the same gene) separate so that each gamete gets only one of the two.

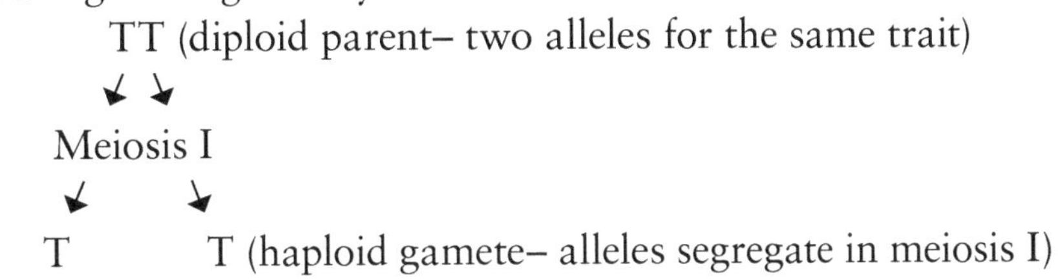

All gametes will be T.

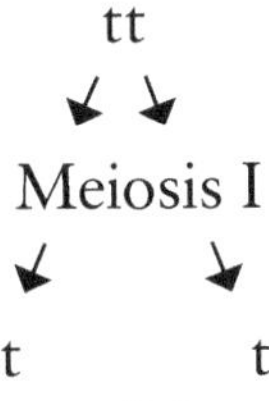

All gametes will be t.

When a T sperm from a TT (homozygous tall) parent fertilizes a t egg from a tt (homozygous short) parent, the genotype of the (F1) zygote will be Tt. The phenotype of the F1 generation, however, was all tall. The reason Mendel only had tall offspring in the F1 generation was that the T allele was **dominant.** That means that even though there was a t in its genotype, the T allele was the only one expressed and the t allele had no influence in the plant's phenotype. When the t allele is not expressed at all, it is said to be **recessive.** Recessive alleles are represented by lowercase letters and dominant alleles are represented by uppercase letters.

MONOHYBRID CROSS

Now let's get back to the results of crossing the F1 pea plants. The short phenotype reappeared in the F2 offspring (¼) and the tall phenotype was ¾ of the offspring. To help easily visualize this cross, Dr. Reginald C. Punnett devised the **Punnett square.** The number of columns designates the number of different sperm and the number of rows designates the number of different eggs. Combining the various gametes in the boxes of the Punnett square reveals the offspring's genotypes and phenotypes and the percentages of each. Since tall pea plants of the F1 generation were all tall hybrids, it is called a **monohybrid cross.** Mono refers to one trait.

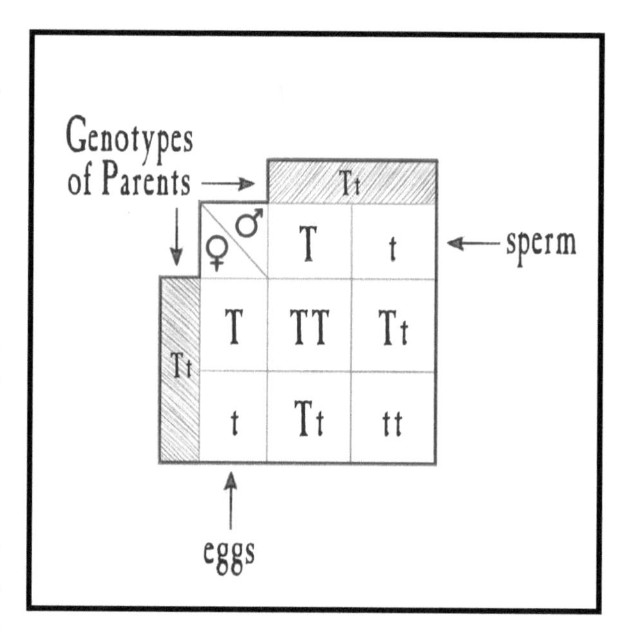

Figure 14.3 Monohybrid cross

The arrows symbolically show how the egg rows could combine (fertilization) with the sperm columns. The four boxes show the phenotypes and genotypes of the resulting offspring.

In this monohybrid cross, the F2 offspring were ¼ TT, ½ Tt, and ¼ tt. A quicker way to put it is to say that the **genotypic ratio** is 1:2:1. The phenotypes as previously mentioned were ¾ tall and ¼ short. In other words, the **phenotypic ratio** is 3:1. Of course one can't tell the genotype by looking at the pea plant. If a tall pea plant has an unknown genotype, a testcross can be done to determine its genotype. This is accomplished by crossing it with a homozygous recessive short plant.

If the tall unknown is TT then the test cross with tt will result in all offspring being tall. However if the tall 'unknown' is Tt then the testcross will result in half of the offspring being heterozygous tall and half being short (Figure 14.4).

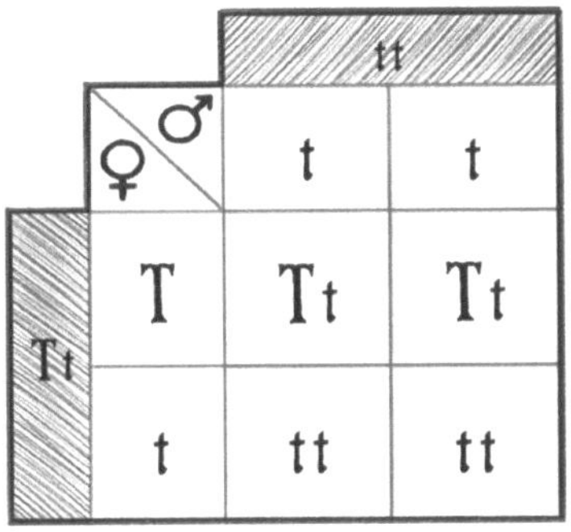

♀ \ ♂ (tt)	t	t
T (Tt)	Tt	Tt
t	tt	tt

Figure 14.4 Test cross

DIHYBRID CROSS

In a **dihybrid cross** we are considering two different traits. The hybrid refers to the fact that the F1 generation is heterozygous for both traits. This cross attempts to determine the genotype and phenotype of the F2 generation. In order to get the F1 generation, Mendel had to first produce purebred (homozygous) strains for two traits. The two traits we will consider from his experiments are plant height and flower color. As mentioned before T = tall plant, t = short plant. The two alleles for flower color are P = purple flower, p = white. He first produced homozygous parent strains through inbreeding. One parent was homozygous dominant for both traits (PPTT) and the other parent was homozygous recessive for both traits (pptt). If we remember meiosis and the Law of Segregation each parent will produce gametes that will have one allele from each trait. So the homozygous dominant parent (PPTT) will produce only one kind of gamete (PT) because even though the Ps and Ts separated, both alleles were the same. Likewise, the pptt parent will only produce one kind of gamete (pt). A possible confusion might be why a gamete with two letters is still haploid. PT and pt are both haploid simply because they each have one p and one t. Now let's cross the parental generation to get the F1 generation.

Now let's do the dihybrid cross (refer to Figure 14.5 on the next page). How many possible gametes can PpTt make? Keep in mind that each parent will do meiosis many times. Each time meiosis occurs homologous chromosomes can line up multiple ways. Let's see how two pair of homologous chromosomes can line up in the figure below. In this case, the genes for these two traits were on separate homologous chromosomes. If the genes for plant height and flower color were located close together on the same chromosome then only two types of gametes would have formed (PT and pt). Since they were on separate pairs, then the **Law of Independent Assortment** (a second law that Mendel described) ensured that four different combinations of gametes could be produced.

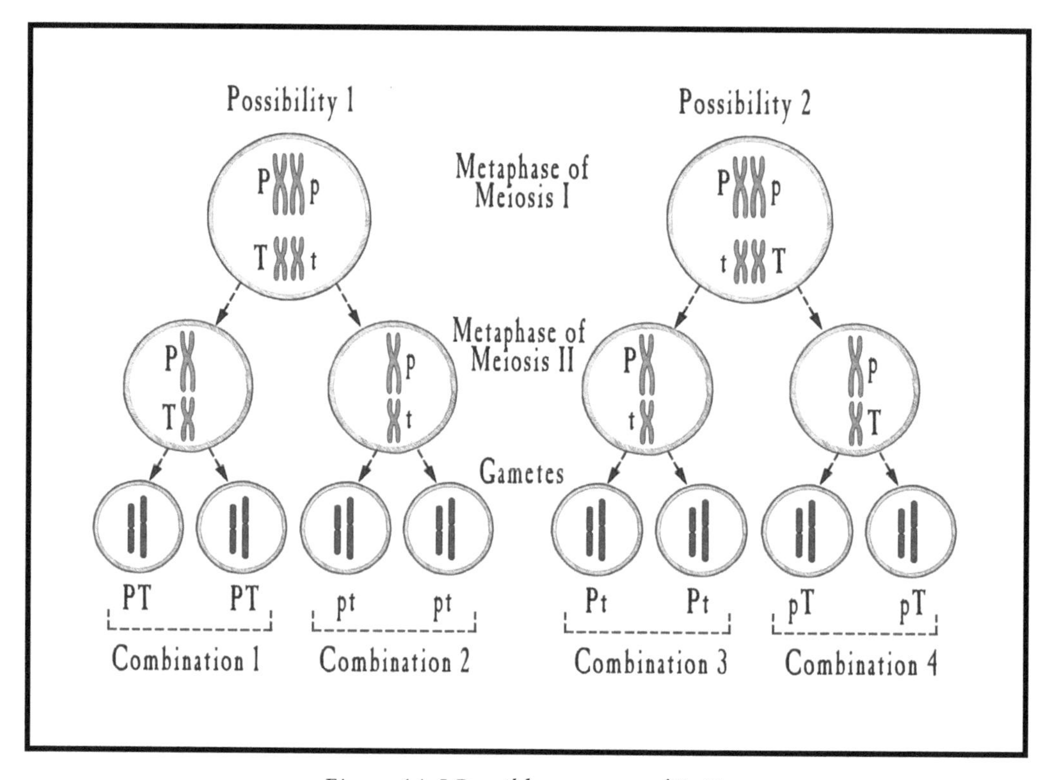

Figure 14.5 Possible gametes of PpTt

These gamete combinations are PT, Pt, pT, and pt. The Law of Independent Assortment holds that separate genes for different traits are sorted into gametes independently of each other. In other words, when anaphase I occurs, P (purple flower allele) doesn't have to wind up in the same gamete as T (tall plant allele). It could just as well wind up with t (short plant allele). Similarly p (white flower allele) doesn't have to wind up with t (short plant allele). It could just as well wind up with T (tall plant allele). As previously mentioned, this law only applies to genes not linked together on the same chromosome. If they were linked, Mendel wouldn't have figured out the Law of Independent Assortment. Also, *crossing over* during prophase I can complicate matters because it can separate linked genes and result in independent assortment. Without *crossing over* linked genes (on the same chromosome) would not be sorted independently of each other.

So to build a Punnett square there must be four columns for the sperm (PT, Pt, pT, and pt) and four rows for the eggs (PT, Pt, pT, and pt). This creates a Punnett square with 16 possible combinations of alleles regarding these two traits. We know that pea plants can produce a lot more than 16 seeds so this really shows us, not exact numbers, but the ratios of genotypes and phenotypes of this cross.

The convention of filling out Punnett squares is that if there is a dominant allele, it is placed first. Also, you put the Ps together, and the Ts together. Several arrows indicate how to combine the gamete rows with the gamete columns. Let's look at the phenotypic ratio of a dihybrid cross. Remember if the offspring's genotype has at least one P, it will be purple flowered, and if it has at least one T, it will be tall. Only when two recessive alleles get together will their phenotype be expressed. If two p's, only then will it be white. And if two t's, only then will it be short. What is the fraction of offspring that are purple-tall? 9/16.

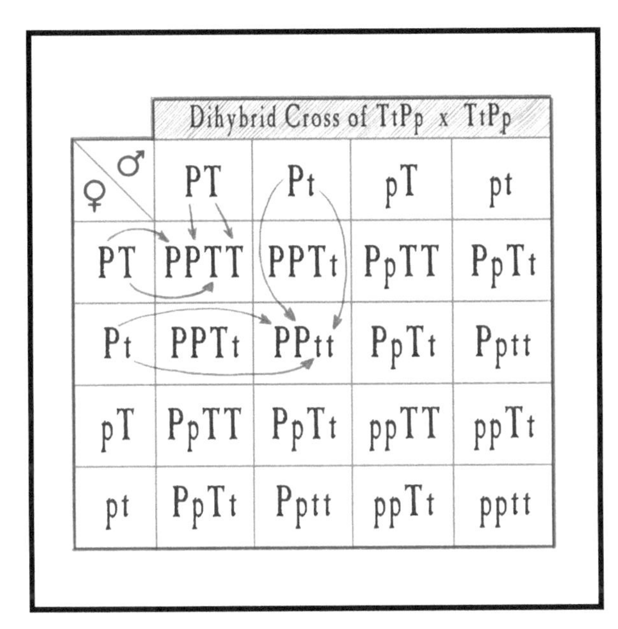

Dihybrid Cross of TtPp x TtPp

♀ \ ♂	PT	Pt	pT	pt
PT	PPTT	PPTt	PpTT	PpTt
Pt	PPTt	PPtt	PpTt	Pptt
pT	PpTT	PpTt	ppTT	ppTt
pt	PpTt	Pptt	ppTt	pptt

Figure 14.6 Dihybrid cross

What is the fraction of offspring that are purple-short? 3/16. What is the fraction of offspring that are white-tall? 3/16. What is the fraction of offspring that are white-short? 1/16.

In short, the phenotypic ratio is 9:3:3:1. Even though Punnett squares were devised decades after Mendel's death, Mendel still discovered the same ratio when he performed this dihybrid cross.

CODOMINANCE

A classic example of **codominance** is the ABO blood group. In this type of inheritance more than one allele is dominant. You are probably familiar with the various blood types of A, B, AB, and O. You may even know your own blood type. First I would like to present a little background on blood types so that you can understand its inheritance. There are three alleles for the ABO gene that determine your blood type. Not surprisingly they are A, B, and O. These three alleles code for an enzyme that modifies a carbohydrate (H antigen) decorating the surface of red blood cells. The A version of the enzyme modifies the H antigen differently than the B version of the enzyme. The O allele is a mutant and nonfunctional, thus the H antigen is left unmodified. Both A and B are dominant, so if you inherit both alleles, both versions of the enzyme will be made and your red blood cells will have on their surfaces a mix of H antigens. Some will have been modified by the A version and some will have been modified by the B version of the enzyme. Thus you will have a blood type of AB. If you inherit two A alleles, then of course your blood type will be A. If you inherit an A allele and an O allele, then your blood type will be A, since the O allele doesn't do anything. If you inherit two B alleles or a B and an O, then your blood type will be B. The only way to have blood type O is to inherit two O alleles. Let's do some Punnett squares to make this clear.

In the first Punnett square a homozygous A (AA) female has offspring by an O (OO) male. All hcr offspring will have the blood type A, but they will all be heterozygous (genotype: AO). In the second Punnett square, a heterozygous A female (AO) has offspring by an O (OO) male. Fifty percent of her offspring will have the A (genotype: AO) blood type and 50% will have the O blood type (genotype: OO).

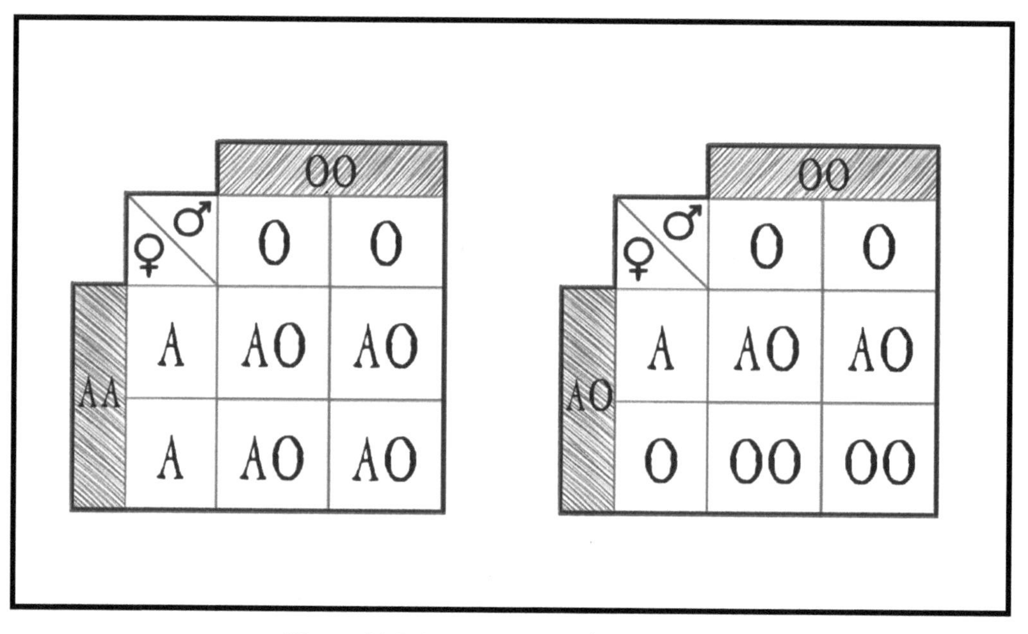

Figure 14.7 AA-O cross and AO-O cross

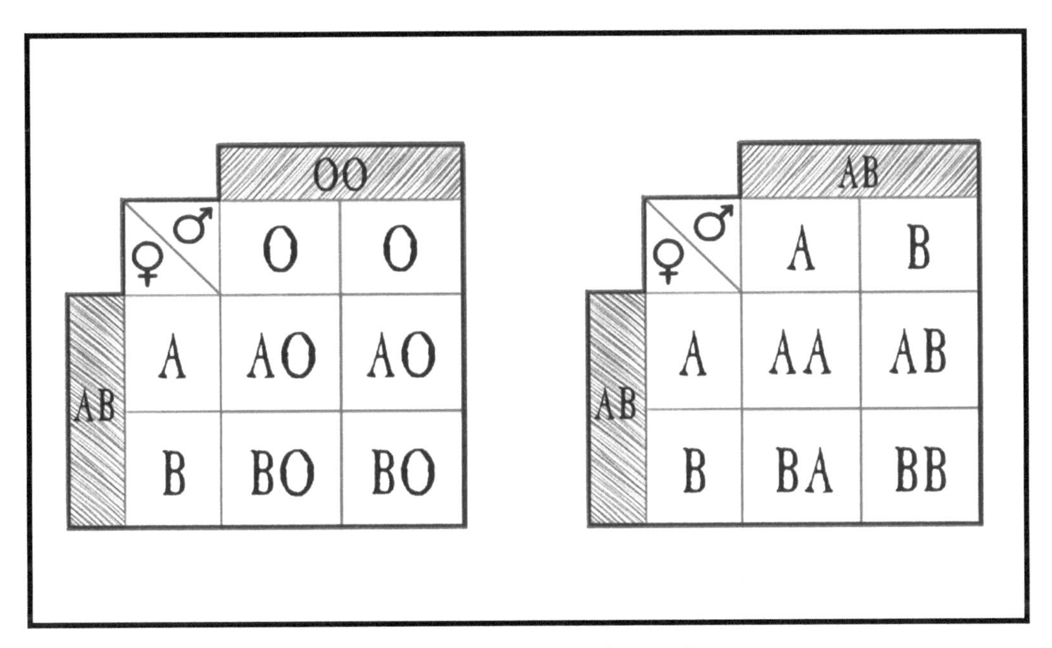

Figure 14.8 AB-O cross and AB-AB cross

Above are two more crosses. The first is an AB female having offspring by an O male. The offspring here have a phenotypic ratio of 1(AO):1(BO). The second square is when both husband and wife are AB. The offspring in the second cross results in a phenotypic ratio of 1(AA):2 (AB):1(BB)

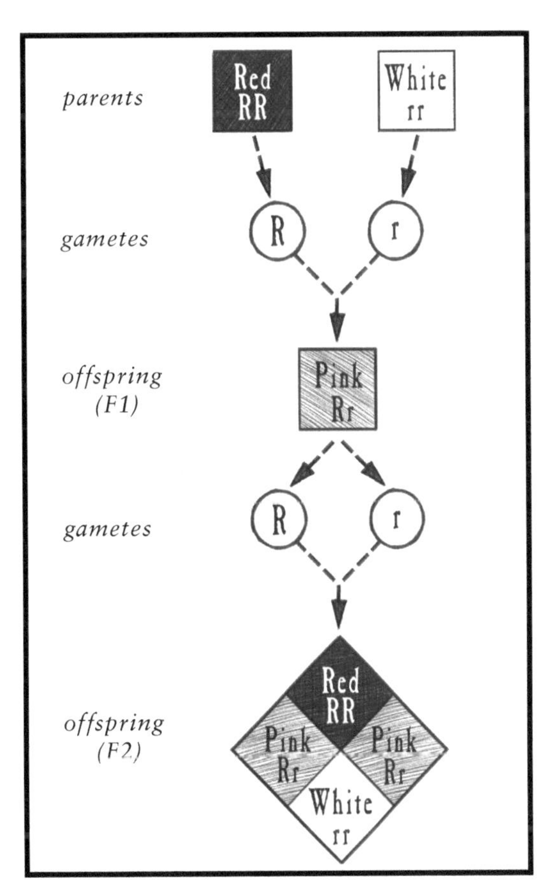

Figure 14.9 Incomplete dominance

INCOMPLETE DOMINANCE

This type of inheritance happens when one allele is not completely dominant over the other allele. A great visual example of **incomplete dominance** is flower color in snapdragons. The R allele codes for an enzyme that helps manufacture the red pigment for the flower petals. The other allele is r which is mutated and consequently the enzyme isn't produced and neither is the red pigment. If a snapdragon has a genotype of RR it will make plenty of red pigment and the flowers will be bright red. If it is rr, no pigment will be made and the flowers will be white. When a snapdragon only has one R allele, it can't make as much pigment resulting in a pink flower color. This is interesting because when you do a parental cross of homozygous red snapdragons with homozygous white snapdragons, then all the F1 offspring will be pink.

When you cross two pink flowers from the F1 generation to produce the F2 generation, things really get interesting. The F2 generation will have ¼ red, ½ pink, and ¼ white flower snapdragons. Or a 1(red):2 (pink):1(white) phenotypic ratio.

THERE IS A LOT MORE TO KNOW

You might wonder if all the traits we see in people, pets, and plants are inherited in this straightforward fashion. To frame it as a question "is one trait determined by the combination of alleles from one gene?" No, in fact the straightforward traits we worked through with Punnett squares are quite rare. Most traits we observe in humans and animals such as eye color, hair or fur color and texture, skin color, height, as well as most plant traits, are not this simple. The inheritance of these traits plus many others can be quite complicated because two or more genes contribute to one trait. This is called **epistasis** or **polygenic** ("many genes") **inheritance**. As is the case in every topic covered in this book, there is a scary amount of information beyond what we have explored between the covers of this book. I have only scratched the surface. If you are interested in going deeper into genetics I recommend checking out an introductory text on the subject. You'll be amazed at how at how much more there is to know and how deep you really can go.

CHAPTER 14: REVIEW QUESTIONS

1. Different versions of the same gene are called ______.

2. When a cell has two complete sets of genetic information it is said to be ______.

3. When a cell has one complete set of genetic information it is said to be ______.

4. When two separate chromosomes match each other in size, shape, and the genes they carry, they are called ______ chromosomes.

5. The combination of alleles for a given gene is the organism's ______.

6. The actual physical appearance of the organism is its ______.

7. Do the following monohybrid cross: F1: Yy x Yy

Pea Traits
Y = yellow seeds (dominant)
y = green seeds (recessive)
R = round seeds (dominant)
r = wrinkled seeds (recessive)

GAMETES		

8. What is the percentage of yellow seeded offspring in the F2 generation?

9. How do you determine whether yellow-seeded offspring is YY or Yy?

10. Do the following dihybrid cross: F1: YyRr x YyRr

First determine the possible gametes and place them in the first column and row; then fill in the Punnett square.

GAMETES				

11. What percentage of offspring is green-round seeded?

12. What percentage of offspring is yellow-wrinkle seeded?

13. What percentage of offspring is green-wrinkle seeded?

14. Do the following dihybrid cross: F1: FfCc x FfCc

*Hydra Traits (*Heterozygotes have six heads)*
F = Fire-breather (dominant)
f = non-fire breather (recessive)
**C = ten headed (incompletely dominant)*
c = two headed

GAMETES				

15. What is the phenotype of these F1 parents?

16. What proportion of F2 offspring can't breathe fire and has six heads?

17. What proportion of F2 offspring can't breathe fire and has ten heads?

18. What proportion of F2 offspring can breathe fire and has two heads?

PART 2

DIVERSITY OF LIFE

PART 2

INTRODUCTION

In Part 1 I presented an overview of the cell's structure and function. Of course, it was a blow-through tour. There are many other parts and processes that occur in cells, but I covered the bare essentials traditionally presented in other introductory texts, to give you a basic understanding of how entire cells work. If Part 1 could be likened to how engines work, then Part 2 is an overview of the common makes and models of vehicles that are out on the market.

CHAPTER 15

CLASSIFYING LIFE

Categorizing living organisms at first glance might seem to be fairly straightforward, like how you might go about organizing a tool box: screwdrivers here, hammers there, crescent wrenches under here, and so on. Unfortunately, it's not that easy. It's more like organizing every Lowe's and Home Depot . . . nationwide. People have been trying to classify life for millennia and it still remains a troublesome affair.

Figure 15.1 Aristotle

Aristotle was a considerably astute naturalist and employed his acumen and logic in a close and detailed examination of many living creatures (although many were dead at the time of examination). As is the goal of most taxonomists, his goal was to create natural groupings according to the features they have in common.

Aristotle was keenly aware that the criteria one uses greatly affects the outcome of the classification scheme. He wanted to avoid artificial groupings (e.g., black animals) because they tend to ignore so many other fundamental characteristics. Instead, he attempted to group creatures to reveal the order implicit in nature, rather than impose an artificial grouping contrary to nature.

For example, artificial groupings based on the coloration of hair, skin, fur, or plumage will result in strange bedfellows, such as black rat snakes, black widows, crows, and black bears. Or if you group together any insect over two inches long, you'd get a motley assortment of big beetles, big roaches, big grasshoppers, big walking sticks, etc., and never arrive at a natural grouping of just beetles.

These examples may seem intuitively wrong but why? We might have greater success at a natural grouping if we selected a pair of characteristics that are less superficial, say, warm-blooded egg-layers. This is definitely closer to the mark of a natural rather than artificial grouping but it still doesn't include enough characters to define birds apart from everything else. There are two warm-blooded egg-laying mammals which would be classified as birds if we used only those two characters.

In short, it's not all that simple. In order to sort the diversity so that it reflects the *true* order of nature, it is of paramount importance that we choose the characteristics that *reveal* that order. This isn't as easy as it may seem.

And, of course, exacerbating this problem is the sheer number of species: right now, around 1.4 million. This includes the known extant species of plants, animals, protists, fungi, archaebacteria, and eubacteria. But due to the fact that many unknown species are very small or even microscopic, live in exotic, out-of-the-way places, are too difficult or expensive to study, or are simply not interesting enough to attract attention (or all the above), the real number of species is probably many times greater.

Some biologists have extrapolated the current rate of new species being discovered and believe it will level out somewhere between 10 to 30 million species. (An exact number will be impossible until all the experts agree on what constitutes a species—another factor which makes this an extremely daunting task.) But even if every species was interesting enough to describe and name, currently there aren't enough biologists to satisfactorily inventory the diversity that's out there. The field is white for the harvest (of classification), but the laborers are few.

Despite these problems, man has always had an innate desire to classify and systematize everything. This is also true of the mind-boggling diversity of life on earth. It has been done by Adam, Solomon, Aristotle, Pliny, Linnaeus, and other systematists all the way to the present and will continue to be done for years and years.

In fact, one of the first jobs given to Adam was to name all the animals (Gen. 2:19-20). The Bible tells us that he accomplished the task of at least the land animals and birds, but we don't know his language, whether it was written down, or whether there was some kind of classification scheme that accompanied his nomenclature. If he did record it, it was apparently lost or destroyed. Whatever the case, we certainly don't have it now. Nevertheless the job was continued, sometimes by believers, sometimes by pagans.

Let's take a look at some history of classification and the worldviews that have shaped it.

ANCIENT TAXONOMY

The most well-known man among the ancients who attempted to classify living creatures was Aristotle (384-322 BC). He wrote up his work in *Biological Treatises.* It's not a riveting read, but it does reveal just how astute the man was–and how keenly aware of the importance of carefully and thoughtfully selecting his criteria for classification.

PLINY THE ELDER

Pliny the Elder was a Roman natural historian (among other things) in the first century. Late in his life, he wrote *Naturalis Historia*—a massive compilation of the accumulated knowledge in the areas of zoology, botany, geology, mineralogy, and astronomy. He dedicated this 37-volume work to Emperor Titus in 77 AD. How much bigger it may have gotten, we'll never know, for Pliny was killed in the eruption of Mt. Vesuvius.

Figure 15.2 Pliny the Elder

CLASSICAL TAXONOMY

The time period known as "Classical Taxonomy" (so-named by Colin Tudge, a British science writer and biologist) began in the sixteenth century and spanned roughly three centuries, ending with the publication of Darwin's *On the Origin of Species* in 1859. During these three centuries, taxonomy was largely motivated by political, commercial, and economic interests in medicine and horticulture. Scientists developed many keys to help the layperson correctly identify plants (and, to a lesser degree, animals) that were described by taxonomists.

Now, we must also pay attention to the religious context of this period of history. Virtually everyone believed in God as the creator of the world and everything in it. The Christian worldview, in other words, underlay all these taxonomic pursuits. Human intelligence itself was rightly considered to be a gift from the Triune Creator. As the teaching of the 16th-century Reformation spread over Europe, scientific inquiry was more and more accepted as a noble and reverent act of exploring the mind of God by attempting to unveil the divine order of His creation.

During the Classical Taxonomy period, many taxonomists realized what Aristotle had realized—that they couldn't determine natural categories using animals' general gestalt or other superficial features. So they brought much more detailed biological data to the table: morphology (detailed gross external anatomy and shape), ultrastructure (microscopic features, both internal and external), and embryology (the study of embryo development from zygote to birth or hatching), to name just a few areas.

During the 18th century (the last 100 years or so of the Classical Taxonomy period), there arose from Sweden an amazing naturalist whose work in the classification of life far surpassed the work of all previous taxonomists in history–including Pliny the Elder and Aristotle. His name was Carl von Linne (1707-1778), but everyone knows him by his Latinized name, which he gave himself: **Carolus Linnaeus.**

Figure 15.3 Linnaeus

Linnaeus is known as the father of modern taxonomy, and his legacy continues to be as large as it was in his own day. During the mid-18th century, he was the king in all matters taxonomic. Many explorers and collectors sent him new plants and animals for him to describe and name—even species from the colonies in North America.

But Linnaeus also got out of the office and collected things himself. He explored Lapland in 1732 and discovered 100 new plant species. He published his classifications of animals, plants, and minerals in a work called *Systema Naturae* in 1735, though he continued to revise and expand it until the 1750s. In 1753, he also published a work devoted to plants, *Species Plantarum.*

Linnaeus developed the basic hierarchy of classification consisting of five ranks or taxa (singular: taxon) which forms the skeleton of our classification system today:

Kingdom → Class → Order → Genus → Species

We have fleshed it out a bit since then:

Kingdom → Phylum → Class → Order → Family → Genus → Species

We can also thank Linnaeus for the binomial system of naming. Sound complicated? It's far simpler than what he proposed at first: the polynomial system, which consisted of a string of Latin words (no more than 12) that attempted to describe the relevant features of the plant or animal. If he'd stuck with this, just imagine what you could be saying today if you went on a hike and spotted a familiar plant: "Look, Bob, I just found *Nepeta floribus interrupte spicatus pedunculatis*." Linnaeus quickly concluded that this was an unwieldy, impractical way to name and identify a plant, even if you are a Latin geek. He thought it prudent to limit it to just two names (hence, "binomial"—bi is "two" and nomial comes from the word meaning "name"), and we are forever grateful. Now you can just say, "Bob, I found *Nepeta cataria*." (Of course, you can always say "catnip.")

WHY ALL THE LEVELS OF CLASSIFICATION?

It's easy to think that all these layers of name-calling are unnecessary. Are biologists just throwing jargon at us to make the lives of biology students more miserable? No. When we understand the diversity out there, we'll understand that biologists actually have very good reasons for this hierarchy. Let's examine the logic of this system.

The most general taxon is **kingdom**. There are, to date, six kingdoms: Plantae, Animalia, Protista, Fungi, Archaebacteria, and Eubacteria.

For an example, let's look at the kingdom Animalia. Anything that is multicellular and able to move about using some sort of muscular tissue is an animal. This includes a surprising array of critters ranging from sponges, jellyfish, worms, clams, starfish, insects, and all vertebrates. This distinguishes them from all the other kingdoms which do not have these basic traits.

After kingdom, the next taxon is **phylum** (plural: phyla). Among animals it is clear that there are huge groups that can be distinguished from all other animals. For example, the phylum Arthropoda includes all critters with segmented bodies, paired and jointed appendages, and some sort of "suit of armor" called an exoskeleton. This includes crabs, shrimp, spiders, ticks, millipedes, centipedes, and insects. Now, crabs share these characteristics with insects, but they are vastly different creatures, hence the need to split phylum Arthropoda into smaller groups called **classes** (the third taxon). We are all fairly familiar with insects so I will use this enormous group of arthropods as a good example of a class. What distinguishes insects from all other arthropods? The main characteristic is that they are arthropods with three body regions (head, thorax, and abdomen) and six legs and two pairs of wings (if they have them) protruding from the thorax. Millipedes are in a different class of arthropods because they have gobs of legs with **two pairs sprouting from each segment** (except the first few). Centipedes are in a different class, because they have one pair of legs per segment.

But we can't stop at class because if you've seen one insect, you haven't seen them all. So the next taxon is **order**. The class Insecta is pretty darn big, so it has a lot of orders, most of which people are familiar with.

Beetles constitute the order Coleoptera. They are very distinct insects with their fairly thick wing covers (the first pair of wings) spreading over their backs. Beetles are such a vast and diverse order (over 350,000 species)

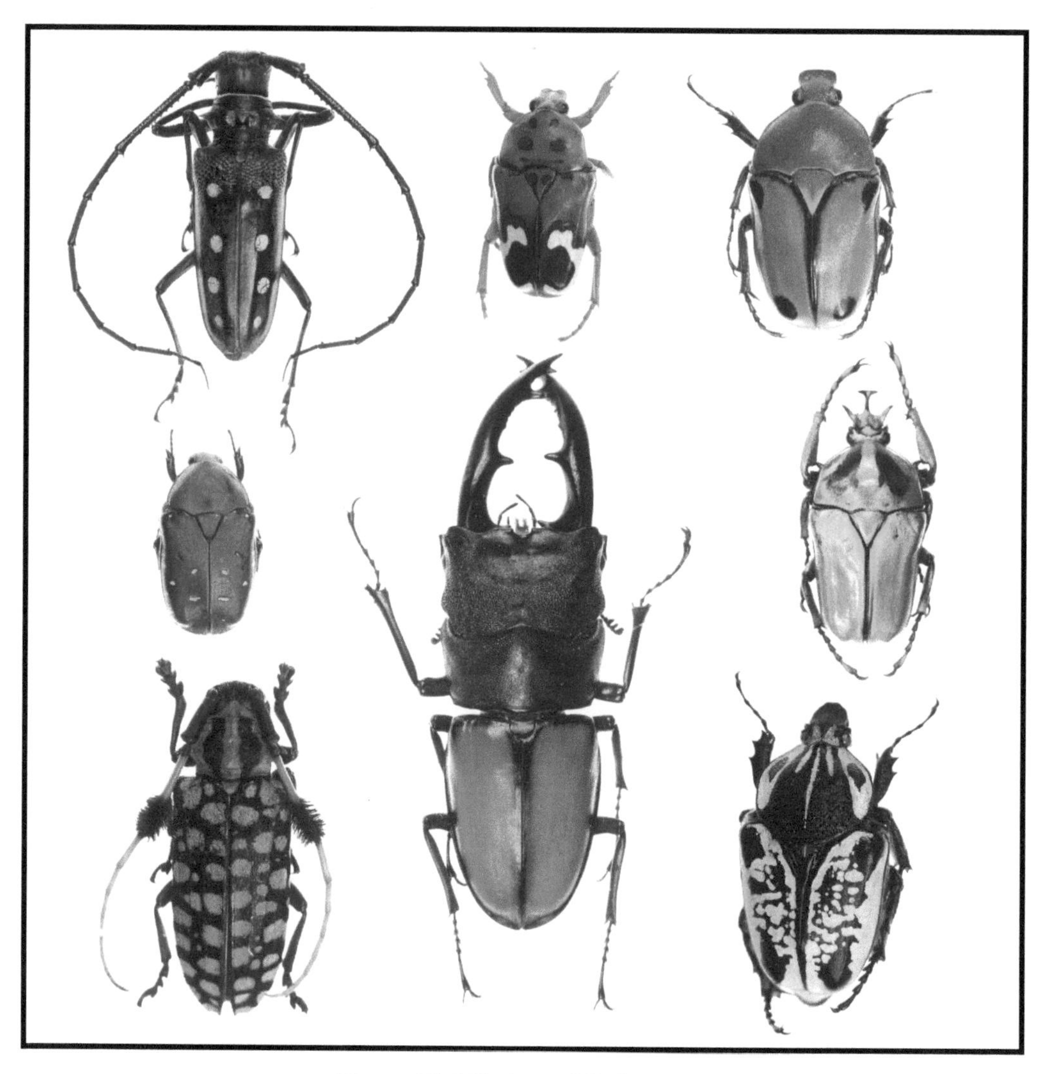

Figure 15.4 Variety of Coleoptera

that it is necessary to break the order Coleoptera even further into **families.**

There are about 160 families of beetles but I will mention just a couple. Ladybugs (properly called ladybird beetles) are in the family Coccinellidae (~400 species in the U.S. and Canada). Weevils (or snout beetles) are in the family Curculionidae (~40,000 species). But we are not done yet. Families are not species. Often families can include tens to hundreds of species. And even among these species, some are more similar to each other than they are to others, which means we need another taxon in between family and species, and that is **genus**. Take weevils, for example.

The boll weevil, *Anthonomus grandis* (pictured to the right), is in the genus *Anthonomus,* but so are the two below, along with many others. . .

Figure 15.5 One of Family Coccinellidae

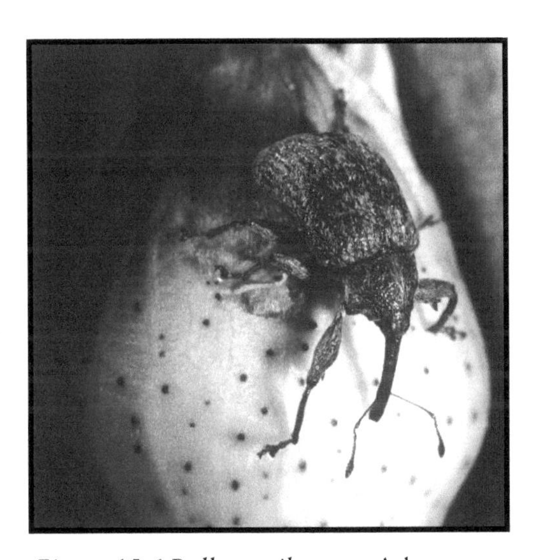

Figure 15.6 Boll weevil, genus Athonomus

Figure 15.7 Anthonomus rubi *and* Anthonomus rectirostri

RULES OF SCIENTIFIC NAMING

Now that we are down to genus, I can discuss scientific naming. Just so you know, when I say "scientific name," I could also say "Latin name," or "binomial," or "species name." They all refer to the same thing, but I usually prefer the term "scientific name," so that's what we're going to use here.

Okay. Let's discuss the rules of scientific naming. I'm a bit fussy about these rules, so pay attention.

The scientific name consists of two names: the *genus* and the *specific epithet* (the specific epithet is often called "species," but technically that's incorrect because species actually includes the genus name). As mentioned above, the boll weevil's scientific name is *Anthonomus grandis. Anthonomus* is the genus name and *grandis* is the specific epithet. Both these names are to be italicized or underlined. This notation demonstrates that it is the proper scientific name and is not to be confused with other higher level taxa such as family, order, etc. The genus (which you *absolutely must include*) is capitalized and the specific epithet is all lower case even if it includes a proper name.

*Figure 15.8 Black Bear (*Ursus americanus*)*

It is difficult to generate different specific epithets for all 1.4 million species, so specific epithets can be named after a scientist. For example, my major professor, Dr. Carl Ernst, has a species of map turtle named after him. The Escambia map turtle, *Graptemys ernsti,* has his last name Latinized as the specific epithet, but it is not capitalized. Specific epithets can also be regional, morphological, or habitat descriptors. Consequently, many unrelated species have the same specific epithet: *Bufo americanus* is the American toad, *Ursus americanus* is the black bear, and *Fraxinus americana* is the white ash.

Figure 15.9
*American toad (*Bufo americanus*)*

If I just use *americanus* or *americana,* I'm not telling my reader anything about its actual identity. Is it a toad or a bear or a tree? Many other plants and animals have the same or similar specific epithets, so, like I said, the genus is essential to make a positive ID. After I use the full genus name once, I am free to abbreviate it thereafter, as in *B. americanus.* This is commonly done when the scientific name is a mouthful like *Escherichia coli.* Microbiologists happily shorten it to *E. coli.*

Figure 15.10
*White ash (*Fraxinus americana*)*

WHY USE THE SCIENTIFIC NAME WHEN THE COMMON NAME IS EASIER?

Common names are fine and I use them myself in the appropriate circumstances. If amateur naturalists want to learn the local flora and fauna, they usually want to learn the common names. It's easier and sounds less pretentious.

But when I teach common names, I take special care to make sure it is the *official* common name. The problem with common names is that they aren't universal. The name of a particular species can change from region to region and county to county, and countless trivial disputes can erupt over the name of some critter because everybody learned it differently from their grandpa or farmer Bob down the road.

Most people, not realizing the overwhelming diversity out there, try to shoehorn some unknown snake into one of the two kinds of snakes he or she happens to know. I call this widespread tendency the know-it-all syndrome. If a know-it-all knows the names of two kinds of snakes, say, copperhead and garter snake, they seem to think that any serpentine, legless critter must fall into one of those two categories. It's like putting an unknown-shaped peg into one of the two known-shaped holes you have in your head. Somehow, knowing nothing is strangely conflated with knowing everything.

Now, some people are refreshingly discriminating and are very certain that this particular critter is in fact what they learned from their grandpa. And they are correct. The problem is not that they are being careless with the knowledge handed down from their grandpa. The problem is their grandpa was wrong.

To silence these petty disputes, just consult a field guide. Or an expert, if you have one of those with you. They also provide the 'official' common names. But I digress. Back to scientific names.

Scientific names are universal ID cards that don't change whether you are in the U.S. or France or Japan. The scientific name of the common box turtle is *Terrapene carolina,* period. If a French biologist decided to study it and write a scientific technical paper in French, the name would appear the same: *Terrapene carolina.* This convention is exceedingly useful because it provides a standardized name under which all scientific information (amassed from scientists past and present from all over the world) can be stored. Knowing the correct name means that I can now access all that information (international in scope) about a particular creature. It might take some work and I might need a translator if it is written in a different language, but I at least have access to it.

Figure 15.11 Western fence lizard

An official common name may also give me ready access to the same information. The western fence lizard (official common name) is *Sceloporus occidentalis,* but is also called the blue-belly and fence swift. If I were searching for accurate scientific information on this lizard, my best bet would be to use either the scientific name or the official common name. If I used the names "blue-belly" or "fence swift," my search would be slower or even altogether futile because both these names can have different meanings, refer to different species altogether, or lead me to unscientific or unreliable sources of the correct species. In short, they all lead me down rabbit trails that hamper an efficient search for reliable information.

Again, the benefit of a standardized scientific name for each species is that it provides a universal label under which all biological data can be stored. This data can then be retrieved by scientists and naturalists worldwide.

SO WHAT'S A SPECIES?

There are many definitions of species and many controversies as to what constitutes a species, but I will give you the one that seems to hold the most sway among most biologists. The definition of **species**:

> a group of organisms that resemble each other quite closely and can potentially, freely, and naturally interbreed producing fertile offspring and do not normally interbreed successfully with other such groups.

Every single word in that definition is vital. Let me comment on a few words and phrases in particular.

"Do not normally interbreed successfully with other such groups." Often, two species can look almost identical but aren't considered the same because they do not freely interbreed at all, or if they do, they don't produce fertile offspring. On the other hand, individuals in the same species can appear quite different physically but freely and naturally interbreed producing fertile offspring. Yes, two similar species may mate in artificial conditions or in a rare union in nature and still produce fertile offspring, but since it doesn't occur naturally or frequently, the two are still considered separate species.

Figure 15.12 Eastern box turtle

In the definition, "potentially" refers to the fact that thc males and females would readily mate and produce fertile offspring, if location details were worked out.

WHAT'S A SUBSPECIES?

It's a subset of a species with one or more shared physical features that are not present in the other subspecies.

Figure 15.13 Florida box turtle

In Figures 15.12–15, you see a favorite example of mine—the box turtle (*Terrapene carolina*). Here's a list of four subspecies. The third name is the subspecific epithet.

Eastern box turtle (*Terrapene carolina carolina*)
Florida box turtle (*Terrapene carolina bauri*)
Gulf coast box turtle (*Terrapene carolina major*)
Three-toed box turtle (*Terrapene carolina triunguis*)

Figure 15.14 Gulf Coast box turtle

MODERN TAXONOMY: HOW THE THEORY OF EVOLUTION IMPACTED TAXONOMY

Almost the entire scientific community is under the influence of Darwin's revolutionary book, *On the Origin of Species.* After the book gained greater and greater acceptance in the scientific community, taxonomists began to construct classification schemes which attempted to trace the supposed evolutionary history (phylogeny) of all life from a common ancestor, and to reveal evolutionary relationships in the family tree of life (systematics).

Figure 15.15 Three-toed box turtle

Now, what's curious to note is that much of Linnaeus's classification did not change. Linnaeus is still greatly respected in taxonomy. His classification schemes have, in principle, remained largely the same. (Things are often reclassified based on new data. Also, new taxa are added to reveal more levels of similarity or dissimilarity.) This is strange because Linnaeus was a *creationist.* How could evolutionary biology build upon the work of a creationist?

This is because when classifying creatures, creationists and evolutionists analyze the same morphological, anatomical, embryological, and biochemical data. If both types of people are intelligent, logical, and observant, they can wind up grouping creatures in very similar patterns and hierarchies. The radical differences are not so much in how they *group* organisms but in how they *interpret* these groupings.

A good way to visually explain the different interpretations is to show you the Linnaean Lawn, the Evolutionary Tree, and the Creationist Orchard. This helps you see how three views of life's history can be very different from each other, and yet classify life in the same or similar ways.

THE LINNAEAN LAWN

Figure 15.16 represents how pre-Darwinian biologists viewed life. Each vertical line represents a species. The top of each line is a species today and the bottom represents its creation. Lines close together represent species that were created according to a similar pattern.

Note that the lines do *not* merge into a common ancestor in the past. Linnaeus was a gifted taxonomist and was fully aware of strong resemblances between certain species; he even classified the orangutan in the same genus (*Homo*) as humans and named it *Homo troglodytes*. Ironically, although he classified it even closer to humans than evolutionists do today (in the same genus), he did not consider it to *share* a common ancestor with us. Evolutionists, on the other hand, classify the orangutan in a different genus and yet believe we share a common ancestor. All this shows that the *logic* we use in grouping doesn't necessarily differ. What differs is the *reason* for the similarity.

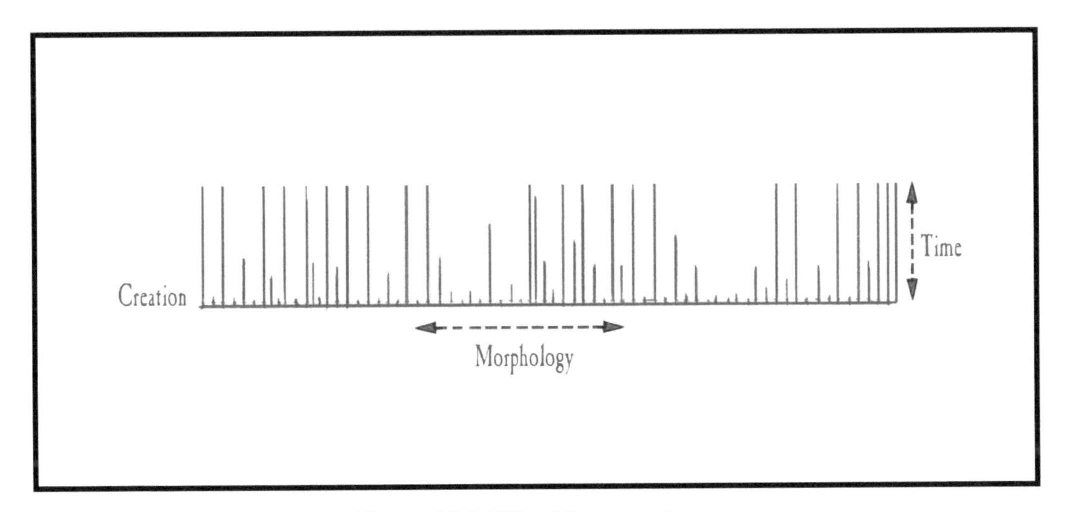

Figure 15.16 The Linnaean Lawn

THE EVOLUTIONARY TREE

With the advent of evolutionary thinking, scientists thought that similar species were similar because they shared a relatively recent ancestor. Instead of blades of grass in a lawn (each separate and distinct), the extant species were twigs on a tree—each of them connected to the others if you traced it back far enough. As you go back in the past, the twigs merge into small branches, small branches merge into bigger branches, and so on down to one trunk. (Like a massive family tree.) In Linnaean classification, a small branch bearing a few twigs would represent a genus. A larger branch bearing a few smaller branches would represent a family, and so on.

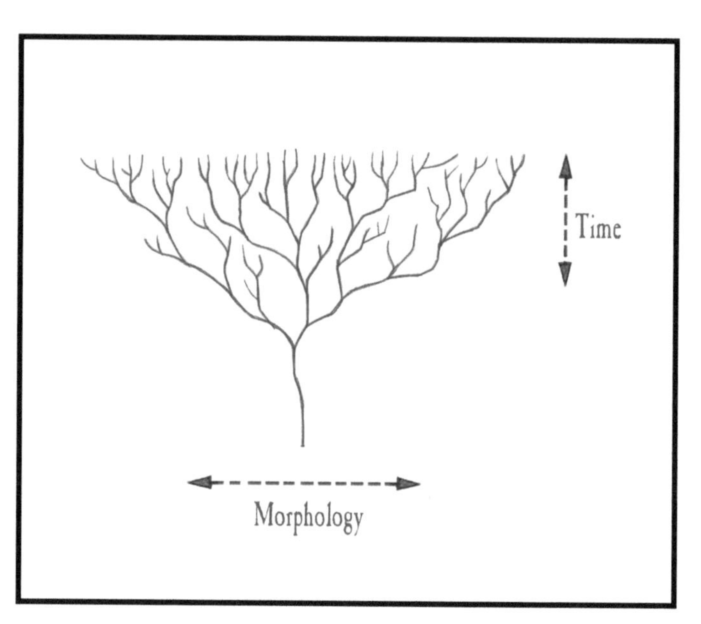

Figure 15.17 The Evolutionary Tree

THE CREATIONIST ORCHARD

Creationists understand that species exhibit *limited* change over time. This change does not exhibit any increase in complexity or net gains in genetic information; it simply means that God created the various kinds with genetic breadth and versatility to adapt to an ever-changing environment. These created kinds (also known as **baramins**, from the Hebrew words, *bara,* "to create" and *min,* "kind") had the innate capacity to diversify (or split) into a number of similar species. These baramins may correspond to certain taxa known today, such as genus or even family.

This is not compromising Scripture or cowing to the evolutionary worldview. The Bible says God created plants and animals "according to their *kind,*" not according to their *species.* Unfortunately, in the history of the church, "kind" was conflated with "species." This position is not only unbiblical, it is also indefensible against scientific evidence for the mutability of species.

In Figure 15.18, each tree in this orchard represents a baramin (a created kind). The branching indicates that each kind could give rise to a number of species. For cxample, the dog family is a baramin and includes wolves, coyotes, jackals, foxes, and domesticated dogs.

Baraminology is an interdisciplinary study which attempts to figure out the boundaries of each created kind. Data from genetics, hybridization studies, biochemistry, biogeography, morphology, and paleontology can be analyzed to try to figure out a particular baramin.

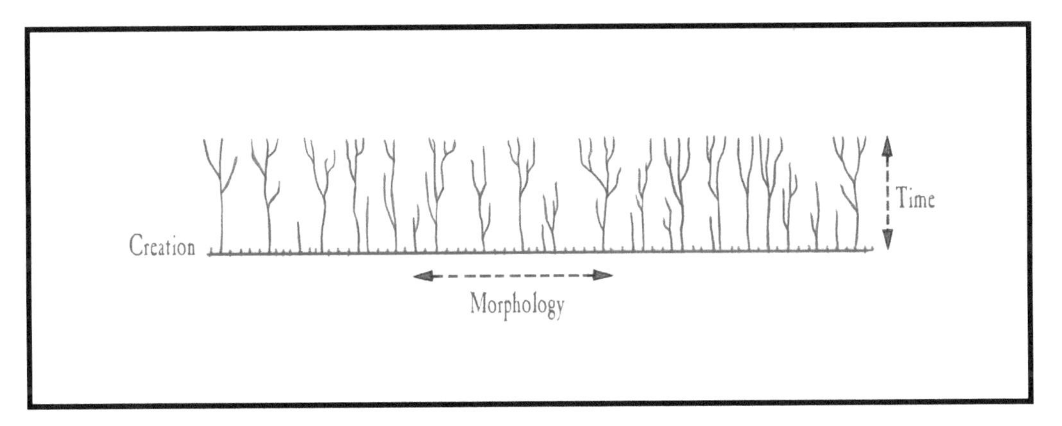

Figure 15.18 The Creationist Orchard

MODERN TAXONOMY THROUGH EVOLUTIONARY EYES

There are several schools of thought regarding classification. **Cladistics** (from the Greek word *klados* meaning "branch") is the dominant method of classification that attempts to classify organisms based on their evolutionary ancestry. This word for branch refers to the branching nature of the evolutionary tree.

The branching pattern, since it is based on certain assumptions about who evolved from whom, is greatly affected by what characteristics are chosen to work out the tree. Cladistics relies heavily on DNA and RNA sequences because DNA and RNA are the stuff of inheritance, but it uses morphological data as well.

Although the technology involved in drawing such a complicated tree is impressive, the Cladist is still beset with a similar problem to the one Aristotle had: which characteristics are the most important in determining who is related to whom?

TERMINOLOGY OF CLADISTICS

To best understand all the terms used in cladistics, let's get inside the head of an evolutionist (just this once) and assume that all creatures evolved from a common ancestor. This is not an evil exercise. Remember, the best way to destroy your enemy's worldview is to know it and be able to think within it. When you know the details of Darwinism, its weaknesses are much more apparent.

Homologous structures are anatomical features which organisms share because they inherited the basic structure from a common ancestor. One common example of a homologous structure is the pentadactylous (five-fingered) forelimb. The science-fiction story of evolution tells us that descendants split into a number of different groups which then adapted to different habitats through variation and natural selection. Consequently, this five-fingered forelimb was molded into a variety of different functions, such as grasping (in humans); walking, running, climbing, catching prey (in cats); swimming (in whales); and flying (in bats). When this occurs during evolution, the structure is said to have undergone **divergence**.

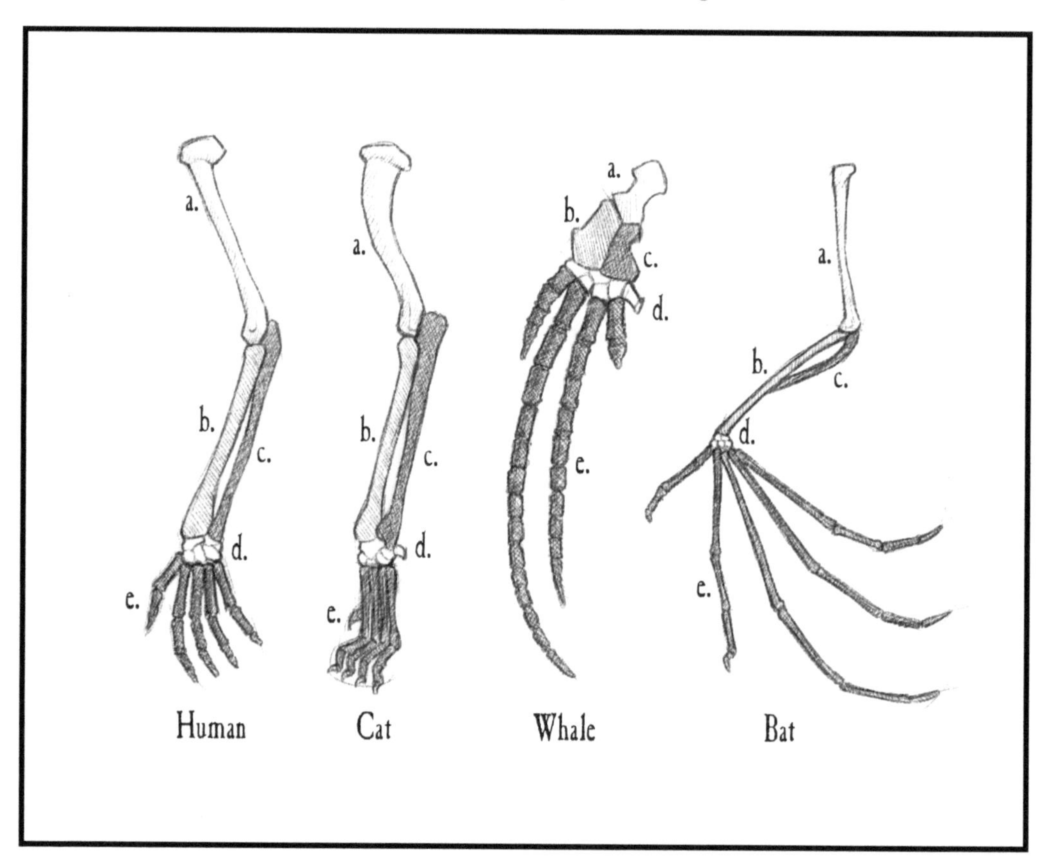

Figure 15.19 Homologous front limbs

Though the limb is used differently by various groups, it is considered "homologous" because it appears to be very structurally similar. For instance, all the above forelimbs have an internal bony skeleton composed of the humerus, radius, ulna, carpals, metacarpals, and phalanges. From an evolutionary perspective, the only sensible reason they would be so similar structurally is that they inherited this basic limb from some common ancestor, like a pre-dinosaur reptile. From a creationist perspective, the similarities are due to a common design from a common Creator. Only if the creatures belonged in the same baramin would they actually be homologous structures.

Analogous structures are anatomical features that have the same basic function, but were not derived from the same *structure* in the common ancestor.

A typical example of this is the wing of a butterfly and the wing of a bird.

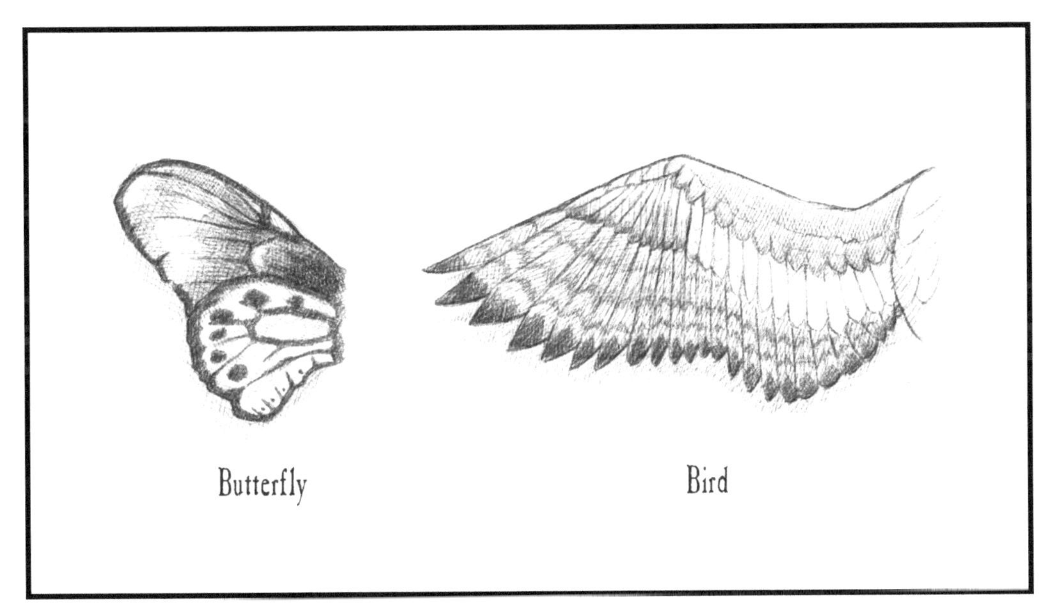

Figure 15.20 Analagous wings

Although evolutionists believe insects and birds have a common ancestor somewhere way back in time, it was long before insects or birds had even become insects and birds, so of course their wings were not on the scene. Insect wings and bird wings thus evolved independently of each other, hundreds of millions of years *after* their wingless lineages split from one another. Their wings are analogous because they have a common *function* (flying), but they actually evolved from different parts of their bodies and developed in completely different ways. When totally different structures in totally different bodies evolve similar functions, it is said (by evolutionists) that they have "converged" or they have "undergone **convergence.**"

A **clade** is a group of organisms: the ancestor and all of its descendants together. A diagrammatic representation of one or more clades is a **cladogram**. The branching pattern is usually two-way. Below is a simple cladogram of a few vertebrates.

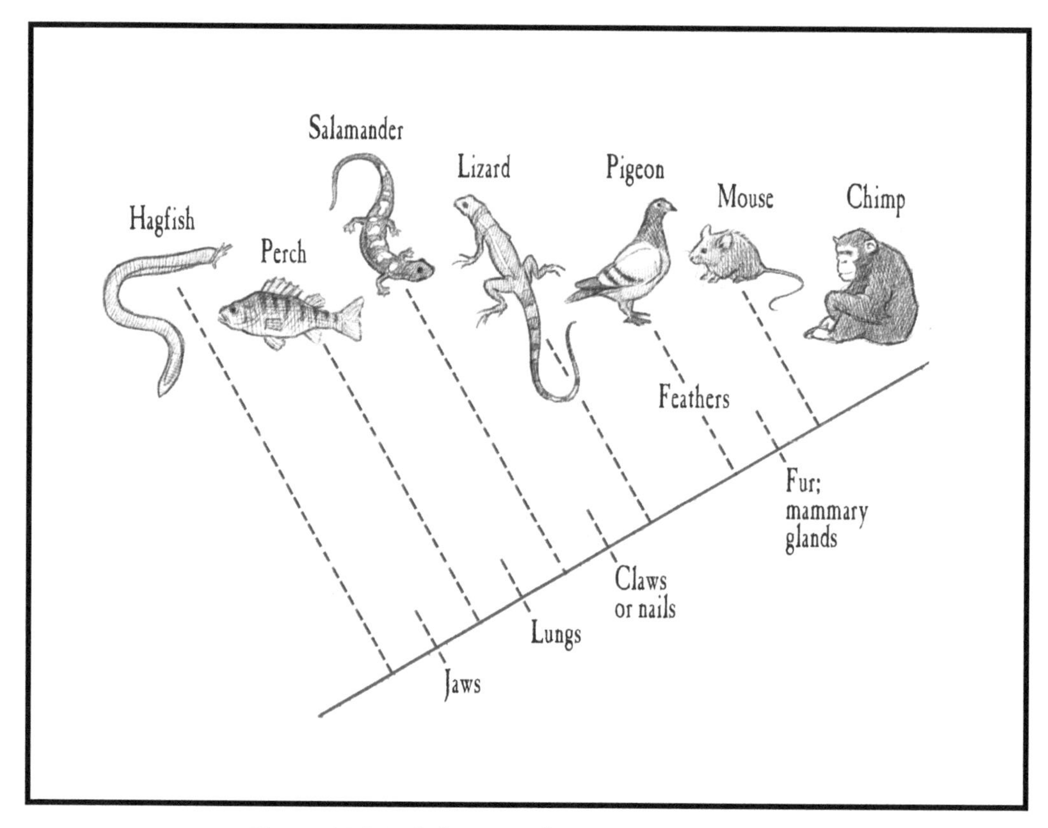

Figure 15.21 Cladogram of an array of vertebrates

SOME MORE TERMS

These may seem like meaningless details, but trust me—they're important. So we're going to go over a few more terms that really help to clarify where evolutionists and creationists part company. You should be thankful that this is barebones cladistics. It could get a lot more complicated.

A **monophyletic** group is a clade. For example, we have both biblical and scientific evidence that all the humans (from Adam and Eve on down) form one clade. Therefore, humans are a monophyletic group.

A **paraphyletic** group is simply a subset of a monophyletic group. A branch or two of a clade of interest is chopped off and excluded. For example, using cladistic logic, if I were to consider the reptile clade (the first reptile and all of its descendants) I would be dealing with way more than reptiles. According to evolution, birds evolved from reptiles, so technically-speaking, birds are in the reptile clade. However, most herpetologists don't let cladistic logic force them to include birds in a herpetology course. They simply exclude birds for several practical reasons (one of which is that they know precious little about birds).

In the cladogram below, the monophyletic reptile clade is highlighted in cream. The paraphyletic group that we call reptiles (excluding birds) is highlighted in blue. A **polyphyletic** group consists of portions of two or more clades, but does not include many of the ancestors that would unite them all into a single clade.

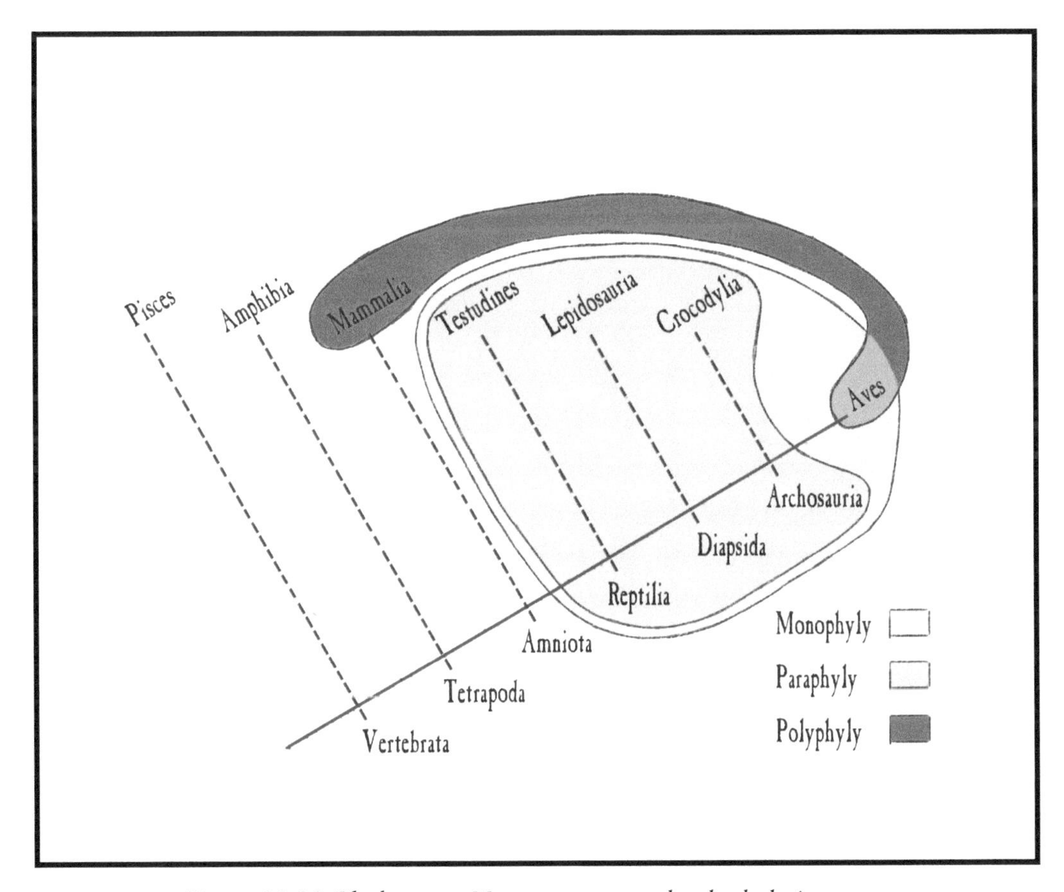

Figure 15.22 Cladogram: Mono-, para-, and polyphyletic groups

For example, endotherms (warm-blooded vertebrates) would be polyphyletic (red) because they would consist of birds and mammals, but would exclude all the cold-blooded ancestors that would unite them all into one big happy clade.

As in the reptile example, cladistic logic often leads to ridiculous clades. According to evolution, everything evolved from bacteria in the primordial soup 3.5–3.8 billion years ago. Consequently, the bacterial clade (ancestor and all descendants) includes the ludicrous assemblage of bacteria, beech trees, boletes, bivalves, bumblebees, bass, bullfrogs, bearded dragons, baleen whales, and ballerinas. Give me a break.

These two terms, "monophyletic group" and "paraphyletic group," are crucial in understanding the fundamental problem with evolutionary thinking. If we creationists believe in a little bit of branching within one baramin (within a tree in the creationist orchard), then why do we have a problem with branching that unites the whole tree? The problem is revealed with the term apomorphy (or derived character). An **apomorphy** is a completely new or novel structure that somehow evolved from scratch within a population of creatures. This structure sets it apart not just as a new species that can no longer interbreed with a sister species, but as something totally new, apart from its own ancestors. The ancestor does not have the structure or the genetic information to code for it.

One good example of an apomorphy is the feather. Before feathers ever existed, some kind of featherless dinosaur had to mutate in a way that gave his offspring the ability to grow feathers (of some sort) out of its skin in addition to its scales, of course. The theoretical problem here is that the information for feather structure and assembly is an exceedingly complex genetic recipe. And these complex instructions are presumed to have magically arisen from random mutations in extra copies of "scale" genes in the featherless dinosaurian ancestor of birds. But feathers are simply too complicated to have sprung from genetic typos in the DNA coding for scales. This kind of change is not the modification of an existing genetic recipe; it is a completely new recipe.

You see, this is the big difference between microevolution (modifications within a baramin) and macroevolution (evolution of apomorphies): the former is testable and observable, while the latter has never been observed nor does it even make sense theoretically.

If one considers the entire evolutionary tree, there are countless examples of organisms with apomorphies (completely new stuff) that had to arise from critters without them: teeth, turtle shells, mammary glands, antlers, scales, fur, hair—I could go on all day. There is no *empirical evidence* for this kind of addition. Yes, it's possible for ancestors to produce offspring with *slight* modifications to existing anatomical stuff (modifications within a baramin), but new stuff from scratch without a Craftsman? Both Scripture and the scientific evidence clearly say "no."

A **plesiomorphy** (or an ancestral character) is a structure already present in the ancestor of a particular clade. In the simple clade of vertebrates shown earlier (Figure 15.21), the ancestor and all its descendants have the vertebral column (that's why they're all vertebrates), which would be the plesiomorphy of this clade. However, you also see a number of apomorphies (hash marks along the right-handed branch) that appear in various points during vertebrate evolution. These include jaws, lungs, claws or nails, feathers, and fur/mammary glands. I should point out that an apomorphy in a larger clade can be considered a plesiomorphy of a smaller clade. For example, as mentioned before, feathers are an apomorphy in vertebrate evolution (starting at jawless fishes). But if we examine the bird clade alone, feathers can be considered a plesiomorphy of birds.

An example of an apomorphy in the bird clade would be the specialized super-extendable and barbed tongue of the woodpecker family. Not all

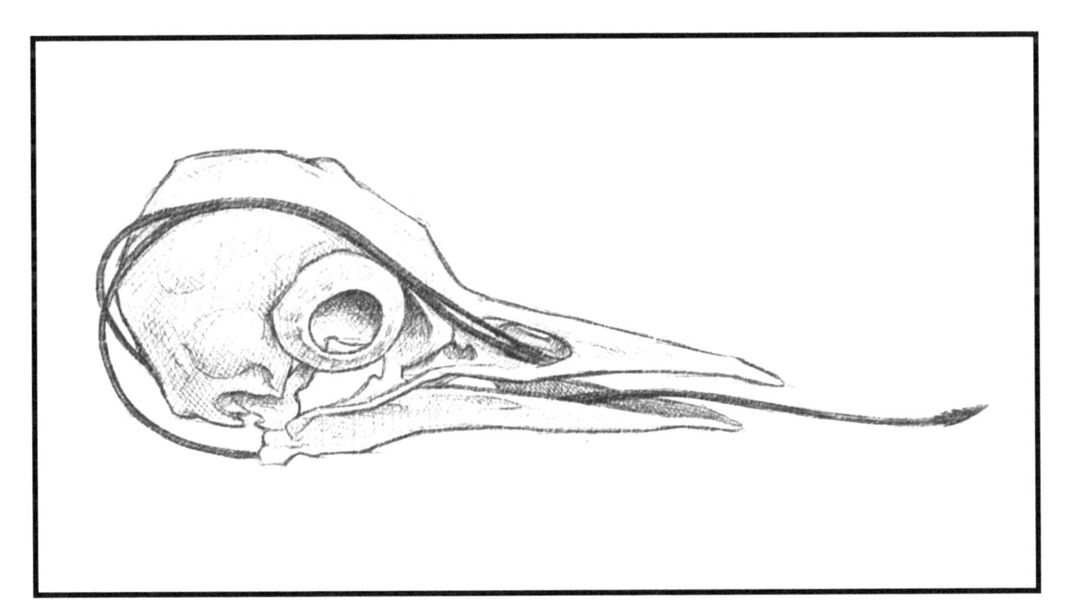

Figure 15.23 Woodpecker's tongue

birds share this feature and, according to evolution, it evolved as a new innovation in this family. Some might argue that the tongue is a plesiomorphy possessed by all birds and the woodpeckers just modified it in a unique way. However, the woodpecker tongue is very unique in structure, arrangement, attachment, mechanics, and development. Many of these features would not be present in an ancestral bird tongue and therefore should be considered an apomorphy.

Well, that wraps up the introduction to classification. Now we will plunge into an overview of God's incredible array of creatures spanning the six kingdoms.

The two bacterial kingdoms will be discussed only broadly at the kingdom level. Most of this overview will include a basic natural history of the viruses, the prokaryotes, and the four eukaryotic kingdoms.

The eukaryotic kingdoms will be treated with more depth and I will cover their major phyla and classes. **Natural history** typically refers to and includes important aspects of physiology (function), morphology (structure), and/or behavior in its natural habitat. Its approach is more observational and descriptive rather than experimental. **Ecology** is also the study of creatures in their natural habitat and is often used interchangeably with natural history. However, it tends to have a more scientifically rigorous, experimental, and quantitative approach compared to 'natural history.' Other ecological relationships such as symbiosis (predator-prey, parasitism, commensalism, and mutualism) and competition will be discussed when good examples arise during the survey. Homeostasis, which is how organisms respond to a fluctuating environment to stay alive, will also be discussed using a variety of examples. For some of the larger or more conspicuous classes, I will even dip down to the order level. I will make every effort to reveal aspects of creatures that are the most representative and/or awe-inspiring.

CHAPTER 15: REVIEW QUESTIONS

1. One of the first taxonomists of the fourth century B.C. was ______.

2. Different classification schemes result from differences of opinion on what ______ are the most important to compare or contrast.

3. A Swedish naturalist named ______ was the father of modern taxonomy. He proposed the ______ system of naming that is still used today.

4. What are the seven ranks (taxa) in the classification hierarchy that Linnaeus developed (although it has been added to)? Go from general to specific.

5. Similar families are grouped into a single ______.

6. A class is split into several ______.

7. What are three synonyms for the binomial?

8. The binomial of the American toad is BUFO AMERICANUS. Rewrite it correctly.

9. What is its genus name? Species name? Specific epithet?

10. Name three ways to visually represent biological diversity according to worldview?

11. Which one above represents fixity of species?

12. From an evolutionary perspective, butterfly wings and bat wings would be considered ______ structures because they didn't evolve from the same feature in their common ancestor.

13. From an evolutionary perspective, front flippers in dolphins and human arms would be considered ______ structures because they did evolve from the same feature in their common ancestor.

14. From an evolutionary perspective, the evolution of a totally new anatomical feature (a derived character) is considered a(n) ______.

15. From an evolutionary perspective, a feature that both ancestor and descendents possess is called a ______.

16. A group of organisms which includes the ancestor and all of its descendents (monophyletic) is called a ______.

17. From an evolutionary perspective, birds are a part of the ______ clade.

18. If birds are excluded from the reptile clade for practical reasons, the remaining reptile group is termed ______.

19. If a two or more clades are lumped into one group because they share a common feature but the grouping excludes the common ancestor and other members that would unite them into a single clade, it is termed ______.

20. Pick one: Creationists object to evolution when it involves the A) Minor modification of a plesiomorphy, or B) Addition of an apomorphy.

CHAPTER 16

THE VIRUSES AND PROKARYOTES

Microbiology is a vast field of study that studies life at the microscopic scale. It can include viruses, bacteria, protists, fungi, as well as aspects of plants and animals that are studied at the molecular and microscopic level.

VIRUSES

Virology is the subset of microbiology that focuses on viruses. Viruses are interesting because they straddle the border between life and non-life. They contain some features of living things (such as protein and nucleic acids), but they don't really *live* in the normal sense. They don't carry out metabolic processes independently. Outside a host cell, they can't eat, grow, or reproduce. They are like little genetic software packages; they literally have to get their DNA or RNA inside a host cell to sabotage it. They take control of the host's metabolic machinery to transcribe viral DNA and make viral proteins. They even use the energy of the host cell to do their dirty work. The host cell is basically converted into a factory to make more viruses. Eventually, this hijacked cell bursts, releasing many freshly minted viruses.

Thousands of different types of viruses infect cells of bacteria, protists, fungi, animals, and plants, and cause a whole host of diseases with a mind-boggling array of symptoms ranging from barely noticeable to lethal.

Needless to say, viruses are tiny even compared to cells. They consist of a protein coat called a **capsid**. The capsid serves as a container of the virus's genetic information (either DNA or RNA).

Figure 16.1 is a diagram of a virus called a **bacteriophage** infecting a bacterium (yes, even bacteria get sick and die) and doing its mischief.

Infecting a single cell is pretty straightforward, but with more complex multicellular hosts the viruses generally need to gain access to the interior where they can find vulnerable cells into which they can inject their genetic

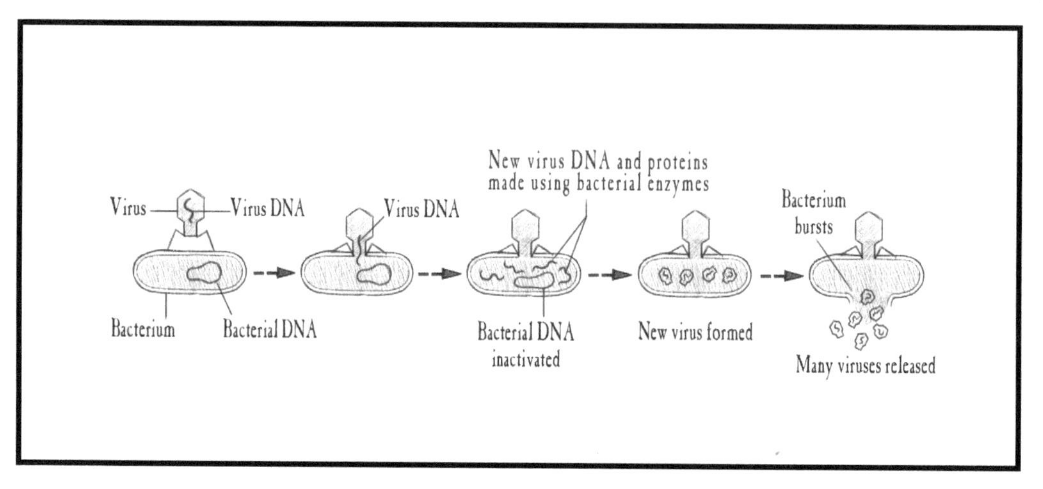

Figure 16.1 Virus infecting bacterium

material. How do they get inside? Many different ways, but here are some of the more common: they are inhaled, ingested, wiggle in through an open wound via soil, water, or air, or get injected in the bite of an insect. (Now you're scared to get out of bed!)

PROKARYOTES

Bacteriology is the subset of microbiology that focuses on prokaryotes. This field is vast, but I will go over some essentials.

Prokaryotes are simply everywhere. Their collective mass in the world's soil, water, and air, as well as in (and on) other living creatures outweighs all the rest of the world's living mass put together—by a lot. Just a pinch of soil will have millions of prokaryotes living in, on, and between the soil particles.

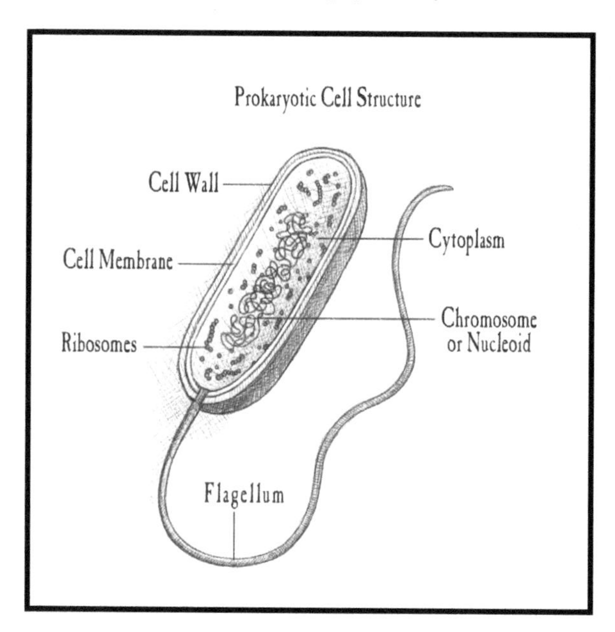

Figure 16.2 Prokaryotic cell structure

There are two major groups of prokaryotes: the **Archaea** and the **Bacteria**, though we don't have time to go into what makes them different.

Before we dive in, you should know that the term

"bacteria" can loosely mean prokaryotes, which also technically includes the Archaea.

Here's a quick review of the prokaryotic cell structure which we covered back in Part I. Bacterial cells are usually much smaller than eukaryotic cells (less than 10 μm) and usually range from .5 to 5 μm in length, although, one rare cell gets up to about 700 μm and can be seen without a microscope.

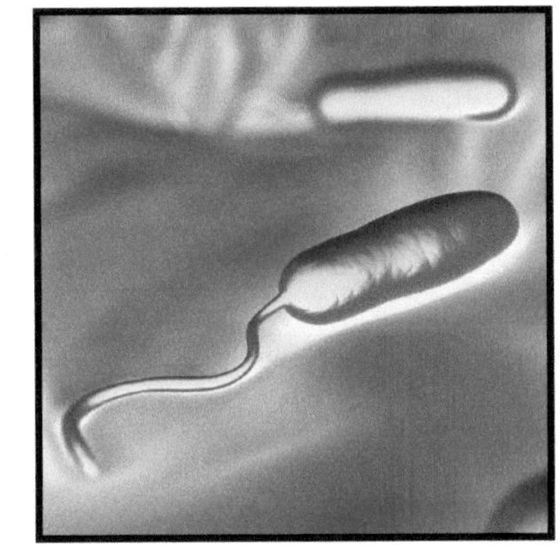

Figure 16.3 Flagellum of gram-negative rod-shaped bacterium

Prokaryotic cells have a cell membrane that is surrounded by a cell wall composed of a polysaccharide called peptidoglycan. They don't have a membrane-bound nucleus or membrane-bound organelles; instead, they have a hoop of DNA (**chromosome** or **nucleoid**) in the cytoplasm which contains many genes encoding their proteins. They do have ribosomes on which the cells carry out protein translation. The many biochemical reactions usually performed by separate organelles in eukaryotic cells can be accomplished in the cytoplasm. Many bacteria in addition to their chromosomes, have smaller hoops of DNA called **plasmids**; these contain extra genetic information. Many also have tiny hollow projections called pili (singular is "pilus"). Most pili help the bacteria to adhere to surfaces, but one type is called a conjugation pilus, which can form a cytoplasmic bridge to another cell that allows one cell to pass genetic material to the other.

Some bacteria have one or more flagella for locomotion. They work more like a rotary engine and are very different from the eukaryotic (9 + 2) flagellum as described on page 77.

Bacteria come in many shapes but here are some of the common ones:

- **Coccus** (spherical) cocci (pl)
- **Bacillus** (rod-shaped) bacilli (pl)
- **Spirillum** (corkscrew-shaped) spirilla (pl)
- **Spirochaete** (tightly coiled)

Bacteria can also form different grouping patterns as they divide. Several prefixes are used to denote these patterns. Here are three examples:

- **Strepto-** (chains)
- **Diplo-** (paired)
- **Staphylo-** (clusters)

If spherical bacteria grow in chains, they are called streptococcus. If the cells form groups of two they are termed diplococcus. When rod-shaped bacteria chain up, it is termed streptobacillus.

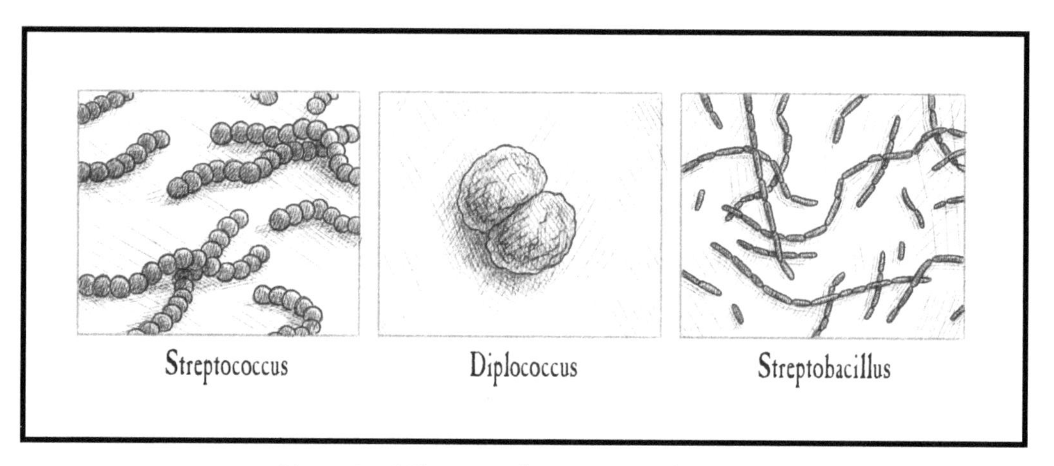

Figure 16.4 Shapes and groupings of bacteria

Let's clear up a common misconception. Many people think bacteria are all disease-causing bad guys, but that's far from true. The vast majority of bacterial species live unobtrusive, beneficial lives in just about every conceivable (and inconceivable) place on this planet. Only a small percentage wreak havoc on the wellbeing of man, beasts, and plants.

Of course, **pathogenic** (disease-causing) **bacteria** will continue to be the focus of most research in bacteriology because man (rightly) wants to have the upper hand in our constant war against bacterial diseases. But try to shake the assumption that bacteria are automatically bad. Many bacteria are environmentally important and are key areas of ecological research.

Many bacteria in association with fungi are called **decomposers** because they are involved in breaking down dead organic matter into simpler inorganic substances that can be reused by nature in countless ways. Other bacteria live in the digestive tracts of innumerable species of animals where they help break down food and release important nutrients for their hosts (in a relationship called mutualism). Other bacteria called **cyanobacteria** are important photosynthesizers and contribute much food and oxygen for certain environments. Still other bacterial species are essential links in the nitrogen cycle. These help convert atmospheric nitrogen into forms usable to plants. Once the nitrogen is incorporated into plant proteins and nucleic acids it is usable to herbivores and eventually to carnivores as it passes through the food chain.

Some Archaea are called **extremophiles** and live in the most inhospitable environments imaginable. **Halophilic** (salt-loving) bacteria can live happily in super saline water like the Dead Sea or the Great Salt Lake. Thermophilic bacteria can live in scalding hot water in hot springs or near hydrothermal vents on the deep ocean floor. The latter is doubly impressive because not only can they take the extreme heat (some live and grow in water above the boiling point), but they can also survive under tremendous pressure. **Acidophilic** bacteria can live in highly acidic environments, usually below pH 2. The biochemical wizardry of extremophiles has made them an interesting area of research, often because scientists see handy applications for us if we can figure out how to harness their secrets.

Another group of Archaea is the **methanogens**. They live in the deoxygenated muck of swamps and produce a gaseous waste product called methane.

Since we are stewards of God's creation (whether we acknowledge it or not), it is important to understand the essential roles these benevolent bacteria play in the cycling of nutrients throughout the world. Once we do, then we can work towards enhancing rather than disrupting their proper balance. If we do our job right, myriads of microbes can silently do theirs so that all life will benefit.

CHAPTER 16: REVIEW QUESTIONS

1. The viral ______ is a protein container for ______ or ______.

2. True or False. Viruses have their own metabolism apart from the host cells they infect.

3. True or False. Viruses only infect animals and humans.

4. The two major groups of prokaryotes are the ______ and the ______.

5. Bacterial cell walls are made of a polysaccharide called ______.

6. Cytoplasmic tunnels that temporarily connect bacterial cells and allow for the transfer of genetic information are called ______.

7. A chain of rod-shaped bacteria hooked end to end is termed ______.

8. Besides the circular chromosome, bacteria often contain smaller hoops of DNA called ______.

9. Most species of bacteria:
    a. Are disease-causing (pathogenic).
    b. Do not cause disease but aren't beneficial to the environment.
    c. Perform many beneficial ecological functions.

10. Which one of the following Archaean groups is not an extremophile?
    a. Halophiles
    b. Methanogens
    c. Acidophiles
    d. Thermophiles

CHAPTER 17

AN INTRODUCTION TO KINGDOM PROTISTA: THE EUKARYOTIC MISFITS

The **protists** are a motley crew of organisms that don't seem to have any unifying features that we could call "protistan." What they do all have in common is a lack of any suite of features that would place them in one of the other three eukaryotic kingdoms (recall that "eukaryotic" means the cell structure has a membrane-bound nucleus and membrane-bound organelles). As a group, protists are all over the map, ranging from unicellular to multicellular, from animal-like to fungal-like to plant-like, from cell walls to no cell walls, etc. They can be anything from single-celled amebas to eighty-meter long kelp.

In this chapter we will cover the **algae**, which are photosynthetic **autotrophs** (self-feeders). (Chapter Eighteen will cover the protozoans, which are heterotrophic protists—they must obtain their food from a different source.) In structure, algae can be unicellular, colonial (which means similar cells aggregate with little or no division of labor), or even multicellular (they form tissues with some division of labor).

EUGLENOIDS

The well known genus *Euglena* is the perfect example of why we moved away from the two-kingdom system of just "plants and animals." Under such a system, anything that photosynthesized or grew out of the ground was a plant. And anything that wriggled was an animal. *Euglena* messed with the tidy-minded taxonomist under this clunky system; it didn't readily fit either the plant or the animal kingdom. Even today it is sometimes hard to decide whether to call a euglenoid a protozoan or an alga since it acts like both. It wriggles like a protozoan but some have chloroplasts like algae. Thus, the kingdom Protista was created for misfit critters like this.

Euglenoids (*Euglena* and relatives) number over 1,000 species and are common denizens of freshwater habitats. These unicellular torpedo-shaped protists range from less than 10 µm to a whopping 500 µm (½ a millimeter). The animal-like traits of wriggling and self-propelled movement are accomplished by two features. For swimming about and getting from point A to point B in a hurry, euglenoids use their **flagellum** (which I describe in detail in Part 1).

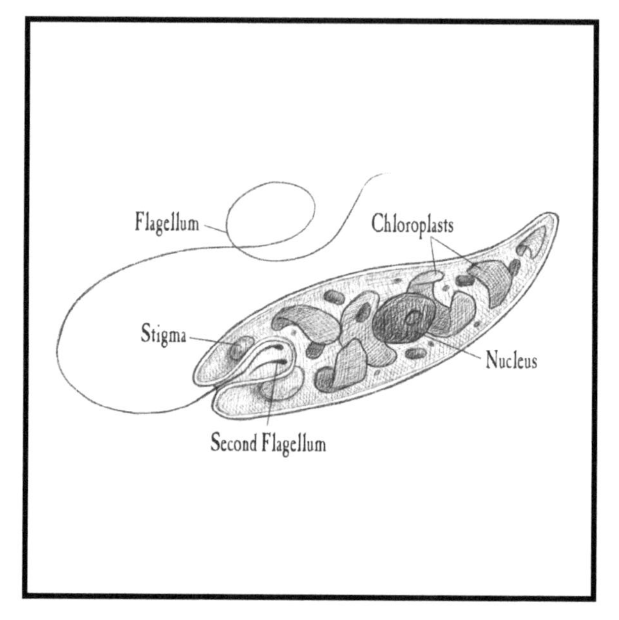

Figure 17.1 Euglena

Now, as I describe features of the genus *Euglena,* keep in mind that what is true for *Euglena* isn't necessarily true for other euglenoids. At the front end of *Euglena* are mounted two flagella within an indentation called a **reservoir.** One flagellum doesn't even emerge from the reservoir, so its locomotive function is dubious, but the other is long and whip-like. This flagellum, unlike a sperm flagellum, is whipped about so that it pulls the little squirt through the water like the propeller of a WWII aircraft.

The **pellicle** is a sophisticated network of contractile proteins just beneath (and linked to) the cell membrane, something like the contractile proteins that are responsible for muscle cell contraction. The pellicle also provides flexible support. Under a good microscope, the pellicle looks like spiral candy striping running the length of the cell. The pellicle enables euglenoids to wriggle, squirm, do the twist, touch their toes . . . I mean their flagellum . . . or even cinch themselves up to be short, fat, and pear-shaped. Pellicle contractions presumably help them worm their way through goopy, muddier water where the flagellum is ineffective.

Near the reservoir is a spot of red pigment called a **stigma,** or **eyespot.** This light-sensitive spot is capable of detecting the direction of the light source. After light direction data is transferred to the flagellar motor, the flagellar motor makes the necessary adjustments to swim toward the light source. Why? So it can catch some rays, of course.

About one-third of Euglenoid species have chloroplasts and thus are capable of making their own food (sugars) via photosynthesis. The other two-thirds must eat by phagocytosis or absorption of food molecules by passive transport. They reproduce by mitosis where the cytokinesis is lengthwise. In other words, during cytokinesis, the two daughter cells look like two canoes side by side.

Because euglenoids live in freshwater habitats, the surrounding water is hypotonic in relation to their cytoplasm. This simply means that the water concentration outside the cell is higher than it is inside. Consequently, water will flow in. Since they don't have a cell wall to keep themselves from over-inflating and popping (called cytolysis), euglenoids need something else to deal with the flooding problem. So they have a contractile vacuole (which I also described in Part 1)—a cellular sump pump or water-bailing device which constantly absorbs the excess water and squirts it out of the cell. Pretty nifty!

Euglena is very common in lakes and ponds and, along with a variety of other microscopic algae, can be responsible for most of the greenish tint of the water. Euglena also comprise a good percentage of the base of the food chain in these aquatic habitats. Many tiny animals consume euglenoids and other algae, which in turn are consumed by insects, which are consumed by fish, which are consumed by bears, and so on up the food chain. The lives of many creatures that we see and enjoy are utterly dependent on many microscopic creatures we don't see, value, or even know exist.

THE DINOFLAGELLATES

The **dinoflagellates** are a very widespread, fascinating, and important group of algae. These unicellular, flagellated algae are found primarily in marine waters. Because roughly half of them can't photosynthesize, dinoflagellates are considered heterotrophs and behave like most other protozoans in getting food. But I'll be

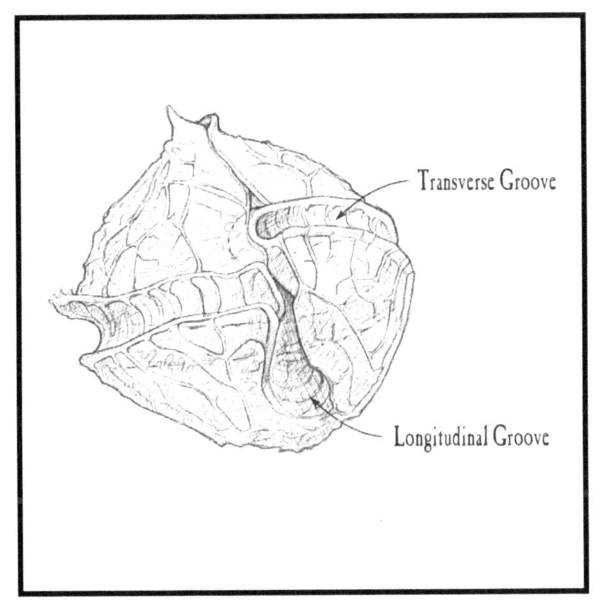

Figure 17.2 Dinoflagellate (flagella not pictured)

limiting my discussion to the other half: the autotrophic (or photosynthetic) dinoflagellates.

Along with diatoms, the dinoflagellates are an abundant, microscopic phytoplankton upon which most marine life depends either directly or indirectly. Dinoflagellates also play a key role as oxygen-generators while they photosynthesize.

A few key features distinguish dinoflagellates from other algae. First, the free-living forms have two flagella situated in two grooves, one longitudinal, one transverse, positioned roughly at right angles to each other. As the tiny algal cell swims, the longitudinal flagellum gives it forward thrust and the transverse flagellum causes it to rotate on its axis, thus making it move through the water like a well-thrown football. In fact, "dinoflagellate" means "whirling whip," referring to their flagella.

Although these autotrophic dinoflagellates have chloroplasts which perform photosynthesis, they are not green; their chlorophyll is masked by abundant antenna pigments (carotenoids). These pigments grant dinoflagellates various colors ranging from red to brown to gold.

Dinoflagellates don't possess cell walls but many do have a **theca**—an internal lattice of cellulose plates just beneath the cell membrane. This structure grants them structural support and gives some of them the appearance of being cloaked in chain mail.

A few groups of dinoflagellates are noteworthy. Certain dinoflagellates have the magical ability to produce light (**bioluminescence**) through a biochemical reaction within their cells. In many marine environments, there is enough algae to cause the water to sparkle and glow when disturbed. When waves, floating objects, or sea creatures churn up certain types of dinoflagellates, the waters glow and the pattern of light matches the pathway of the moving object, making it look like glowing hair under the water. This glow quickly fades to black. My students and I have seen glowing dinoflagellates on one of our field trips at the Friday Harbor Labs in the San Juan Islands. We went down to the dock at night, and when we swished an oar or our hands through the water, the dinoflagellates lit up.

It is quite possible that dinoflagellate activity is mentioned in the Bible. In Job 41:32, when God speaks of the great sea monster, Leviathan, He mentions what appears to be light produced by dinoflagellates: "Behind him he leaves a glistening wake; one would think the deep had white hair" (NIV).

Red Tide

Another notable phenomenon caused by dinoflagellates is **red tide.** Red tide is a massive bloom of algae, caused by nutrient-rich waters that trigger the population explosion of the local dinoflagellates. Those of you who live near the coast of the southeast U.S. may be familiar with red tide alerts. The culprit of Florida red tide is *Karenia breve.* When their numbers skyrocket, the water turns reddish due to the dominant photosynthetic pigment in the little algae cells.

Red tide's toxicity, however, is not due to the dinoflagellates' pigments but rather the deadly *neurotoxins* they naturally produce. Dinoflagellates are always there, of course, but their levels are usually low enough that their toxins don't pose any threat, nor do they turn the water red. When their numbers are high, however, their neurotoxins also become dangerously high. During red tide alerts, people are warned not to go to the beach or to eat fish or shellfish that has been tainted by the tide. The toxins can even go airborne and cause skin, throat, and eye irritations.

Zooxanthellae

Another group of fascinating dinoflagellates live as mutualistic symbionts in other sea creatures (*symbiosis* means two different species living together and *mutualism* means that both creatures benefit from the partnership). These symbiotic dinoflagellates are called **zooxanthellae.** They literally live in the skin of a wide variety of sea creatures, including certain kinds of coral, sea anemones, sponges, marine snails, octopuses, squid, sea squirts, and other protists. They produce food for their hosts in the form of surplus sugars which they manufacture through photosynthesis. In fact, their photosynthesis helps grow healthy coral reefs. Because they live within animal tissue, zooxanthellae don't have (or need) flagella or thecae.

THE DIATOMS

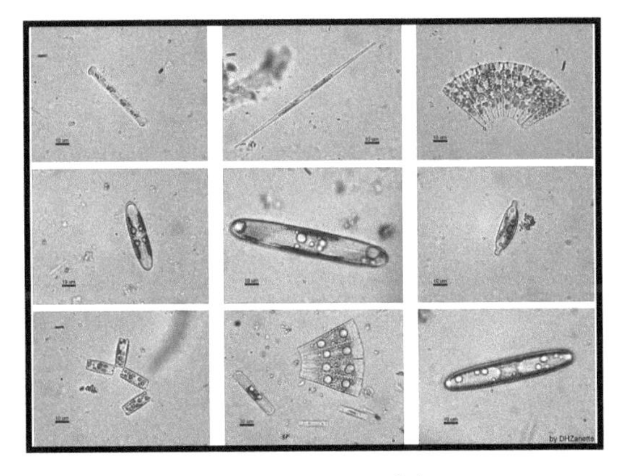

Figure 17.3 Variety of diatoms

Although dinoflagellates are important producers in aquatic environments as they photosynthesize, the indisputable champions in this department are the **diatoms.** It's been estimated that planktonic diatoms are responsible for approximately 25% of the world's (land and sea) total photosynthetic production!

But besides being important, diatoms are magnificent, unicellular algae in their own right. Like the dinoflagellates, diatoms have brownish chloroplasts due to a carotenoid pigment that masks the presence of chlorophyll. Their cell wall, called a frustule, is made of silica-containing (glass-containing) material and consist of two overlapping halves called valves which fit together like a petri dish: that is, one sits inside the other. These frustules are intricately sculptured with various patterns of pores that allow the cell membrane direct access to the photosynthetic ingredient, CO_2, that is dissolved in the seawater.

When these algal cells die, their frustules sink to the bottom and form very fine sediment called *diatomaceous ooze*. Due to the radically changing shorelines of the earth soon after the great Flood, vast deposits of this wound up above sea level and became **diatomaceous earth**. Today we mine thousands of tons of this diatomaceous earth yearly to make all kinds of stuff: water-filtering material, fine abrasives (which we use in toothpastes and polishes), pest control agent (this fine abrasive promotes water loss through insect exoskeletons), thermal barriers (which we use in some fire-resistant safes), toxic spill absorbent, livestock feed additive, etc. So not only do diatoms support a large percentage of life on earth through photosynthesis when they're alive, but their remains are pretty useful when they die.

THE BROWN ALGAE (PHAEOPHYTA)

The planktonic algae we've covered so far would be invisible without a microscope. The only thing you could see with the naked eye is the tint of the water or the glow of many algae when the water is disturbed. Most brown algae, however, you can actually see.

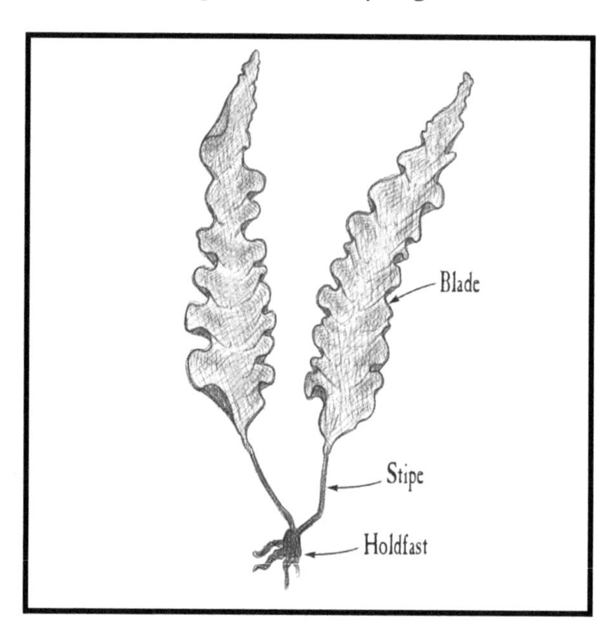

Figure 17.4 Anatomy of kelp

There are over 1,500 species of **brown algae**, most of which live in the ocean. Taxonomists group the brown algae based on chloroplast pigments they all share (chlorophylls *a* and *c* and a type of carotenoid called *fucoxanthin*). This blend of pigments gives them a brownish to olive-green color.

Brown algae can be found in a variety of marine habitats, but they dominate the rocky coasts in the cooler temperate latitudes. They are quite diverse in size and shape. Some are microscopic and filamentous, but most are visible to us as greenish-brown growths ranging from cushiony to crusty to familiar plant-like forms that we affectionately call seaweed. The largest species of kelp, which is one familiar group of brown algae, can grow to an impressive eighty meters long.

The basic structure of the plant-like brown algae consist of a root-like base called a **holdfast**. This is not a true root because the function of water and mineral absorption (which is typical of plant roots) does not occur in the holdfast. Rather, the holdfast simply serves to anchor the alga firmly to a hard underwater surface (typically rock, seashells, wood pilings of docks and piers, etc.) They don't like soft-shifting surfaces like sand or mud.

The flexible stem-like structure of the holdfast is called the **stipe**. The viscosity of water necessitates a rubbery stipe. If algae had more rigid or woody stems typical of land plants, they would snap like matchsticks under the tremendous flow of water that occurs during the movement of the tides, surf, and ocean currents.

Figure 17.5 Bull kelp

Brown algae usually have some portion of their body flattened out into one, several, or many leaf-like **blades**. These structures function as the main site of photosynthesis.

Since these algae are often submerged in water, many have air-filled floatation devices called **pneumatocysts** to buoy their stipe and blades up to well-lit surface water.

The brown algae, particularly the kelps, form large and important ecosystems on which countless sea creatures depend for food and lodging. Even from a strictly utilitarian standpoint, they justify their own existence. Within their tissues is an intercellular substance called **alginate** (a muco-polysaccharide) that contributes to the rubbery texture of brown algae. We harvest the massive blades from certain kelp forests and extract the alginate to use in a variety of commercial applications: coatings on paper and textiles, water-and fire-proofing material in fabrics, and thickening agent in soups, ice cream, jellies, cosmetics, and paints—to name just a few. Alginate is also an excellent substance used in mold-making for dentists and prosthetists. (And you thought it was good-for-nothing seaweed!)

THE RED ALGAE (RHODOPHYTA)

As you probably guessed, the unifying feature of **red algae** is the mix of light-capturing pigments contained in their chloroplasts. The predominant reddish pigment that masks the chlorophyll is *phycobilin.* This pigment is designed to absorb green to blue-green wavelengths of light, thus turning the algae red.

The red algae are the most diverse group of the seaweeds, containing roughly 5,000 to 6,000 species. Almost all are marine-dwellers except a hundred or so freshwater species. While the brown algae prefer more temperate waters, the red algae are more abundant in the tropics than the brown algae. They are more diverse than the browns, but they don't have any giants in the tribe: just a vast assortment of red seaweeds. Here is one species (Figure 17.6).

Other than their pigments, red algae have so many different growth patterns and life histories that it is difficult to discuss them as a group. One group that is especially peculiar is the coralline algae.

The coralline form reddish or pink calcareous branching or encrusting growths on rocks and other hard surfaces. The encrusting forms look like pink lichens. Because green and blue-green light is capable of penetrating water quite deeply, some record-holding coralline algae can photosynthesize in the places seemingly devoid of light over 800 feet deep.

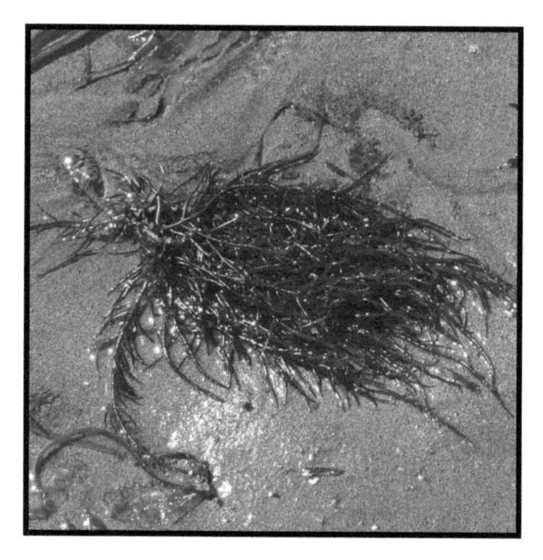

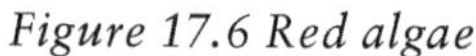

Figure 17.6 Red algae

Figure 17.7 Green algae: Ulva

We extract **agar** (a muco-polysaccharide similar to alginate) from a variety of commercially grown red algae. This substance also has many commercial applications, including gel capsule material for vitamins and drugs, mold-making material (again, similar to alginate), cosmetic base, gelling agent in some jellies and deserts, petri-dish culture medium (used universally by microbiologists to grow bacteria), and an electrophoresis medium (a highly purified agar called agarose) used in molecular biology experimentation.

THE GREEN ALGAE (CHLOROPHYTA)

You guessed it. **Green algae** are also characterized by their set of pigments. They, as their name implies, are clearly some shade of green. The chloroplasts contain chlorophyll *a* and *b* and carotenoids (carotenes and xanthophylls).

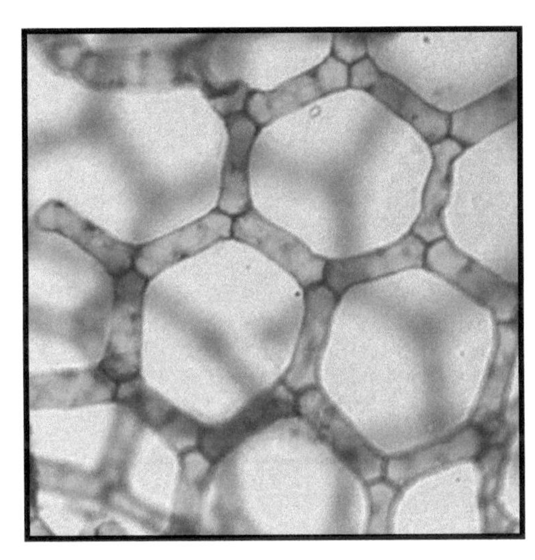

Figure 17.8 Green algae: Hydrodictyon

This is a huge group containing over 17,000 species. Although some are marine-dwellers, few species are sizable enough to be called seaweed. They are highly diverse in size and shape ranging from unicellular (*Chlamydomonas*) to net-forming colonies (*Hydrodictyon*). There are larger multicellular species such as dead man's fingers (*Codium*), sea lettuce (*Ulva*), and mermaid's wine glass (*Acetabularia*). Green algae inhabit quite a wide range of habitats. Many colonial species form tangles of thin green filaments in ponds and marshes or flowing green "hair" covering cobble stones in streams and rivers. Some are pond-dwelling miniscule hollow spheres (*Volvox*). One colony is about the size of the period at the end of this sentence. And some green algae even grow on the surface of snow, on rocks, and on the bark of trees.

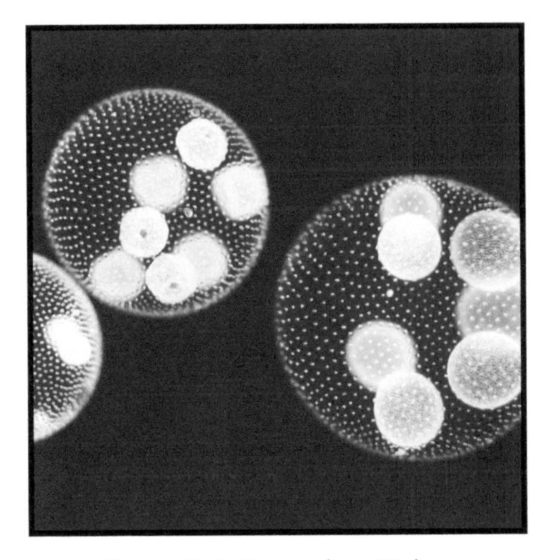

Figure 17.9 Green algae: Volvox

Though the red and brown algae dominate the oceans, some green algae also thrive there. Sea lettuce (as pictured previously in Figure 17.7) is a common marine-dweller and is often found washed up on the shore.

Because of similarities in the types of chloroplast pigments and other cellular structures involved in cell division, evolutionists consider the green algae to be the ancestors of the plant kingdom. Creationists never deny these clear similarities between groups, but we don't automatically assume that similarity implies common ancestry.

CHAPTER 17: REVIEW QUESTIONS

1. A complex arrangement of contractile proteins beneath the cell membrane of euglenoids that enable them to change shape is called a ______.
2. Some photosynthetic euglenoids have a ______ that is light sensitive and enables them to determine the direction of the light and swim towards it.
3. Free-living dinoflagellates have two flagella. One is situated in a ______ groove. The other is in a ______ groove.
4. Red tide is caused by a population explosion of certain species of ______.
5. The toxic chemicals that make red tide dangerous to certain sea life are ______.
6. What lives in the tissues of corals that enables them to live in such nutrient poor water? What do these microscopic tenants produce and how do they produce it?
7. Certain ______ are able to undergo bioluminescence.
8. The beautiful cell walls of diatoms are composed of ______ compounds.
9. Which marine protist is the most important photosynthesizer of the oceans?
10. All photosynthetic (autotrophic) protists are termed ______.
11. Large, marine autotrophic protists are colloquially called ______.
12. What are the technical names of the three algae groups that are largely multicellular? What are the common names for each?
13. The types of their ______ serve as the basis of their classification.

14. The brown algae often have four major organs that compose their body. They are:
    a. The ______ which is used for anchoring the algae to the sea floor.
    b. The ______ which acts a flexible stem or stalk.
    c. The ______ which is analogous to a leaf and serves as the primary site of photosynthesis.
    d. The ______ is gas-filled and grants buoyancy to some underwater seaweeds.

15. Two important commercial polysaccharide products of seaweeds are ______, which is extracted from certain types of red algae and ______, which is extracted from certain types of brown algae.

CHAPTER 18

ANIMAL-LIKE & FUNGAL-LIKE PROTISTS

THE PROTOZOANS

The **protozoans** are also an informal grouping of protists. They are **heterotrophs** which literally means "different feeders"—i.e., they must obtain food from a source different than themselves. "Protozoa" means "first animals," so the name clearly has evolutionary undertones. Protozoans are animal-like in that they wriggle around and obtain food, but since they are unicellular they are not actually considered animals.

FLAGELLATES (MASTIGOPHORA)

The mastigophorans (mastigo = "whip," phora = "to bear") or **flagellates** are very diverse in size, shape, and natural history. The one thing they all have in common (besides being unicellular) is the possession of one or more eukaryotic flagella. Although I can't do justice to any of these groups, I'll try to pick a few good representatives to give you an idea of the breadth of diversity in this group.

Figure 18.1 Termites carry Trichonympha

Trichonympha

The average layman has probably never heard of this little guy, but the enormous damage it does when in cahoots with its partner in crime, the termite, is all too familiar. The many termite species that make their home by eating away ours are indebted to the flagellate *Trichonympha*. This flagellate looks like a hairy pear or Cousin Itt from the Adam's family.

Trichonympha simply digest wood pulp into usable sugars for the termites. Wood cell walls are made of mostly cellulose (a polysaccharide) that's indigestible to most animals since they lack the enzyme cellulase, but *Trichonympha* do make cellulase, so wood cell walls are no problem for them.

These flagellates reside happily in the guts of termites where they secrete the enzyme *cellulase* which breaks down the cellulose in wood into glucose for their own sustenance. Their termite hosts absorb whatever sugars it can glean from the digestive powers of the *Trichonympha*. In this mutualistic relationship, the termites digest food that they couldn't otherwise get, and the flagellates benefit from the termite's subsidized housing and a constant supply of pre-chewed food. Although it's an amicable arrangement for the termite and flagellate, the homeowner in termite territory gets the short end of the deal.

Trypanosoma

This flagellate does nothing positive for its host whatsoever. It's a parasite, and parasites damage their hosts in some way—in this case, unto death.

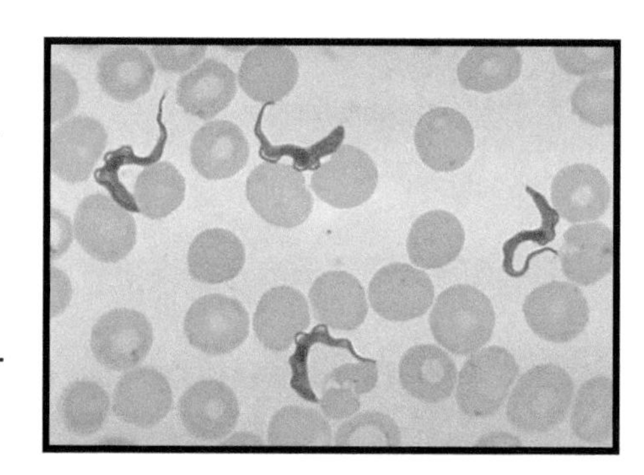

Figure 18.2 Trypanosoma

This insidious spindle-shaped flagellate spends part of its life cycle inside another host called a Tsetse fly. Once the blood-sucking fly obtains the flagellate by feeding on an infected person, the parasite eventually migrates to the fly's salivary gland. Then, when the fly bites a person, the trypanosomes are injected into the blood and lymph. Here they swim about with their flagellum which forms an undulating membrane along one side of the parasite, similar to the fin of a fish. The disease wreaks havoc throughout the body, eventually reaching the brain. It is called *African sleeping sickness* and, without treatment, is 100% fatal.

Giardia

Another flagellate which leads a parasitic lifestyle is *Giardia*. Many people have heard of it, but few could tell you that it's a flagellate shaped like a flattened teardrop sporting several flagella. It enters your body when you drink fecal-contaminated water (even if it's a clear-looking mountain stream). In its infective form, *Giardia* attacks the cells that line your digestive tract and disrupts their proper function, leading to severe diarrhea, gas, nausea, vomiting, and gastrointestinal cramps. It's a pretty flagellate with an ugly personality. The illness is a nasty affair so you'd be wise to seek medical treatment, though people do recover without treatment.

AMEBAS AND RELATIVES (SARCODINES)

Distinguishing **amebas** and their relatives from flagellates can be problematic. In some classifications, the two groups have been lumped together. The reason is that some groups of amebas (at certain times of their life cycle or due to certain stimuli) have a habit of dispensing with their pseudopods and manufacturing their own flagella. (Like I said earlier, protists are known for not respecting our tidy categories.) With that as an intro, let me mention the hallmark features of the sarcodines.

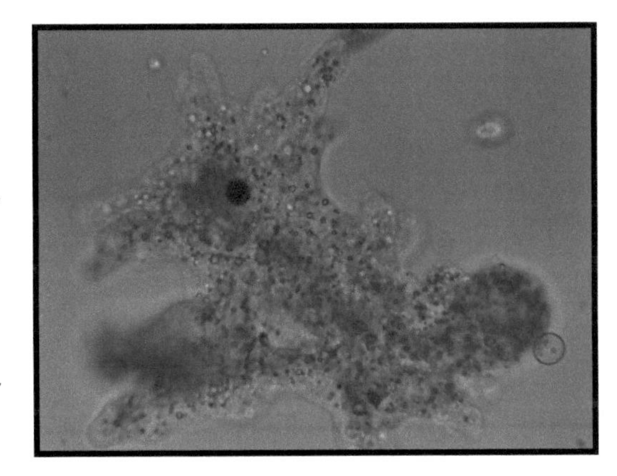

Figure 18.3 Ameba

Sarcodines have the ability to make pseudopods of some sort: little cellular protrusions which are generally used for locomotion and for feeding through phagocytosis.

Many kinds of amebas are free-living in a variety of freshwater habitats, but others have taken up a parasitic existence. The most well-known parasitic ameba causes the gastrointestinal malady called amebic dysentery. This disrupts the large intestine's ability to absorb water. Diarrhea with a vengeance results from this infection.

Most freshwater forms are naked in that they have no test (cell wall-like structure). Their shape is constantly changing as new pseudopods sprout and older ones disappear along their cell membranes. Their cytoplasm also has a granular appearance due to many vesicles and vacuoles being carried about the cell's interior by *cytoplasmic streaming.*

The freshwater amebas also have contractile vacuoles to rid themselves of excess water flowing into the cell due to the hypotonicity of their surroundings.

Marine Sarcodines

There are two major groups of ameba-like creatures that are abundant in the oceans: the **foraminiferans** and the **radiolarians.** While most freshwater amebas are naked, both of these groups do have a **test**, which is essentially a miniature shell that surrounds their single-celled body.

Foraminiferans produce a test made of **calcium carbonate** (lime). They often make diminutive tests that have spirals like snail shells and are perforated so that their little pseudopods can protrude. The foraminiferan pseudopods are net-like, forming many interconnections with other pseudopods. For this reason they are called *reticulopods* (*reticulo* = net).

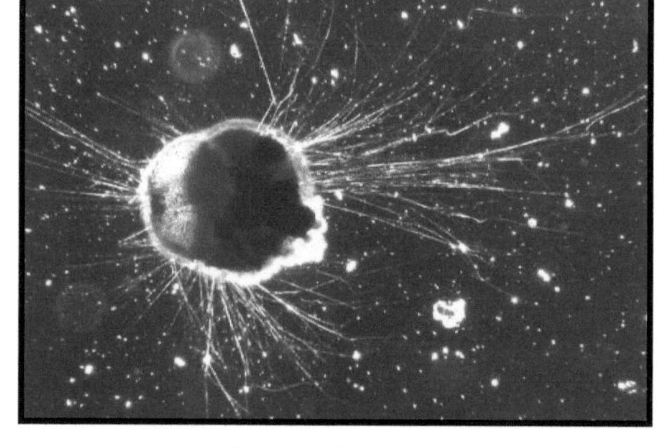

*Figure 18.4 A foraminiferan (*Ammonia tepida*)*

These wonderful creatures form a huge part of the microscopic zooplankton (animal or animal-like plankton) in the oceans, particularly in temperate waters. They float freely, trapping and phagocytosing smaller one-celled organisms with their reticulopods. When they die, their tests, which don't decompose, sink to the bottom of the oceans, accumulating into large deposits called *foraminiferan ooze*. In the past, when the sea level dropped radically (like when the waters receded after Noah's flood), many of these deposits wound up above sea level. The most famous of these are the White Cliffs of Dover.

Figure 18.5 White Cliffs of Dover

These huge deposits are composed mostly of remains of Coccolithophores (marine algae containing $CaCO_3$), though foraminiferan tests also make up a significant portion. All these microbe remains have solidified into rock called chalk. In fact, old-fashioned chalk was quarried from deposits like this. (Now most chalk is artificially made.)

The **radiolarians** are also amazing. Their tests are made of **glass-containing compounds**. The radial symmetry and beauty of their tests truly make them microscopic jewels. The perforated tests again allow the little pseudopods to extend from their cell bodies. Their pseudopods, called axopods, are thin and spoke-like; they don't interconnect with each other.

Radiolarians tend to be in more tropical waters. They are planktonic, but can also roll along a surface by shortening the leading axopods and lengthening the trailing ones. These stiff, skinny pseudopods have a cytoskeleton made of hundreds of parallel microtubules running lengthwise like a package of spaghetti (each noodle represents a microtubule and the plastic bag is the cell membrane). In addition to locomotion, pseudopods are used for getting food. They may be skinny, but they can actually phagocytose tiny one-celled prey.

*Figure 18.6 A radiolarian (*Carpocanium solitarium*)*

Just like the tests of foraminiferans, radiolarian tests also don't decompose. When radiolarians die, their tests sink to the bottom and form radiolarian ooze. Radiolarian fossils above sea level are found in rocks called radiolarian chert. These rocks, however, are not as widespread or as impressive as the chalk deposits like the White Cliffs of Dover.

CILIATES

While many other groups get split and lumped according to the latest ideas in taxonomy, the **ciliates** have remained relatively stable as a taxon. The reason for this is that, although they are very diverse, ciliates don't mess with our categories by possessing traits that should belong to another group. Rather, they all share the following unifying characteristics: they are all unicellular, they all possess cilia (these are short versions of flagella in that they have the same internal 9 + 2 arrangement of microtubules we covered

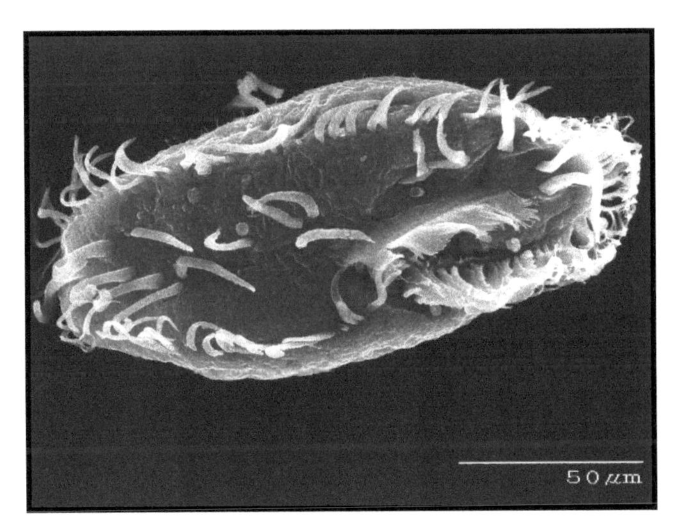

*Figure 18.7 A ciliate (*Oxytricha trifallax*)*

on page 77), and all have more than one nucleus. Beyond this, ciliates have tremendous diversity in size and shape and can be found in both freshwater and marine habitats. Compared to sarcodines and flagellates, most ciliates have a larger cell size; some get up to 3 mm, though some pipsqueaks are only 10 µm. We will only look at two of the approximately 8,000 known species.

Paramecium

The most well-known freshwater ciliate is the *Paramecium*, which has been used in countless introductory biology labs in high schools and colleges.

There are several species of the genus *Paramecium,* but *P. caudatum* is probably the most studied. Like the euglenoids, *P. caudatum* has a cytoskeletal **pellicle,** but unlike the euglenoids, it doesn't contract. It lies just beneath the cell membrane and maintains the classic shape of the *Paramecium.*

This species ranges from 150 to 300 µm long and sports approximately 10,000 to 14,000 cilia arranged in parallel bands running lengthwise over its entire surface. Most of these cilia are responsible for the *P. caudatum's* speedster reputation among the protozoa. It can go from zero to a 1,000 µm/second in no time, do a three point turn, and head off in another direction in the blink of an eye (literally). If you get the opportunity to watch them zip around under a microscope, your eyeballs will dry out as you watch, bug-eyed in unblinking amazement. They move like a well-thrown football, with glass slipper-like curves and contours.

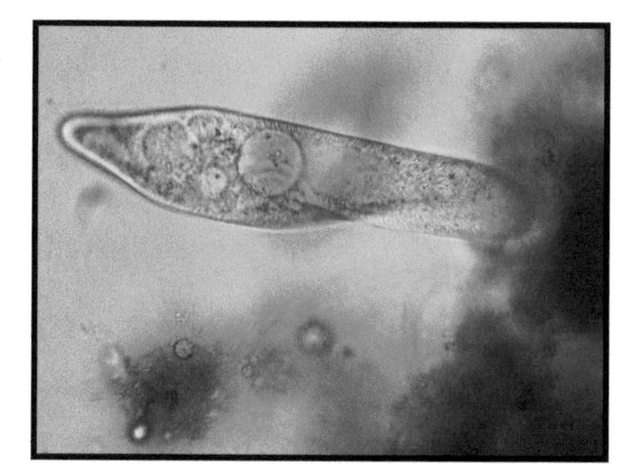

Figure 18.8 Paramecium

The arch of the "slipper" is the oral groove. The cilia lining this groove are involved in sweeping and funneling small microbes down into a tiny opening called a **cytostome** (cell mouth). This directs the food down a short tube to a food vacuole where phagocytosis occurs. Having a specified place on the cell to do phagocytosis is common in ciliates, and puts them in stark contrast with the amebas which engulf prey anywhere on their cell surface.

Once the food vacuole is filled, it pinches off and begins a journey through the cytoplasm. During this circuit, lysosomes fuse with it so that the food is digested. The nutrients are absorbed into the cytoplasm while the waste remains. The resulting waste vacuole also has a particular location on the cell surface where it does its business of exocytosis, dumping waste from the cell. *P. caudatum* also have wonderful **contractile vacuoles** which provide the water-baling service so necessary in freshwater protozoa.

In other ciliates, the pellicle is more similar to the euglenoid in that they are contractile proteins tethered to the cell membrane (again, much like the contractile proteins for muscle cell contraction). Like the static pellicles, it also provides flexible support, but the contractile proteins also allow many ciliates to radically change shape if the need arises.

Stentor

Stentor is probably my favorite of the ciliates because they are so large and fantastical. When attached to a surface by their tapered end, they are shaped like a hairy fanfare trumpet (Stentor was a Greek herald in the Trojan War, noted for his loud, trumpet-like voice) and can stretch over 2 mm (2,000 μm) in length. But when *Stentor* goes for a cruise, it uses its muscle-like pellicle to roll up like a hairy rugby ball, and spirals through the water at a leisurely pace.

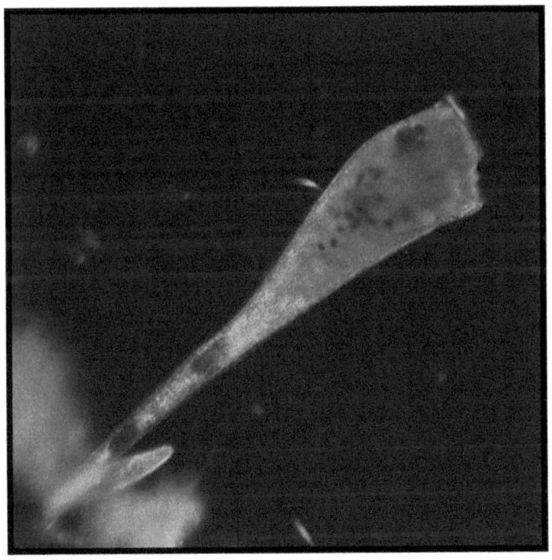

Figure 18.9 Stentor

If the *Stentor* is attached, its feeding end flares out like the bell of a trumpet where there is a curving **oral groove** leading to a food vacuole. The cilia lining the rim of the bell are longer than the cilia covering the rest of the cell. These beat vigorously, creating a deadly current. Any bacteria or even sizable single-celled algae or protozoans swimming too close can be caught in the vortex and sucked into the oral groove of death.

So far, I've introduced you to two groups of protists: the plant-like algae and the animal-like protozoa. Now we're moving on to the fungal-like protists.

THE FUNGAL-LIKE PROTISTS

These organisms are also heterotrophic, but unlike protozoans, they are colonial or multicellular. They are informally called "molds" because part of their lifecycle and growth are reminiscent of fungi; however, they have subtle characteristics that exclude them from Kingdom Fungi.

The Plasmodial Slime Molds (Myxomycota)

This group is almost the subject matter of a B horror film (like *The Blob*). These alien creatures are kind of animal-like and fungal-like in that they move about like an animal and form fruiting bodies to disperse spores like mushrooms. There are approximately 700 described species worldwide. (The best known example is in the genus *Physarum*.) Each individual slime mold is composed of one multinucleated cell and each nucleus is diploid.

Figure 18.10 Plasmodial slime mold

Though these blobs can grow to several feet across, they are usually only a few inches in diameter. They generally ooze along the forest floor, consuming microbes in the moist, decaying vegetation. Usually, the creeping slime mold fans out like a river delta in the direction it is moving. When conditions grow bleak due to lack of food or moisture, the slime mold stops crawling about and begins to mound up into small excrescences called **sporangia** which number from one to many (sporangium means spore container).

Each diploid nucleus in the sporangium is encapsulated inside its own cell wall, thus becoming a diploid **spore**. Each spore nucleus undergoes meiosis and produces four haploid nuclei, three of which disintegrate. This results in each spore having one haploid nucleus. When the sporangium opens up, the tiny spores are liberated into the air and wafted through the air currents. If some of the spores chance to land on a suitable moist surface, they germinate and become microscopic amebas or flagellated gametes.

These amebas (still haploid) cannot grow into the big multinucleate blob. Instead, they have to find and fuse with another ameba of the same species. In what is essentially the same as fertilization, their nuclei fuse to become a diploid zygote. Now in the diploid state, the slime mold is able to grow again into a large multinucleate cell. (The many nuclei result from the zygote nucleus dividing by mitosis without cell division.)

Slime molds are usually not very conspicuous. They live out their bizarre lives in dark, damp, secretive places and are unnoticed by the casual hiker. Occasionally, when the conditions are right, slime molds grow large and crawl across roads, up trees, and onto patios, bringing them into contact with unsuspecting citizens. Some encounters with slime molds, needless to say, have evoked mild panic in ignorant, excitable folk because they think some blob-like alien has invaded their domain. If you had a yellow, slimy blob about three feet across ooze onto your back stoop, what would *you* do?

The Cellular Slime Molds

This strange group is very inconspicuous and you're not likely to stumble across it unless you're an ardent naturalist with a keen eye and a fondness for tiny, clear slimy growths on the ground. I have put this group alongside the plasmodial slime molds because they form spore-producing bodies, even though one of its stages is very similar to amebas. There are about 50 known species of cellular slime molds and probably many more yet to be discovered. It is likely that the numbers of species known is a reflection of the number of biologists that are actively looking for this sort of creature.

LIFECYCLE

Let's start with its spore stage. Microscopic spores fall to the ground from a spore-bearing body. If the ground is an appropriately moist substrate, the spores germinate into tiny amebas. These move about in moist, humus-rich soils, consuming bacteria (phagocytosis) and multiplying by mitosis. When the available food runs out, the amebas begin to migrate towards one another. As they congregate, they form a small, clear, elongate blob several millimeters long and begin moving in one direction. This stage is called the **slug** (not to be confused with a naked snail).

Eventually the slug parks itself and the little amebas begin to crawl on top of each other. In this way, the slug begins its transformation into a spore-bearing body (**sporocarp**) that looks like a miniaturized water tower. The leading amebas (of the slug) form the supportive stalk by producing cellulose cell walls and then dying. The trailing amebas crawl to the top and form the knob. These develop into dormant spores which are eventually released starting the life cycle all over again.

The Water Molds (Oomycota)

Water molds, like the slime molds above, are organisms you don't see everyday. Nevertheless, they do have important ecological roles that are worth knowing and appreciating. Unfortunately, some members of this group are also responsible for widespread pestilence and famine, but I ask you—what phylum *doesn't* have their bad guys that are strong reminders of the curse?

Though water molds don't belong to the Kingdom Fungi, they are much more like fungi than the slime molds above. Water mold's growth form is thread-like in that their "cells" form thin filaments called **hyphae**. I put "cells" in quotation marks because the idea of cells is inaccurate with these molds. Their hyphae *don't* have distinct cellular units hooked end to end. Instead, their threads are a continual filament of cytoplasm, bounded by cell wall and membrane with multiple nuclei scattered about inside. There are no cellular partitions dividing up the thread. If Robert Hooke looked at water mold instead of cork under his microscope, he never would have coined the word "cellulae" to describe this odd arrangement. Instead of being called "cells," hyphae lacking septa ("partitions") are termed **aseptate** or "coenocytic" (guess which term I prefer).

These water molds are important **saprobes** (decomposers) in aquatic habitats. They do an indispensable job of digesting and consuming much of the dead organic debris (mostly leaves and twigs) that falls into the water. True fungi (mushrooms and such) do much the same work on land. So what's the difference? Why aren't water molds true fungi? Other than habitat, the differences are not apparent to the naked eye. Rather, there are subtle biochemical and genetic differences.

Water molds have **cellulose** cell walls; true fungi have **chitin** cell walls. Both chitin and cellulose are polysaccharides but their monosaccharide building blocks are quite different. Another difference is that water molds are usually diploid (2N) during most of their lifecycle, whereas fungi are typically haploid (1N) for most of their life cycle. Also, water molds have flagellated spores, whereas fungi don't have flagella at all at any point in their lifecycle. Water molds have filamentous growth (hyphae), and at the end of the day, that's why we call them molds. They decompose organic debris in much the same way (*extracellular digestion*) as fungi (but I'll discuss fungi next chapter).

As I mentioned earlier, some water molds are plant parasites. Two species in particular have etched themselves into the annals of European history as a devastating pestilence. One water mold to bring major devastation was the **late blight of potatoes** *(Phytophthora infestans)*, causing the Great Famine of 1845-1852 in Ireland.

But if they are water molds, why attack land plants? Water molds grow within the tissues of a plant, which is a highly moist environment, and the summers of the late 1840s in Ireland were cool and wet. These conditions were ideal for the blight. In damp conditions, the blight can reach full stride and reduce a field of potatoes plants to a black mess in just a few days.

This devastated the peasant population of Ireland. Since the landowners took the meat and almost everything else, the peasants' major food source was potatoes. (The average adult ate nine to thirteen pounds of potatoes a day to get enough protein.) As the blight ravaged the potato crop from 1845 to 1851, the population of Ireland dropped approximately 2 million (8.5 million to 6.5 million). Of these, almost half starved to death.

Figure 18.11 Healthy versus blighted potatoes

Yet another water mold that had a historical impact was the Downy Mildew in Grapes. In the 1870s, many vineyards in France were being attacked by a water mold called *Plasmopara viticola*. It attacked both leaves and immature grapes and was on the verge of undermining the entire French wine industry. Providentially/fortunately, a professor from the University of Bordeaux noticed that the grape vines near roadsides and byways of Medoc, France, were virtually unscathed by the pestilence. This was because the vineyard owners in this area made a point of preventing pedestrians from picking their precious grapes. They had an unpalatable concoction of lime and copper sulfate which they applied on the vines within easy reach of passersby. The professor, after discussing the problem with the vineyard owners, made up his own concoction ("the Bordeaux mixture") and made it available by 1882. This was the first recorded instance of chemical treatment to control a plant disease.

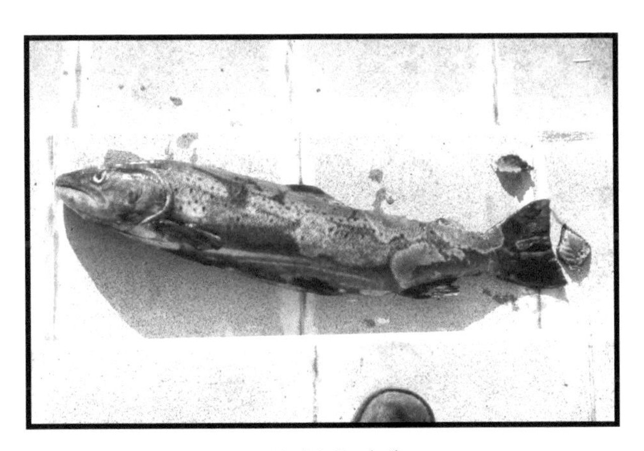

Figure 18.12 Fish fungus

Keep in mind that most water molds do us a great

service as saprobes in aquatic ecosystems, but I will focus on one more water mold that misbehaves: *fish fungus*. It does have a good side. Fish fungus is a proper saprobe, consuming dead organic matter in freshwater habitats, but it can also switch to the dark side.

This parasitic water mold attacks fish and fish eggs in unclean conditions. Aquarium fish (as well as wild) that are well fed and live in clean water usually stay healthy and are very resistant to fish fungus attack. But when fish get infected, white cottony growths sprout from their scales. Whole sheets of skin slough off, and if left untreated, the fish will die.

CHAPTER 18: REVIEW QUESTIONS

1. The flagellates share a locomotion device called a ______.
2. Shelled amebas that produce a calcium carbonate test (shell) are called ______.
3. Giardia, Trichonympha, and Trypanosoma are all examples of a disease-causing ______.
4. Shelled amebas that produce a test composed of glass compounds are called ______.
5. White Cliffs of Dover are partly composed of the shells of which protozoan group?
6. Protozoans that get around with and obtain food with cilia are classified in the group called ______.
7. The common feature of all amebas is the ______ which is an extension of the cell used for locomotion and feeding.
8. Single-celled, non-photosynthetic (heterotrophic) protists are colloquially called ______.
9. Many freshwater protozoa have an osmotic problem because they live in a hypotonic environment. What organelle do they possess that helps them cope with the constant influx of water?
10. Many ciliates have a depression on their cell surface where they channel food to be phagocytosed. This is called the ______.

11. A plasmodial slime mold is a gigantic multinucleate ______. They resemble fungi in that they produce ______ which produce spores.

12. The 'slug' in cellular slime molds differs with the plasmodium in that it is composed of many ______ moving together.

13. Water molds differ from Fungi in two significant ways.
    a. They have a cell wall made of ______ rather than chitin.
    b. They are ______ (ploidy) for most of their life cycle.

14. Name one water mold that had a great historical impact.

15. What was the historical impact? In other words, what did the water mold do?

CHAPTER 19

KINGDOM FUNGI

Kingdom Fungi is not as troublesome as Protista, which is desperately lacking in characteristics that unify them as a kingdom. Fungi, though a very diverse kingdom with around 100,000 *known* species, at least has some clear unifying characteristics with very few exceptions. Let's go over these characteristics.

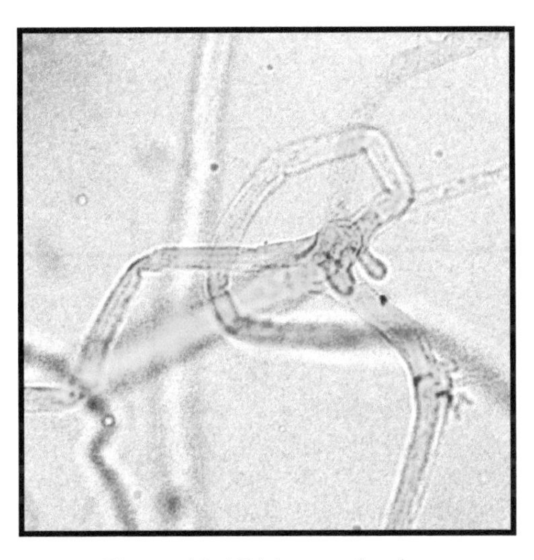

Figure 19.1 Rhizopus *hyphae*

The characteristics that are not exclusive to fungi are that they are multicellular (with the exception of yeast), they have a eukaryotic cell structure (membrane-bound nucleus and organelles), and they are also heterotrophic saprobes (they consume dead organic matter).

Fungi are filamentous (with the exception of yeast). Their cells generally link end to end in long branching filaments called hyphae. The term **hypha** (pl. **hyphae**) is usually used to denote one to several threads viewed under the microscope, while the term **mycelium** is reserved for larger quantities as easily seen by the naked eye. When mold is growing all over your food in the refrigerator, "mycelium" is a good word (along with "gross") to describe it at that scale. If you've ever ripped open a rotten log

Figure 19.2 Mycelium

and found branching networks of yellow or white threads woven through the log, this is also mycelium (but it is not gross). The only odd-man-out with regard to the filamentous growth form is the well-known yeasts, which I will discuss later.

When I said that water molds are not true fungi, I mentioned that they had cell walls of *cellulose*, whereas true fungi have cell walls made of *chitin*. Also, chitin is a type of polysaccharide made up of the monosaccharide called *N-acetylglucosamine*. Below is a two monosaccharide segment of a chitin chain.

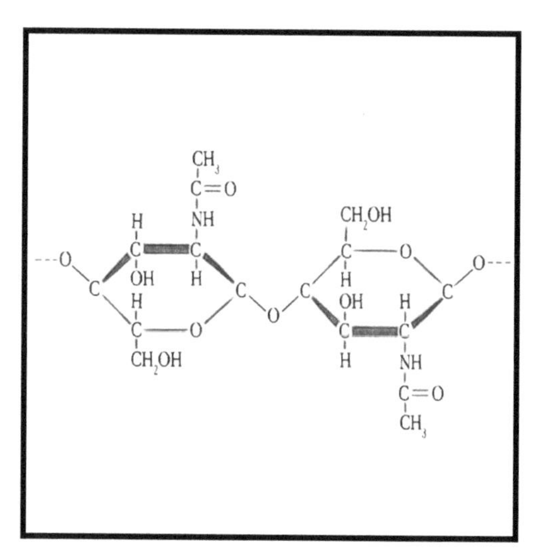

Figure 19.3 N-acetylglucosamine

Another interesting feature is that fungi have no cilia or flagella. In fact, no part of their life cycle contains these biological outboard motors. (That's another reason water molds don't qualify as true fungi: their spores are flagellated.)

Fungi are haploid for most of their life cycle. Their nuclei have only one complete set of genetic information, whereas most eukaryotic nuclei are diploid (2N: two complete sets of genetic information). For example, most animal cells have a complete set of genetic information from their father and a complete set from their mother.

Fungi reproduce by spores–single cells shrink-wrapped in a membrane and resistant cell wall to survive adverse environmental conditions. Spores are very tiny and light and can easily be wafted by air currents all the way up to the jet stream. This means that fungal spores can get around, hopping from continent to continent without a passport. I'll discuss more about spore reproduction later when we get to the different fungal groups and their own peculiar way of making and dispersing spores.

Fungi also have a bizarre variation on mitosis and meiosis. The most obvious difference is that when they go through mitosis or meiosis, the nuclear envelope doesn't break down; all the chromosome movement occurs within the nucleus.

Fungi are very diverse. The current count is around 100,000 but knowing how much more we need to explore the earth, the grand total probably far exceeds that.

In describing how fungi affect mankind, I will be a little more even-handed than I was with water molds. I will highlight both the injurious as well as the salubrious qualities of fungi.

DESTRUCTIVE FUNGI

Although they consume untold amounts of **detritus** (dead organic matter), fungi don't distinguish between wanted and unwanted stuff. If the stuff used to be alive, the fungi will eat it no matter what, indiscriminately consuming many natural products and much stored food. In the tropical rainforests where there are moisture and humidity aplenty, fungi mercilessly attack all sorts of stuff they are not supposed to, such as leather goods, paper products and every form of fabric made from natural fibers (cotton, wool, linen, etc.).

Of course, not every fungus attacks everything mentioned. Fungi are either specialists (very picky about what they feed on) or generalists (they'll feed on a variety of different substances given the right circumstances). Some fungal species partake of exotic dishes like the emulsion on photographic film and the coatings on optical lenses. Some even consume jet fuel!

Although most fungi are saprobes (eaters of dead things), there are some fungi that don't wait around for their food to die before they dig in. Such a fungus is called a parasite or pathogen. Countless fungi cause a variety of fungal diseases on live plants. It is of special concern to farmers and horticulturalists when the victimized plants are crops or ornamentals. When a weed is afflicted no tears are shed.

Much agricultural research is focused on these disease-causing fungi. At some universities, entire departments are devoted to the study of plant diseases. By studying these fungi and their life cycles intimately, we can develop better techniques to combat these destructive diseases.

Figure 19.4 Rust (a fungal disease) on corn

Still other parasitic fungi attack both animals and humans. Some very well known examples are athlete's foot, ringworm, and yeast infections (a.k.a. thrush or candidiasis).

Athlete's Foot

How do fungi eat? I've been saying "fungi feed on" or "fungi eat this or that," but I'm not implying that they actually have miniature mouths. No, they go about obtaining food in a very different way than animals and people do. This bizarre technique is called **extracellular digestion**.

As mentioned already, fungi are composed of tiny threads called hyphae. As a hypha is growing through its particular environment (whether it's dead leaves, dead wood, a living leaf, or the skin between your toes), the Golgi bodies within the hypha are making lysosomes filled with digestive (hydrolytic) enzymes. These lysosomes are then directed to the cell membrane where they are released by that wonderful process called exocytosis. After exocytosis, the enzymes are outside the cell membrane. They diffuse through the cell wall (chitin) and digest the various nutrient molecules such as proteins, carbohydrates, lipids, etc., that make up the surrounding organic matter (dead leaves, wood, skin, and the like). Once this stuff is digested down into basic building blocks (e.g., amino acids, monosaccharides, fatty acids, and glycerol), these nutrients are absorbed into the cytoplasm of the hypha to be used for energy and hyphal growth. (By the way, since lysosome membranes fuse with the cell membrane during exocytosis, the surface area of the hypha increases and elongates as the cytoplasm gains mass with the absorption of nutrients and water.)

If it wasn't for fungi, dead material would continue to build up faster than it is broken down. Yes, as we've already seen, bacteria and scavengers play an important role in consuming a good deal of this dead matter, but fungi take care of a very significant portion. Just think of a forest. Most of the dead leaves and wood are rotted by the activity of the mycelium weaving through moist leaf litter and fallen logs, releasing gazillions of lysosomes. All this decomposing or rotting stuff is largely due to the extracellular digestion of fungi.

BENEFICIAL FUNGI

Now let's consider some salubrious qualities of fungi. Probably the most celebrated member of the kingdom Fungi is yeast. Although it is not a typical fungus in that it doesn't grow as hyphae, it does share many other fungal traits not apparent to the naked eye.

Yeast (leaven) has been employed by brewers, vintners, and bakers for thousands of years. In short, the desirable trait of yeast is actually their waste. Let's explore how.

Figure 19.5 Yeast

When yeast is added to a sugary solution of wort (pre-fermented beer) or grape juice, the yeast cells absorb the sugars for food and then ferment (partially metabolize) the sugars for energy and growth.

$$C_6H_{12}O_6 \rightarrow 2CO_2 + 2C_2H_5OH + 2\ ATP$$

This metabolism doesn't burn glucose all the way down to the typical waste products of cellular respiration (CO_2 and H_2O), but only partially burning it down into $2C_2H_5OH$ (two ethanol molecules) and $2CO_2$. Brewers and vintners alike are interested in both of these waste products. The ethanol is what they're after to make their beverage alcoholic, and the CO_2 is the gas that makes the beverage bubble after the lid is popped off. (Often the natural CO_2 made by the yeast escapes before bottling, in which case the beer is pressurized with CO_2 canisters to make it fizzy.)

Bakers add yeast to dough to make it rise. The yeast feasts on the sugars in the dough, producing ethanol and CO_2 and it's CO_2 that makes the dough rise. As the dough rises, it is also becoming alcoholic; the reason you can't get drunk by eating lots of bread is because the bread is baked. The heat of the oven causes almost all the ethanol to evaporate. (You can sometimes, however, catch a whiff of alcohol when you open the oven door.)

Figure 19.6 Blue cheese

Certain cheeses, like Roquefort, Blue, Camembert, Brie, Gorgonzola, Stilton, and Limburger, get much of their distinctive flavor from mold growing in their cracks and crannies. All these cheeses have either the fungi *Penicillium roquefortii* or *Penicillium camemberti*, growing on them. Their peculiar flavor is due to their unique recipe of curdling milk in combination with one of these two species of fungi.

The advent of antibiotics was the result of a classic serendipitous discovery. In 1928, Alexander Fleming (a Scottish microbiologist working in

London) discovered that one of his old cultures of bacteria was contaminated by a fungus. He noted that there was a clear zone which indicated no bacterial growth around the fungus colony. It was evident that the fungus was actually manufacturing and secreting some mysterious substance that killed bacteria or inhibited their growth.

The practical application of this discovery did not get underway until about 10 years later when the antibacterial substance was isolated. The substance, **penicillin**, was named after the fungus that contaminated Fleming's bacterial petri dish, *Penicillium notatum*. Before World War II ended, American scientists figured out how to mass-produce the mold, extract the antibiotic penicillin, and use it extensively against a variety of bacterial diseases such as scarlet fever, gonorrhea, pneumonia, and meningitis. Penicillin quickly replaced sulfa drugs since it was much more successful at fighting infections. Even though it was introduced partway through the war, it saved the lives of countless soldiers. Up to that time, deep bacterial infections were impossible to stop and wounded soldiers often died of sepsis (the spread of multiplying bacteria through body) because deep bacterial infections were hard to stop. Penicillin was the new wonder drug that could stop an infection dead in its tracks.

Figure 19.7 Penicillium *and* Aspergillus *molds on lemon*

Some fungi are used directly as food, not just growing on food like a living spice. Many people (including myself) are fungiphiles at heart and love edible mushrooms on pizzas, in omelets, in salads, or just by themselves.

But there are many different edible fungi, not just mushrooms. Morels, for example, are a fungi that are considered a delicacy for those who don't have a delicate bank account.

Cyclosporine, an interesting chemical isolated from a fungus in the genus *Beauveria,* was discovered to be effective in suppressing our immune system. Now, normally we like our immune systems; they protect us from all sorts of pathogens that weasel into our bodies. In short, they're essential to our survival. But the down-side is that our immune systems will just as vigorously attack a life-saving organ from an organ donor *because it's foreign.* Consequently, organ transplants are a very dangerous business unless the donor's tissue matches the recipient's tissue perfectly. Cyclosporine saves the day here, suppressing the recipient's immune system so that it can't detect or react to the new organ.

Compost is simply a nutrient-rich, soil-like medium used to enrich the soil for growing plants. It is produced by the decomposition of food wastes, yard clippings, manure, etc. Not surprisingly, fungi (along with bacteria) are a major decomposer in compost. In compost, fungi transforms unwanted waste into a useful product for anyone who wants richer soil for their plants.

I will discuss this in a little more detail later, but another beneficial fungus is **mycorrhizae** or fungus roots. Certain species form intimate symbiotic relationships with plant roots where both the fungus and the plant benefit (+/+). This is another example of mutualism. The fungus helps the plant by extracting a number of useful minerals from the soil and delivering them to the plant roots. The plant returns the favor by allowing the fungus to help itself to some of the photosynthate (products of photosynthesis) stored in the root's tissues.

GROUPS OF FUNGI

Fungi may look exotic, strange, or beautiful; they may even make themselves useful by being edible, medicinal, or agriculturally beneficial, but they just don't rivet our attention like animals. Why? Because animals actually get up and move around and do stuff like eat (each other), sleep, run, walk, climb, fly, mate, and fight.

But in spite of their inability to do all this, fungi can be quite interesting. (And actually they *do* do some of this stuff; they just don't do it in a way that readily captures our attention.) I hope to make you sit up in awe as I highlight the subtle yet fantastical aspects of fungal life.

The Zygomycetes

This group is one of the smaller groups of fungi, containing over 1,000 species. They are mostly saprobes, consuming dead organic matter of plants and animals in the soil. A few, however, are parasitic on plants, insects, and other small soil animals.

Zygomycetes don't have large fruiting bodies designed for reproduction like mushrooms. Instead they usually have a hypha that terminates in some kind of knob-like structure called a **sporangium** filled with—you guessed it—spores. The sporangium is sometimes more like a pepper shaker, sprinkling its spores about.

Another notable feature of zygomycetes is that their hyphae, rather than being cellular, are long branching threads of membrane-bound cytoplasm. There are no internal septa or partitions (**aseptate**) to delineate one cell or nucleus from another. Their many nuclei just wander freely about this continuous thread of cytoplasm. (Robert Hooke never would have coined the word "cell" if he'd looked at these fungi under the microscope, either.)

Figure 19.8 Pilobolus

One notable zygomycete has taken spore dispersal to a jaw-dropping level. *Pilobolus,* a fungus that often grows on cow patties and the droppings of other cloven-hoofed herbivores, has hyphae that look like tiny glass fibers growing on the surface of the dung. When it's ready to make spores, the fungus sends up vertical hyphae called **sporangiophores** (sporangium-bearers). Perched at its tip is a little black shiny sporangium. This fungus doesn't sprinkle spores; rather, the entire sporangium is fired like a cannonball. There is a bulge in the transparent sporangiophore directly below its sporangium and as the sun rises over the cow pasture, the light rays are refracted by the bulge and effect the growth of the sporangiophore so that it is aimed toward the light. If tall grass blades cast a shadow, the sporangiophore will not be aimed in that direction; it will only point at the light, wherever it shines through.

Now, the cytoplasm of the bulge is very hypertonic, drawing water into the bulge and increasing its fluid pressure. Eventually the building pressure causes the bulge to burst. Like a water pistol plugged with a spit wad, the pressure suddenly launches the sporangium at about 45 to 55 mph. This acceleration amounts to the sporangium experiencing 180,000 g. The little black sporangium is shot through the grass blades and lands on a grass blade a meter or two away from the cow patty. Now, a cow chances by, but is too fussy to graze that close to a cow patty. (The grass around a patty, in case you didn't know, is repugnant.) The fresh grass, on the other hand, which is right where that tiny sporangium landed, is far enough away. So the cow munches it down and eats the sporangium. After the grueling passage through the cow's digestive tract, the spores are released and plopped out in fresh manure. And its life cycle begins anew.[1]

Another familiar zygomycete fungus is the Black Bread Mold in the genus *Rhizopus*. This is the culprit behind so much of the mold that grows on your food when it sits around too long (in or out of the fridge.) To the naked eye it ranges from whitish to grayish-black fuzz (mycelium).

As you've noticed, there are different kinds of hyphae. Mycologists have given them special names. As noted in *Pilobolus*, the hypha bearing the sporangium (spore container) is called the sporangiophore (sporangium-bearer; see Figure 19.9.) The hyphae that spread out over the surface, prospecting for new sources of food, are called **stolons**. Whenever these pioneering stolons touch down, root-like hyphae called **rhizoids** grow into the food. These are designed to penetrate and consume the food through extracellular digestion. New sporangiophores sprout up opposite the rhizoids and form new sporangia filled with spores. When the sporangia are fully developed, spores are released and if they land in a suitable place, they can grow into more mycelia. This is asexual reproduction, so any mycelia produced from these spores will be a clone of the parent.

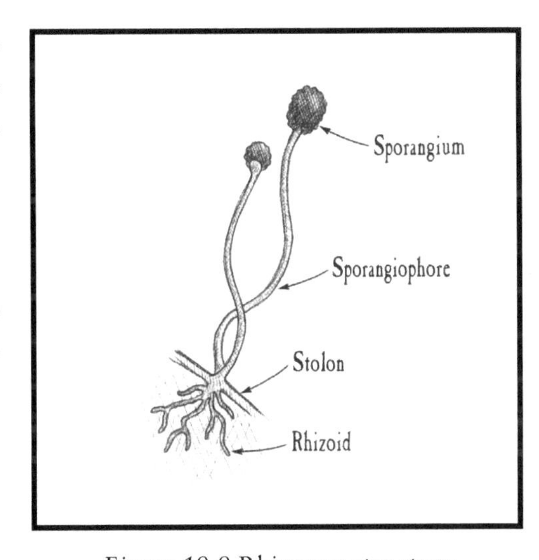

Figure 19.9 Rhizopus *structure*

The sporangia are black and are barely visible to the naked eye. When these form, they darken the overall appearance of the light mycelium to shades of gray or black. This fungus has been well studied, so I will use it as the representative life cycle of this phylum.

In sexual reproduction of *Rhizopus stolonifera,* there are two mating strains. (This is not always the case; some are self fertile.) Since the strains can't be visually distinguished from each other as male or female, they are simply designated as + and –. When the + strain is near the - strain, they sense each other chemically. Stolons from the two opposite strains sprout short hyphae which reach out to meet each other. When they touch, each strain forms a **gametangium** (gamete container) which walls itself off from

1. You can find more details in this article I wrote for *Answers Magazine*: "Fungus Firearms," http://www.answersingenesis.org/articles/am/v5/n2/fungus-firearms [accessed June 20, 2014].

the hypha that produced it. Inside a gametangium are several nuclei that will serve as gametes (hence the name).

The two gametangia then merge into one compartment called a **zygosporangium**. The + nuclei would fuse with the – nuclei, forming several diploid nuclei. The zygosporangium then undergoes a transformation, developing a thick, resistant wall that can survive adverse environmental conditions such as dryness, cold, etc. And sooner or later, when the conditions are right, the zygosporangium germinates.

When it does, the diploid nuclei undergo meiosis, producing equal numbers of + and – nuclei. The emerging hypha develops directly into a sporangiophore topped with a sporangium. The resulting haploid nuclei become spores within its sporangium. In this case, the sporangium will have spores of both mating strains whereas the asexual sporangia will produce either + or – spores, but not together. Since there is crossing over during meiosis, all the spores will be genetically different from each other and different from the parent mycelia that joined. When the sporangium is ready, spores of both strains are released to the four winds.

The Ascomycetes

Commonly known as the sac fungi, this is a large and motley crew of fungi consisting of approximately 64,000 species. Although they may be the largest group, they aren't the fungi we're most familiar with. They include cup fungi, morels, truffles, yeasts, lots of colorful food-spoiling molds, *Penicillium* (of antibiotic and cheese fame), and, unfortunately, quite a few plant pathogens, or powdery mildews. (The most infamous of the plant pathogens are Dutch elm disease and Chestnut Blight. You've probably heard of those.)

Figure 19.10 Morel

Since this is such a diverse group, why are all these fungi categorized together? Let me explain by going over the life cycle of a common cup fungus of the genus *Peziza*. Most of the basic features described in this life cycle are shared by the other members of sac fungi, and you'll be able to see why they all belong in the same group.

The hyphae of all sac fungi are **septate**. As you might remember, this means that the hyphae actually have cells with septa (cell wall partitions) between them, unlike the zygomycetes which are aseptate.

In asexual hyphae, one nucleus per cell is the status quo. This is called **monokaryotic hyphae** (which means "one nucleus per cell"). In asexual reproduction, monokaryotic hyphae will produce **conidiophores** which terminate in several strings (like pop-it beads) of asexual spores called **conidia**.

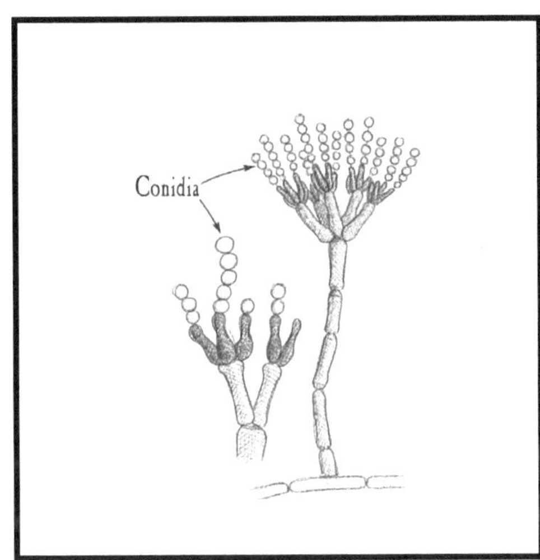

Figure 19.11 Conidia

Figure 19.12 Cup fungus, a type of ascoma

When conidia are dispersed, they can travel by air. When they land in a suitable place, they will germinate into a genetic clone of the parent mycelium. In sexual reproduction however, two different mating strains (+ and -) must come in contact with each other. Their monokaryotic hyphae merge to form **dikaryotic hyphae** (two nuclei per cell; one nucleus from each strain). This kind of hyphae is able to grow into a fruiting body (spore-producing body). Fruiting bodies in this group are much larger than a tiny microscopic sporangium sitting atop a sporangiophore (zygomycetes). The dikaryotic hyphae grow in a very organized way, not just into a tangled web of mycelium. It weaves itself into a highly sculptured macroscopic fruiting body that can easily be seen by the naked eye and may often grow quite large. This fruiting body is called an **ascoma**. Figure 19.12 above shows an ascoma (in the genus *Peziza)* that I photographed in Virginia.

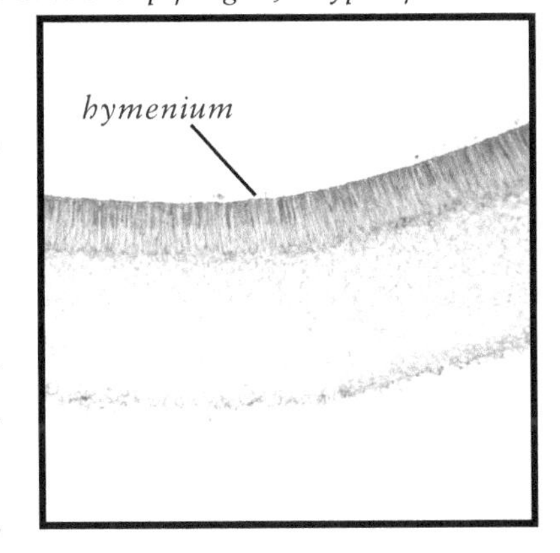

Figure 19.13 Hymenium of ascoma

The inner surface of this cup is the spore-producing surface called the **hymenium**. To view the hymenium up close, microscopists use a microtome (tiny blade) to make extremely thin slices of the cup. A slice is then placed on a glass slide and is covered with a preserving resin and a cover slip. The slide can then be viewed under the microscope so that you can see the details of the hymenium (Figure 19.13).

The hymenium is composed of parallel arranged **asci**. Each **ascus** is an oval cell filled with eight **ascospores**. To keep these names straight, I provided a table.

FUNGUS GROUP	Ascomycetes
FRUITING BODY	Ascoma
SPORE-PRODUCING CELL	Ascus
SPORES	Ascospores

How are the asci formed? As I said before, dikaryotic hyphae need to form first before an ascoma grows. As a new ascoma is growing, many dikaryotic hyphae dead-end at the cup's inner surface. The terminal cells (each containing two nuclei, one from each mating strain) become the asci. The first step that occurs in the young ascus is for the two nuclei fuse to form a diploid nucleus. This can be likened to fertilization. This nucleus then undergoes meiosis to form four nuclei. These four nuclei do one round of mitosis to make a total of eight ascospores (4 of each mating strain). Because crossing over and independent assortment of chromosomes occurred during meiosis, each ascospore will be slightly different genetically from the others. When each ascus is fully developed it explodes, releasing its octet of ascospores. I have seen this happen. Once on a family hike I found a large ascoma. I plucked it up to add to my fungus collection. As I held it in my hand I saw something like a puff of smoke come from the cup. It seemed that many asci exploded synchronously such that a little cloud of ascospores wafted out of the cup fungus. This happened several times while I was carrying it.

If an ascospore lands in a suitable place, it will germinate into monokaryotic hyphae and the life cycle begins anew.

The Basidiomycetes

Finally we come to the most familiar group of fungi, the basidiomycetes or club fungi. Some common examples of this group are mushrooms, boletes, shelf fungi, puffballs, stinkhorns, earthstars, coral fungi, and birds nest fungi, to name a few general groups.

They also have outlaws, namely plant pathogens. Two well-known villains are corn smut and wheat rust.

And don't think that if you've seen one mushroom, you've seen them all. There are over 13,000 species of gilled mushrooms.

Many of the terms used in describing the ascomycetes can be recycled in our discussion of the basidiomycetes. Since the mushroom is familiar to most of us, we will use it to describe the general life cycle and most of the unifying features of this group. Most species are saprobes that feed on dead plant matter.

Figure 19.14 Mushroom, a type of basidioma

Like the ascomycetes, this group also has monokaryotic hyphae that are incapable of forming fruiting bodies. However, unlike the ascomycetes, they don't make asexual spores like conidia. Their only mode of asexual reproduction is simple fragmentation of mycelium. The sexual phase corresponds somewhat to the ascomycetes. Two different mating strains (+ and -) grow and feed underground or in dead plant material as monokaryotic hyphae. When they come in contact with each other, they merge and become dikaryotic hyphae. When this type of hyphae forms, it weaves itself into a fruiting body. The fruiting body of this group is called a **basidioma.** Most of the common names of different types of basidiomycetes are named after their distinctive basidioma, since that's the most visible and familiar structure they exhibit. Mushrooms, puffballs, and shelf fungi are examples of different types of basidiomas. The anatomy of a mushroom is found above.

In the gilled mushrooms, the hymenium (spore-producing surface) lines the surface of the gills. On close inspection, many dikaryotic hyphae terminate at the gill surface. The same basic thing happens here as in the hymenium of a cup fungus. The two haploid nuclei (one of each mating strain) in the terminal cell, fuse producing a diploid nucleus. The cell is a young **basidium** and would be equivalent to an ascus. This diploid nucleus then undergoes meiosis producing four genetically different nuclei. Here is where basidiomycetes clearly depart from the ascomycetes and fortunately it is a bit less complicated. Instead of one round of mitosis producing eight, division stops at four. The four nuclei then migrate into four outpocketings of the basidium. These outpocketings, once they contain one nucleus each, pinch off at their base. Eventually each basidium has four **basidiospores** perched on its surface (and there are millions of basidia covering all the gills in a single mushroom).

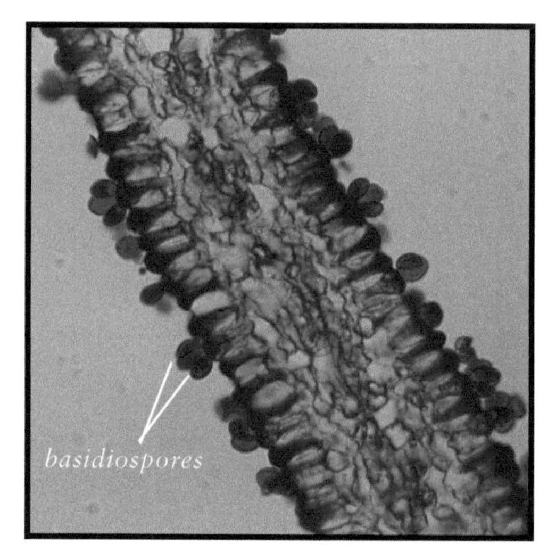

Figure 19.15 Gill basidiospores

Each basidiospore's attachment is so narrow and delicate that it eventually drops off. Most spores land on the ground below the mushroom but a few may be wafted to dizzying heights and travel staggering distances from their origin. This can be the case with most other fungal spores.

FUNGUS GROUP	Basidiomycetes	Ascomycetes
FRUITING BODY	Basidioma	Ascoma
SPORE-PRODUCING CELL	Basidium (plural = basidia)	Ascus (plural = asci)
SPORES	Basidiospores	Ascospores
ASEXUAL REPRODUCTION	Fragmentation	Conidia on conidiophores

Where is the hymenium located on these other non-mushroom basidiomas?

Shelf fungi and boletes: On close inspection of the underside of shelf fungi or boletes (mushrooms that have pores instead of gills) you can see hundreds to thousands of medium or tiny sized pores covering that surface. If a cross section is made of those holes and placed under a microscope you would discover that the hymenium lines all those holes. This means that basidia drop their basidiospores out of all those holes.

Puffballs and earthstars: These basidiomas don't have a proper hymenium. Within the interior of the ball basidia and their basidiospores form everywhere inside. Once they mature, the puffball or earthstar is designed to form a hole or is easily perforated. Any object that strikes the ball (raindrops included) will cause countless basidiospores to be shot out of the hole and into the air.

Stinkhorns: In stinkhorns, the hymenium is on the surface of the cap. It is designed to liquefy and stink like poo. Not surprisingly, this strategy draws in flies and other creatures who find excrement to have an appealing aroma. They land on it and, of course, get basidiospore goo all over their feet. The next place they happen to land they will track basidiospores all over it.

Figure 19.16 Variety of basidiomycetes

Bird's nest fungus: This little fungus is probably the fanciest in spore dispersal. The basidioma superficially looks like a cup fungus (shaped more like a teacup than a bowl) but inside the cup are several 'eggs' that are shaped like discs. Within these discs, basidia and basidiospores are produced. When the discs are ready and a drop of rain chances to land in the cup, it may splash one to several discs out. These thin walled discs easily rip open and shed their basidiospores wherever they land. Some discs are designed with a built-in trailing thread with a sticky end opposite the disc. When it is splashed up into the air, the trailing thread may chance to brush past a low-hanging twig. The sticky end adheres to the twig. The momentum of the disc causes the anchored thread to wrap around the twig like a tetherball rope. If the disc manages to lash itself to a twig a couple of feet off the ground, it's in a better position to scatter its spores farther. [2]

Coral fungus: These basidiomas look like coral growing out of the ground. The surface of these 'coral branches' are lined with a hymenium that produces basidia and basidiospores.

2. For more details read this article I wrote for *Answers Magazine*: "Bird's Nest Fungus—High-Flying Eggs!," http://www.answersingenesis.org/articles/am/v7/n4/birds-nest-fungus [accessed June 20, 2014].

LICHENS

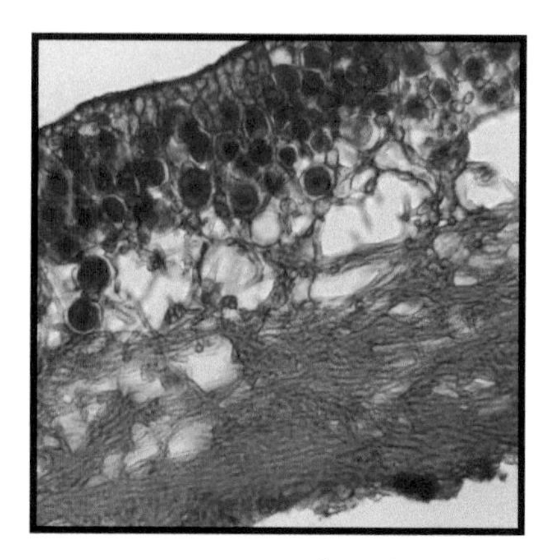

Figure 19.17 Lichen thallus

You can't go outside, even in town, without seeing lichens somewhere nearby. They are most commonly found on undisturbed big rocks and tree bark. These cool little growths are often overlooked because many don't know what they are. Each **lichen** growth is actually a combination of two totally different organisms growing together so intimately that it looks like one organism. They are an excellent example of a symbiotic relationship called mutualism. The two organisms are: 1) a fungus (usually an ascomycete; sometimes a basidiomycete), and 2) an algae (green algae or blue-green algae). In Figure 19.17 the oval reddish things are the algal cells. The greenish stuff is fungal mycelium. The upper side is densely woven hyphae called the *upper cortex*. The middle, loosely woven hyphae is called the *medulla*. The lower side is also densely woven hyphae called the *lower cortex*.

How do they benefit each other? As you may guess, the algae does photosynthesis and provides itself and its fungal partner with carbohydrates for growth and energy. The fungal partner provides the algae with the right microenvironment for it to collect needed minerals from rain or dust. This relationship is most definitely mutualistic because together they can grow in habitats that they otherwise could not grow in separately.

There are three basic growth forms most commonly found. These distinctions are not to be confused with different species of lichens. **Crustose** lichens look like they are spray-painted on the surface. Essentially they grow in such a way that they are tightly affixed to the surface. These are most frequently found on rocks and can sometimes look like the rock if they aren't a different color.

Foliose lichens have a flakey or leafy appearance.

Fruticose lichens have a bushy or branching appearance.

Lichens definitely have important God-given roles in nature. They are known to produce lichen acids which aid in the transformation of rock into soil. They have also shown that some lichens have very important nitrogen-fixing roles (converting atmospheric nitrogen into usable nitrogen compounds essential to life) in certain forest ecosystems. Apart from their many practical roles in nature, lichens are aesthetically pleasing with their interesting and diverse shapes and textures. They also provide artistic splashes of color on trailside rocks and trees. The next time you're outside, seek them out, observe them closely and enjoy their subtle beauty.

Figure 19.18 Crustose, foliose, and fruticose lichen

MYCORRHIZAE

Mycorrhizae means fungus roots. It's another good example of symbiotic mutualism (living together intimately for the mutual benefit of each party involved). More specifically it is mutualism between a species of fungus and the roots of vascular plants. The species of fungus varies with the type of plant but certain members of zygomycetes, ascomycetes, and basidiomycetes have been involved in *ectomycorrhizae* associations. In ectomycorrhizae, fungus hyphae grow within the root but they do not actually penetrate root cells. On the other hand, *endomycorrhizae* takes intimacy to another level. In *endomycorrhizae,* certain species of another fungal group called the Glomeromycota (not discussed in this text) form highly branching invaginations that interface with the root cell membranes (interior to the plant cell walls but not penetrating the plant cell membranes) so more efficient nutrient exchange can occur between the fungus and the plant.

So how do they benefit each other? Although the plant's root hairs can absorb water and minerals from the soil, the fungus is better at it and has a greater reach. The fungal hyphae essentially absorb water and minerals from the soil that the plant's root would otherwise not be able to get. The plant helps out the fungus by allowing it to partake of some of the bounty of photosynthesis (mostly sugars stored in root cells). The benefits can be visually obvious between two plants of the same species. On the next page, in Figure 19.19, the seedling on the left was grown without mycorrhizae, and the one on the right was grown with it.

CHAPTER 19: REVIEW QUESTIONS

Figure 19.19 Redwood seedlings with and without mycorrhizae

1. List six characteristics of Fungi other than eukaryotic, heterotrophic, and multicellular.

2. Fungi obtain nutrients through a process called ______ digestion. This occurs when the hyphae exocytose ______, releasing digestive enzymes onto the surrounding organic material.

3. Name three destructive activities of fungi.

4. Name three beneficial activities of fungi.

5. The zygomycete fungi reproduce asexually from spores that have been released from knob-like spore containers called ______.

6. In the black bread mold, tough spore containers called ______ are formed from the sexual union of two different mating strains.

7. Zygomycete hyphae with different job-descriptions have different names. The ______ supports the sporangium and the root-like ______ penetrate the substrate and absorb nutrients.

8. Ascomycete fungi reproduce asexually by spores called ______ which form pop-it bead-like chains.

9. Ascomycete fungi, during the sexual phase form fruiting bodies called ______. The concave (usually) spore-producing surface called the *hymenium* is formed by one layer of densely packed parallel ______, each containing eight ______.

10. Name two examples of ascomycete fungi.

11. An atypical ascomycete is ______ and is essential in the brewing and baking industry.

12. The shelf fungi, mushrooms, puffballs, earthstars, and coral fungi are all examples of ______.

13. In mushrooms, the hymenium is found on the surface of the ______. The hymenium is composed of parallel-arranged ______ instead of asci. Each one forms four ______ which eventually get placed on the outside surface until they drop off.

14. Septate hyphae is found in:
    a. Zygomycetes
    b. Ascomycetes
    c. Basidiomycetes
    d. Both a and b
    e. Both b and c

15. Dikaryotic hyphae induce the formation of the fruiting body in:
    a. Zygomycetes
    b. Ascomycetes
    c. Basidiomycetes
    d. Both a and b
    e. Both b and c

16. Two infamous plant pathogens of basidiomycetes are the ______ and ______.

17. Lichens are formed by a mutualistic relationship between ______ and ______.

18. The growth form of lichen that is bushy and branching is called:
    a. Fruticose
    b. Foliose
    c. Crustose

19. The growth form of lichen that looks like it was spray-painted on a rock or bark is:
    a. Fruticose
    b. Foliose
    c. Crustose

20. The mutualistic relationship between vascular plant roots and fungi is called a ______ relationship. The fungi benefits from the ______ of the plant and the plant benefits because the fungi enhances ______ and ______ absorption for the plant.

CHAPTER 20

KINGDOM ANIMALIA

A SHORT INTRODUCTION

Everyone knows that lions, tigers, and bears are animals. That's easy. In everyday conversation, we usually say "animal" for furry critters, and that, too, would be easy (and correct) but the furry ones aren't nearly all the animals out there. It doesn't occur to many people that birds, insects, reptiles, worms, fish, sea anemones, starfish, and sponges are animals, too.

That's quite a diverse bunch. Just what are the defining characteristics of an animal? Well, simply put, an animal is any multicellular critter that wriggles. To be more scientific, the characteristics of all animals include the following:

- Eukaryotic cell structure—the cells have membrane-bound nuclei and membrane-bound organelles.
- Cells that lack cell walls.
- Multicellular: animals have many cells that manifest division of labor, i.e., differentiation of cells into tissues; tissues into organs, etc.
- Heterotrophic: they obtain food from sources other than their own bodies (they eat).
- Motile: can move body parts or entire body using muscle tissue of some sort.

Animals also exhibit a variety of symmetries (or lack thereof). These are:

Asymmetry: This simply means "no symmetry." In other words, no imaginary plane can pass through the center of the animal and

Figure 20.1 Asymmetry of a sponge

produce mirror-image halves. The bath sponge exhibits this kind of symmetry.

Radial: This means the animal has a central axis and that two or more imaginary planes passing through it would roughly divide it into similar halves. Starfish and sea anemones exhibit this kind of symmetry.

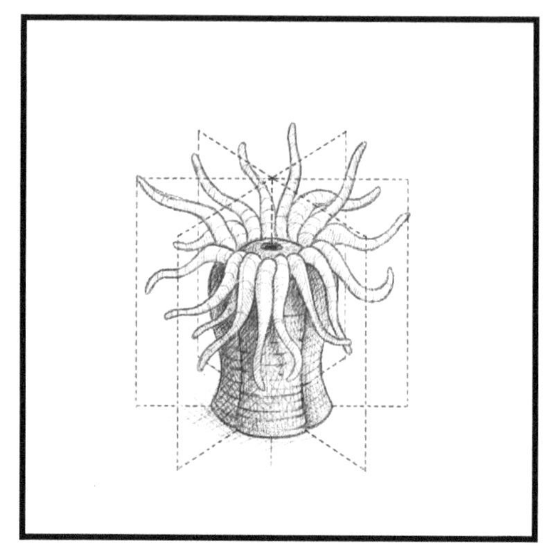

Figure 20.2 Radial symmetry

Bilateral ("two sides"): This is by far the most common symmetry in animals. "Bilateral" means that only one imaginary plane that passes through the center of the animal that would produce roughly mirror-images. Worms, mollusks, insects, and vertebrates of all flavors (including we humans) exhibit this type of symmetry.

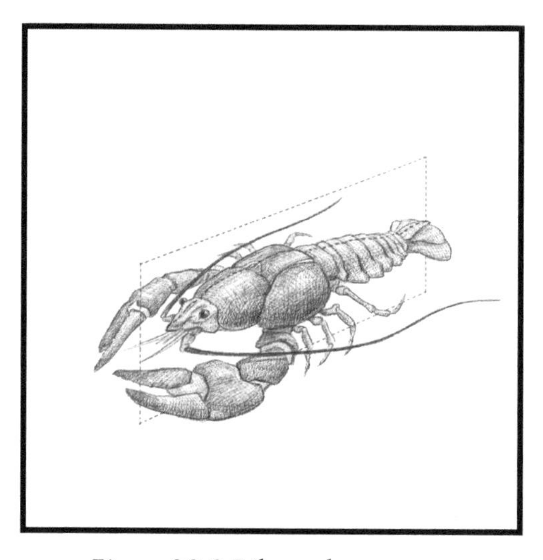

Figure 20.3 Bilateral symmetry

All animals that do not possess a backbone are called invertebrates and those that do are called vertebrates. In this book, I will cover eight phyla (there are many more) that are invertebrates. I will cover just one phylum (Phylum Chordata) that, with the exception of a tiny fraction of invertebrates, is composed of "card-carrying" vertebrates.

CHAPTER 20: REVIEW QUESTIONS

1. List five general characteristics of all animals.

2. What is the most common symmetry of animals?

3. If an animal can be divided into similar halves by two or more planes running through the central axis of an animal it has ______ symmetry.

4. Name one animal that is asymmetrical.

5. Name one animal that is radially symmetrical.

6. Between invertebrates and vertebrates, which has the most diversity?

7. Phylum ______ is almost entirely composed of vertebrates.

CHAPTER 21

PHYLUM PORIFERA

THE SPONGES

Nowadays we mostly use artificial, synthetic sponges for cleaning our dishes and such, so we aren't very familiar with the living (or dead) creatures that are the real deal. In the old days, actual bath sponges were used for cleaning pots, pans, and people. Of course, the sponge was dead by that point. All the living cells in its body had been killed and removed, leaving just a skeleton of sorts.

The rubbery consistency of many **sponges** is due to an extracellular network of fibers made of an elastic protein called **spongin**. Many sponges also have microscopic glassy or calcareous particles called **spicules**. These often have beautiful shapes reminiscent of diatoms shells, and they add rigidity to the sponge matrix. Sponge skeletons may have both spongin and spicules, or just one or the other.

Now, these animals are not usually thought of as animals. After all, they are sessile (anchored to the surface on which they grow), they don't move (much), and they don't seem to have any organ systems to speak of. They seem more like a loose confederation of cells, which is quite true. But they are animals nonetheless. They manifest all the major characteristics of the animal kingdom.

Figure 21.1 Sponge spicules

Porifera (the name of the phylum) means "pore-bearing." A sponge's entire surface is covered by pores called **ostia, dermal ostia,** or **prosopyles** through which water is sucked into the sponge's body. As water enters the sponge, tiny planktonic bacterial, algal, and protozoan cells are filtered out of the water by specialized collar cells. These cells capture the food, take what they need, and then pass on the nourishment to other cell types within the sponge. Hence, sponges are a good example of filter feeders.

Figure 21.2 is a simple sponge diagram (*Syconoid* canal system) to give us an idea of the filter-feeding process. The arrows indicate the direction of water flow.

The flagellated collar cells lining the **radial canals** (the black areas are where the collar cells are located) not only capture plankton but also generate the water current. As all the collar cells vigorously beat their little flagella, a one-way water current flows into the **incurrent canals**, through the prosopyles, and then into the radial canals.

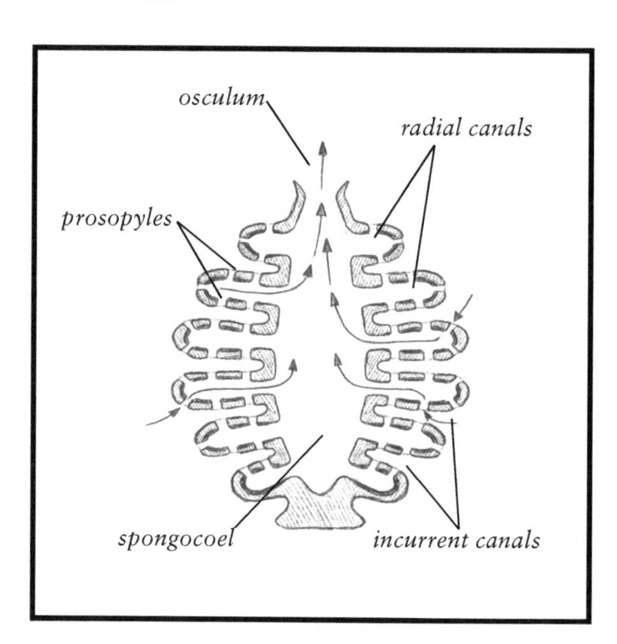

Figure 21.2 Syconoid sponge diagram

Figure 21.3 is a cartoon of **collar cells**. Notice the sieve-like collar (like the skirt on a badminton shuttlecock) surrounding the base of the flagella. Due to the beating of the flagella, much of the water will be pulled through the sieve-like collar. As algae and protozoa collect on the collar, they slide down to the cell body where they are phagocytosed. The water continues out the open top of the collar, through the radial canal, and into the centrally located cavity called a **spongocoel**. Lastly, water moves up the chimney-like spongocoel and out through the **osculum**. ("Osculum" is Latin for "little mouth." How appropriate.)

Complex sponges have intricate branching waterways called the Leuconoid canal system, but the basic idea remains the same: water is pulled into the sponge through small ostia and through a catacomb-like system of canals. These canals lead to a series of "rooms" called **flagellated chambers** that are "wallpapered" with collar cells. No matter which way the water flows through the sponge, it is bound to flow through a number of flagellated chambers. Any unicellular plankton that makes it through a leuconoid sponge without being consumed in those "rooms" is mighty lucky. These canals merge into larger canals that lead to oscula (many little mouths!)

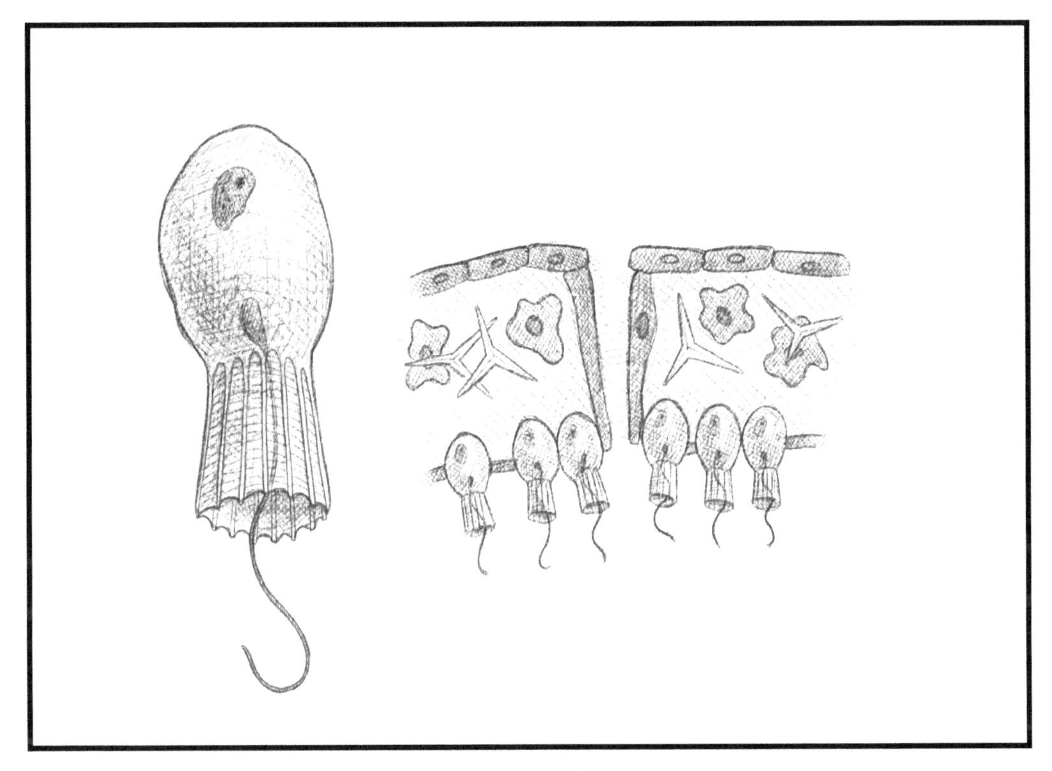

Figure 21.3 Collar cells

which then let the water out of the sponge. In Figure 21.4, the black areas indicate the flagellated chambers:

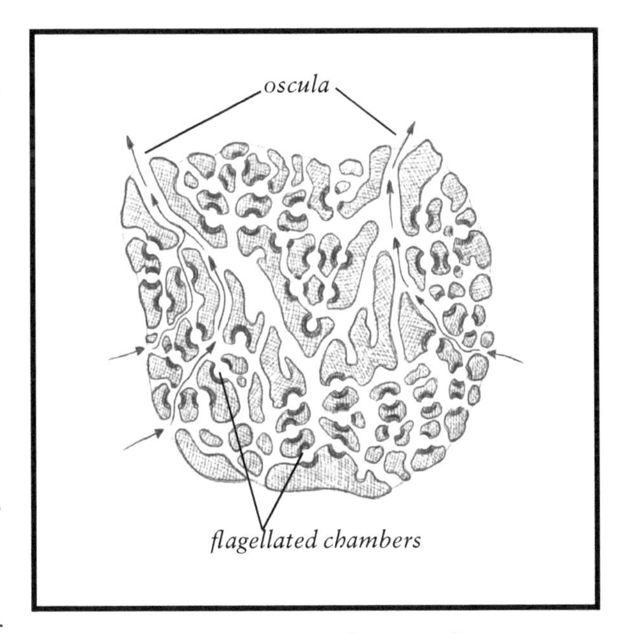

Figure 21.4 Leuconoid sponge diagram

Now, we know that if sponges are animals, they must exhibit at least *some* movement using muscle or muscle-like tissue. While sponges don't have muscles per se and certainly cannot waltz around the ocean floor, they do have skin-like cells that have contractile proteins that cause them to shorten—somewhat like a muscle cell. Consequently, the sponge can slightly change the shape of its "skin." The skin-like cells are most handy in forming weak, sphincter-like rings around ostia and oscula so that the sponges can regulate the size of these little doorways and thus control the flow of water.

Figure 21.5 Variety of Porifera

Sponges can reproduce both asexually and sexually. Asexual reproduction occurs by growing and budding. The sponge can form a branch which eventually detaches to take up its own existence. Or many sponges form little packets of sponge cells encased in a rugged coat of spongin and spicules. These little capsules are called **gemmules**, and are designed to ride out harsh environmental conditions that may kill the parent sponge. When conditions become favorable, the cells climb out and grow into a clone of the parent sponge.

Sexual reproduction usually occurs within a single sponge (which means it is able to make both sperm and eggs), though some species have separate "male" and "female" sponges.

There are somewhere between 5,000 and 10,000 sponge species. Most are marine dwellers; only a few live in freshwater. Marine sponges can inhabit the frigid arctic or Antarctic waters, warm tropical waters, and everything in between. They can be found in shallow seas just below the low tide mark or out in the deep sea bottom, 29,000 feet down. Sponges can basically survive anywhere. Above are two sponges representing some of the diversity of Phylum Porifera.

Sponges are invaluable biological water filters in many different ecosystems, doing their part to keep microscopic plankton levels in check. Sponges also provide many different microhabitats to a host of tiny creatures lurking in their catacomb-like interiors.

And from a purely aesthetic perspective, sponges greatly enhance the beauty of the ocean floor with their tremendous variety of shapes, sizes, and colors.

CHAPTER 21: REVIEW QUESTIONS

1. Sponges are ______-feeders because they strain out microscopic plankton from the water that circulates through them.

2. Sponge skeletons are composed of beautiful siliceous or calcareous ______ that provide rigidity.

3. The specialized cells in a sponge that generate the water current, capture, and phagocytose the microscopic plankton are called ______ cells.

4. What is the protein that serves as a flexible skeleton for sponges?

5. What canals are lined with collar cells?

6. Asexual reproduction in sponges occurs through budding and by the production of tiny tough capsules containing sponge cells called ______ that can survive adverse environmental conditions.

7. Be able to draw a simple body outline of a syconoid sponge (using dashes to show the pores (prosopyles). Label the incurrent canal, radial canal, spongocoel, and osculum. Use an arrow to show the pattern of water flow through the sponge.

8. In the more complicated leuconoid sponge, what is lined with collar cells?

9. What important ecological service do sponges perform as they filter feed?

10. What types of cells do they contract to change the size of their openings?

11. In sexual reproduction of most sponges, the sperm and egg cells are produced in:
    a. the same sponge.
    b. different male and female sponges.

CHAPTER 22

PHYLUM CNIDARIA

JELLYFISH, SEA ANEMONES, CORAL, ETC.

The phylum Cnidaria (the c is silent) includes the jellyfish, sea anemones, coral, and Portuguese man-of-war, but many people are familiar with these creatures without knowing the phylum that they belong in. Overall, Cnidaria includes over 9,000 species that may, at first glance, defy our attempt to put them in the same phylum. They range from the tiny hydra (a few mm long) to enormous jellyfish with a diameter of eight feet. So what do they all have in common?

Despite the fact that they exhibit two different body forms (the **polyp** and the **medusa**), they do conform (loosely) to the same general body plan. They all have one opening (called the **mouth**, not surprisingly) and the mouth leads to an internal space called the **gastrovascular cavity.** (Ready for weirdness? There is no one-way traffic through their gut, which means waste must be expelled back through the mouth.)

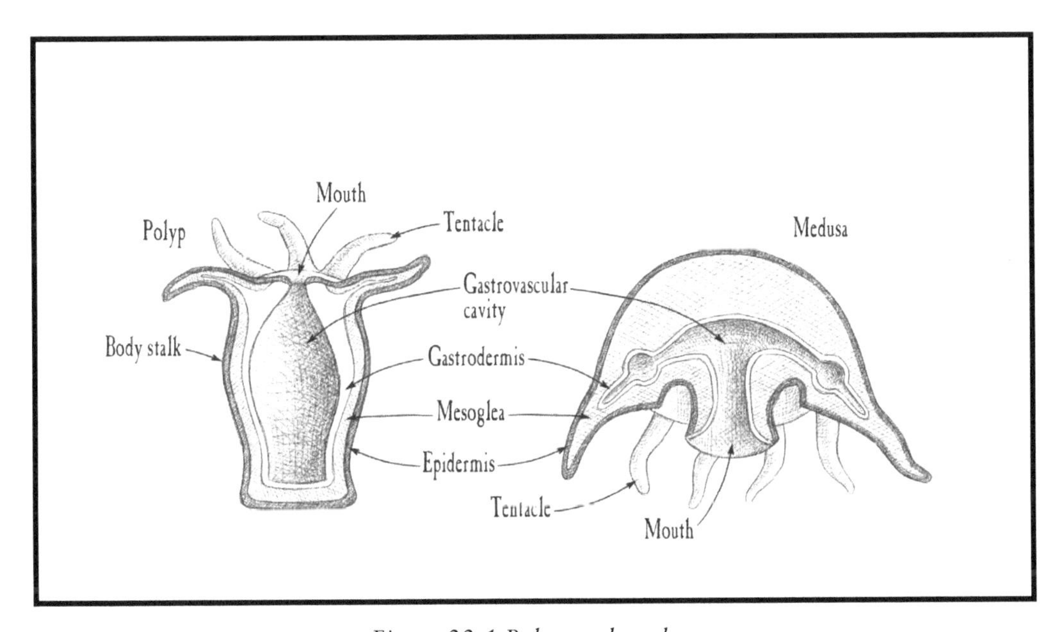

Figure 22.1 Polyp and medusa

Although the different species span a multitude of shapes and can be quite convoluted and elaborate, the body wall of all species remains the same: it consists of a non-cellular, jelly-like substance called the **mesoglea,** sandwiched between two layers of cells. The layer facing the outside is the **epidermis** and the layer facing the gastrovascular cavity is the **gastrodermis.** Together the epidermis and gastrodermis layers are usually one cell thick.

Figure 22.2 Coral

The polyp body form is sessile (attached to a surface). Examples of creatures with this body form are hydras, colonial hydroids, sea anemones, and coral.

The medusa body form (named after the monstrous gorgon Medusa whose head was covered in venomous snakes instead of hair) is exhibited by the jellyfish. Its body isn't drawn out into a stalk with a **pedal disc** sticking to some surface. Rather, the medusa is free-floating with a body shaped more like a bell. The medusa is often transparent or translucent, and the mesoglea is usually thicker compared to the polyp's mesoglea, especially in the bell region.

Figure 22.3 Sea anemone

In both the polyp and the medusa forms, the mouth is surrounded by radiating **tentacles** like petals on a flower. These tentacles can be used both for defense and for catching prey. As you may have already discovered while swimming in the ocean, the tentacles sport numerous cells called cnidocytes that contain the infamous stinging organelles called nematocysts (more on this later).

In the polyp form, there's a pedal disc opposite the tentacles and mouth. The pedal disc is what makes the polyp stick to the substrate (with the help of some secreted mucus). This doesn't prohibit movement; hydra and anemones can still mosey along very slowly by sliding on their pedal disc.

They can even technically let go. The polyp *Hydra* can actually move by cartwheeling "head over heels" (or tentacles over pedal disc) along the substrate.

Depending on the species, the polyp or medusa catches prey by discharging their nematocysts, which can either sting or entangle the prey. (There are also sticky nematocysts but these are not usually used for capturing food.) These **nematocysts** are exquisitely designed, microscopic, hypodermic harpoons produced within cells called **cnidocytes.**

Although they can be found all over the surface of the body and even in the gastrodermis, the highest concentration of cnidocytes are on the tentacles. They are situated in dense clusters or bands among regular epidermal cells, with each cnidocyte's apical surface facing the watery environment. If any prey bungles into a tentacle, a trigger-like structure on each cnidocyte is physically stimulated and causes molecular H_2O gates in the nematocyst capsule membrane to open. Due to the extremely high hypertonicity within the nematocyst capsule, water rushes into it from the cytoplasm by osmosis. The sudden influx of water rapidly increases the capsule's pressure.

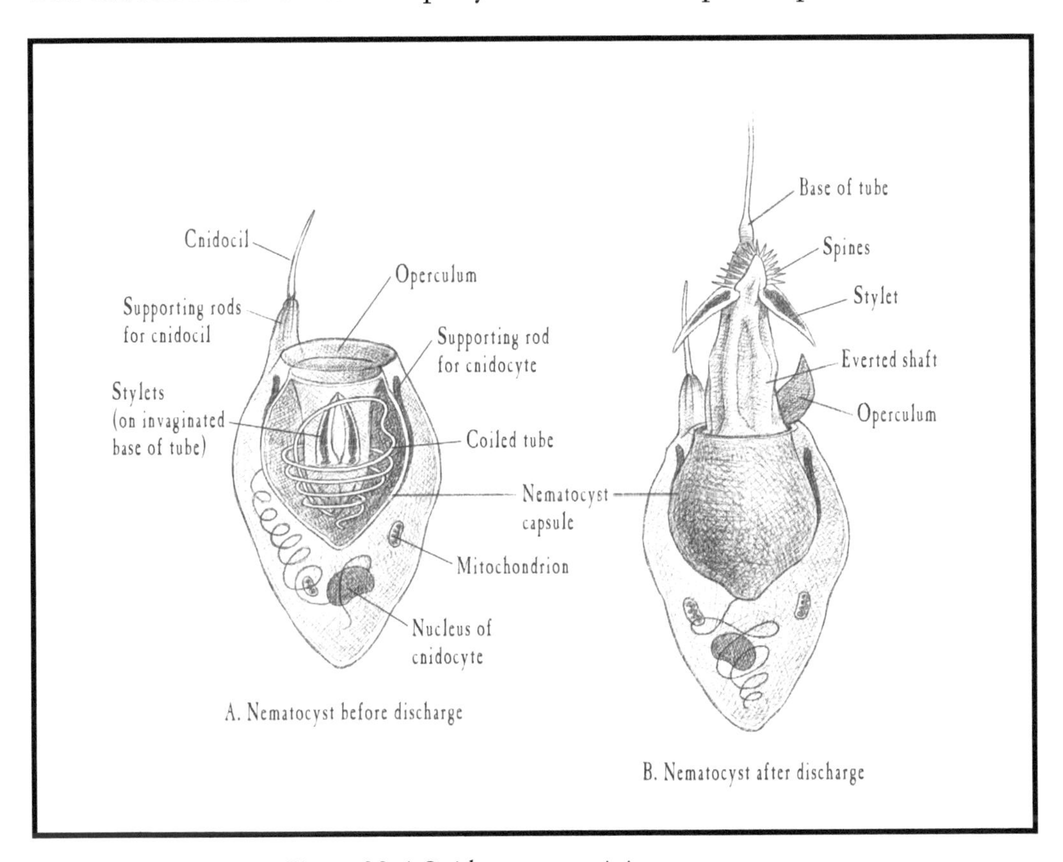

Figure 22.4 Cnidocyte containing nematocyst

Now, within the capsule is an inverted, hollow, thread-like tube, all coiled up. But the sudden increase of pressure forcibly turns it inside-out, just like blowing air into a latex glove will get its inverted fingers to pop straight out.

Near the base of this thin tube are *spines* and *stylets* that snap out like blades on a pocketknife. These cut a tiny hole in the prey and in goes the thin little thread. The tip of the thread is open-ended. The same pressure that made it pop out of the capsule now also expels the capsule's venom up through the hollow interior of the thread and into the prey's skin.

With the exception of a few species, cnidarians are inconsequential to humans. They either don't sting us or when they do, it's usually just a painful irritant. This is because we (thankfully) are not the intended prey. To the prey, however, the nematocyst is a formidable weapon designed to paralyze and kill.

When prey comes in contact with the tentacles, a great many nematocysts are simultaneously shot into its body. Paralysis and death quickly follow. Once the prey has been sufficiently immobilized, the polyp or medusa begins to manipulate the prey towards the mouth and eats it whole. It's actually quite incredible how wide they can open their mouths to accommodate their prey, rather like a medium-sized snake eating a large rat.

Once it has ingested the prey, the cnidarian begins the business of digesting its meal within the gastrovascular cavity. Digestion is a job for the gastrodermis. Countless lysosomes of the gastrodermis are exocytosed into the gastrovascular cavity and the digestive enzymes get to work breaking the prey down into the basic building blocks: amino acids, monosaccharides, glycerol, fatty acids, etc. Once this is accomplished, the nutrients are absorbed by the gastrodermis. Any nutrients not used by the gastrodermis pass through the mesoglea to provide nourishment for the epidermis. And as I already mentioned, there is no anus, so any waste left in the gastrovascular cavity is eliminated back through the mouth.

Since Cnidarians are considered animals, you know that this means they must be able to contract, bend, and wave their body parts around. In the following example of ***Hydra*** (which is more or less representative of other Cnidarians), you might ask, "But how does it move since it has only two cell layers, the epidermis and the gastrodermis (both of which are epithelial tissue)?"

Well, the magical trick is that these layers actually multitask. In *Hydra*, the bases of most epidermal cells flare out to form long myofibrils parallel to the axis of the tentacles and body. These serve as a quasi longitudinal muscle layer. As for the bases of most gastrodermal cells, they flare out to form long myofibrils perpendicular to the axis of the tentacles and body. These serve as a weak quasi circular muscle layer. By contracting these in various ways, the Hydra can shorten, elongate, bend, or wave both body and tentacles around.

CLASS HYDROZOA: HYDROID COLONIES, HYDRA, AND PORTUGUESE MAN-OF-WAR

Hydroid colonies are colonies of connected polyps. However, the colony is, in one sense, a single creature, since the body wall and gastrovascular cavity are continuous through all the polyps. Food taken by one polyp will be shared within the colony through the connecting gastrovascular cavity.

The colony has a branching pattern which can be likened to tufts of algae. They are often found on submerged surfaces like rocks and piers or on the surface of many kinds of marine creatures.

Hydras, common denizens of freshwater habitats, are lethal Lilliputian hunters who prey on tiny crustaceans.

Figure 22.5 Hydroid colony

CLASS ANTHOZOA: SEA ANEMONES AND CORAL

The members of this group live exclusively as polyps and can range from ¼-inch to six feet in diameter. Most **anemones**, however, are one to several inches. The small anemones sting and feed on tiny critters their own size or collect organic debris on secreted strands of mucous that they reel into their mouth. Bigger anemones can sting and consume a variety of prey including fish, sea stars, shrimp, crabs, or any other critter that they can manage to paralyze and stuff into their gastrovascular cavity. Often very colorful, anemones greatly enhance the beauty of the intertidal zone of rocky shores.

Coral are basically miniaturized sea anemones that live and grow as colonies. The most familiar type of coral is stony or hard coral. Their countless coral polyps are interconnected by sheets of tissue. The underside of this living sheet of polyps secretes a calcium carbonate (lime) skeleton that forms a sort of grand apartment complex for the entire coral colony.

These often branch into a variety of sizes and beautiful shapes indicative of each species. Each polyp resides in a small depression.

When you look at a piece of dead coral up close at a tourist shop, you see numerous circular cavities covering the coral rock. A coral polyp used to reside in each one of those, but all the living tissue has been removed so the stony skeleton can be sold as a souvenir.

Figure 22.6 Sea anemones

Coral polyps are versatile feeders. They can use their tentacles to catch any tiny prey that happen along, but most tropical waters are very clear and don't provide enough prey to allow coral to grow into coral reefs. So how do they grow into reefs with so little food around?

Coral often supplement their diet by having mutualistic unicellular algae called zooxanthellae performing photosynthesis inside their tissues (see Dinoflagellates in Chapter 2). With zooxanthellae partners, coral can make their own food with CO_2 and water (and there is plenty of that around). Food produced by photosynthesis enables coral to grow into colossal structures called coral reefs. If they didn't have these photosynthetic friends, coral would never have enough food and energy to make that happen.

CLASS SCYPHOZOA: JELLYFISH

As previously mentioned, **jellyfish** exhibit the medusa body form. They range in size from less than an inch to eight feet in diameter (like Lion's mane jellyfish). Jellyfish can inhabit both freshwater and marine habitats, but they are much more common in the latter. They can be found in the shallows or at great depths.

Like most cnidarians, jellyfish sting their prey with their nematocyst-loaded tentacles and haul the hapless creature through their mouth (with the help of oral arms) and into the gastrovascular cavity. There is an impressive diversity of colors and shapes. They feed usually on fish and other free-swimming prey that blunder into their tentacles.

Reproduction is usually accomplished by separate male and female jellyfish. Gonads (testis or ovaries) develop in the gastrodermis of the stomach.

Figure 22.7 Variety of jellyfish

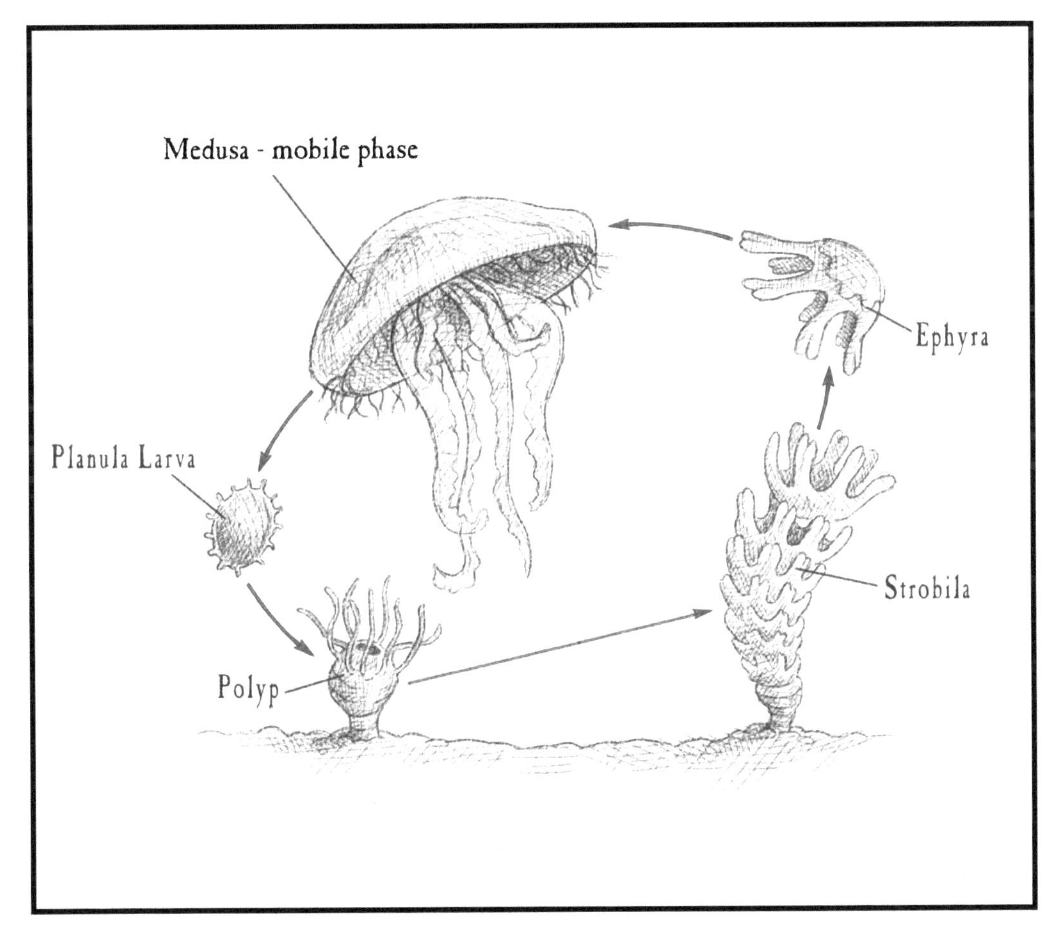

Figure 22.8 Life cycle of jellyfish

Sperm and eggs are released through the mouth so that fertilization takes place outside the body, and each zygote (fertilized ovum) grows into a ciliated larva called a **planula,** either in the open sea or within the oral arms of the female. The planula, a tiny, flattened, oval larva covered with cili, then sinks to the bottom and takes up a sessile existence as a polyp.

This small polyp stage buds repeatedly so it begins to take on a segmented appearance called a strobila and looks like a stack of cups. Eventually the terminal bud on the strobila detaches as a cute little free-living medusa, which then eventually grows up into an adult medusa thus completing the life cycle.

CHAPTER 22: REVIEW QUESTIONS

1. The hallmark characteristic of phylum Cnidaria are the possession of cells called cnidocytes which contain stinging organelles called ______.
2. Cnidocytes are mostly concentrated in bands in the epidermis on which body part?
   a. Stalk
   b. Pedal disc
   c. Tentacles
   d. Mouth
3. Are all nematocyst designed to sting?
4. Finger-like projections of the body wall surround the mouth and are called ______.
5. Describe the structure of a nematocyst and how it discharges.
6. There are two general body forms of Cnidaria: the ______ and the ______.
7. Hydra, coral, hydroid colonies, and sea anemones exhibit the ______ form while jellyfish exhibit the ______ form.
8. The digestive system of Cnidarians is composed mostly of the mouth and the ______ cavity. Solid waste must be excreted out of the ______.
9. Nutrients are absorbed by which cell layer?
10. Generally there are two cell layers that comprise the body wall: the ______ and the ______.
11. Name two or three prey items of larger sea anemones.
12. Name two very different ways coral polyps can feed themselves.

13. The Portuguese Man-of-war is a:
    a. colony of polyps.
    b. jellyfish.

14. Sperm and eggs from the gonads are released out of the ______ of separate male and female jellyfish. Fertilization happens in the open sea water and the zygote grows into a small ciliated larva called a ______.

15. A thin to thick non-cellular layer is sandwiched between the epidermis and gastrodermis and is called the ______.

CHAPTER 23

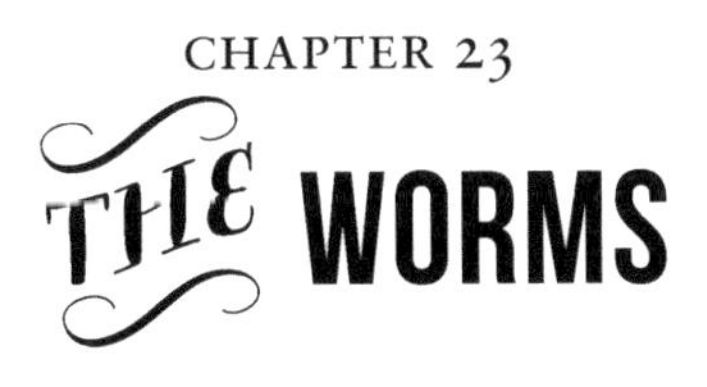

THE WORMS

PHYLUM PLATYHELMINTHES: THE FLATWORMS

This is the first of three phyla of worms I will summarize. **Platyhelminthes** all have a dorso-ventrally flattened body with no body cavity. Their digestive system (if present) is incomplete and reminiscent of the Cnidarian-style gastrovascular cavity: their mouths serve as both the entrance for food and the exit for waste.

This group includes some unpleasant parasites, including flukes and tapeworms as well as free-living forms called turbellarians.

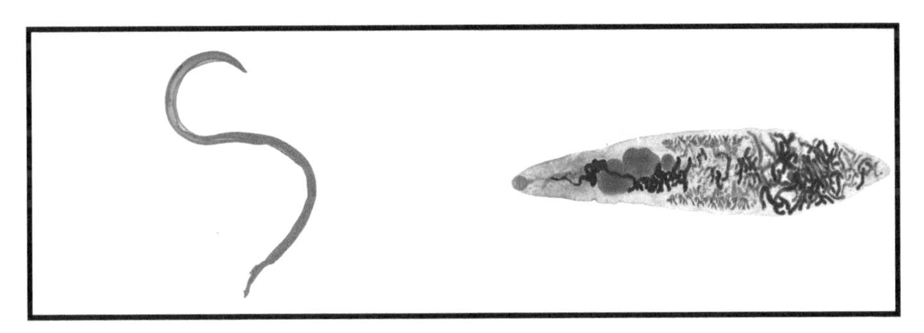

Figure 23.1 Blood fluke and liver fluke

The **flukes** (Class Trematoda) have diverse and complex life cycles involving very different developmental stages existing in several hosts. The first host is a mollusk and the final host is some kind of vertebrate. Sometimes, depending on the species, intermediate hosts occur between the first and final host. In humans (yes, we could be their final vertebrate host), different kinds of adult flukes take up residence and do their mischief in different parts of the body (including the circulatory system, digestive, urinary, respiratory, and reproductive tracts) and cause a whole host of miserable diseases.

Tapeworms (Class Cestoda) are parasites so accustomed to easy living that they don't even have a digestive tract. They just don't need one, living in the digestive tract of vertebrates as they do. The tapeworm simply hangs onto the lining of the gut and absorbs the predigested nutrients through its body surface. How do they hang on? They have a head-like structure called a **scolex** armed with suckers and/or hooks that enable them to stay anchored in the constant flow of digestive juices through the gut.

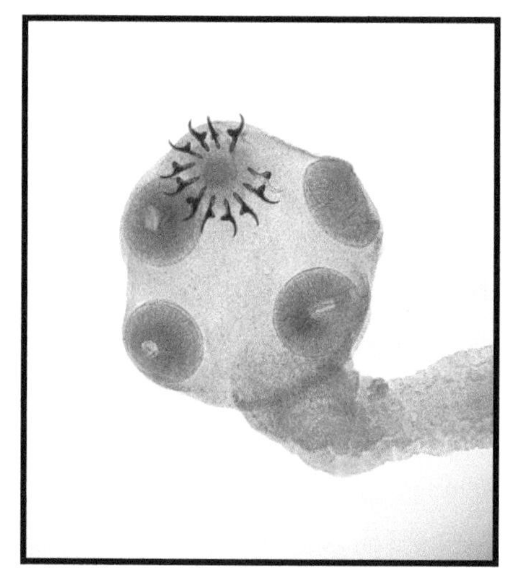

Figure 23.2 Scolex of pork tapeworm

The tapeworm body is divided up into repeating segments called **proglottids**. As new ones are made near the scolex, older proglottids mature and grow and get pushed further from the scolex.

Each proglottid is outfitted with gonads for both sexes. The eggs are fertilized by sperm from the same or different proglottid. Eventually, the terminal proglottids (loaded with fertilized eggs) detach and leave the gut with the excrement. In the beef tapeworm, the proglottids crawl out of the feces to a place where they may be consumed by grazing cattle, and the eggs later hatch within the cattle's gut. During a roundabout journey, the larvae develop into juveniles which eventually take up residence as stationary cysts within the muscle of the animal (beef). If the infected meat (measly beef) is consumed without adequate cooking, the life cycle unfortunately starts all over again. Although disgusting, tapeworms don't appear to cause serious health problems. They do, however, cause some weight loss, appetite loss, and abdominal pain. In the nineteenth and twentieth centuries, some diet pills purposefully contained tapeworm eggs! That's what you call a gross weight loss plan.

Figure 23.3 Giant land turbellarian

Planaria and relatives (Class Turbellaria) are, in the main, a respectable group of flatworms due to the simple fact that most species are free-living. With the exception of a few parasites and symbionts, they are predators or scavengers in freshwater, marine, and moist terrestrial environments. Most species are black, brown, or gray, but many marine species are beautifully colored. Although the majority are just a few millimeters long, some land flatworms grow to two feet.

As is true of all the gut-bearing members of Platyhelminthes, they possess one entrance to or exit from the gastrovascular cavity: the mouth. The freshwater **planarians** (size: 1 mm to almost an inch) are the most well-known members of the group. Their mouth is located on the end of a vacuum-cleaner-hose-like pharynx located near the middle of the underside of its flat body. As they prey on small animals (or scavenge bits of dead ones), they suck food into the mouth, through the pharynx, and then into the gastrovascular cavity where the food is digested. Since the gastrovascular cavity pervades most of its interior, absorbed nutrients don't have far to diffuse to all the tissues of the body.

Planarians also bear light-sensitive eyespots on the head and are famous for regenerating missing body parts when sliced or diced by curious biology students.

PHYLUM NEMATODA: THE ROUNDWORMS

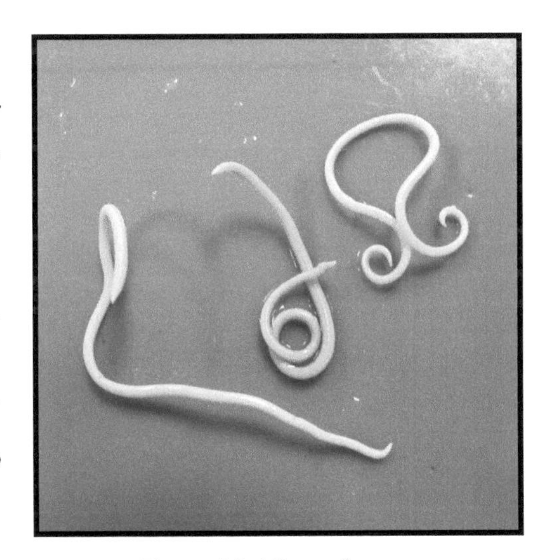

Figure 23.4 Roundworms

Nematodes are very different structurally from Platyhelminthes worms. They aren't flat, for one. They have a complete digestive system from mouth to anus and range in size from microscopic to over 1 meter in length. There are over 28,000 described species that live in every conceivable habitat including soils, saltwater and freshwater, tropics, to the polar zones, high mountains to ocean depths, and inside the bodies of plants and animals. Over half of the known species are parasitic in humans, animals, or plants, and wreak major medical and agricultural havoc worldwide. Because young students tend to have a morbid curiosity, I will mention a couple of parasitic nematodes.

The **pinworm** is fairly common in the U.S. and grows to about 1 cm in length. The adult pinworm lives in the large intestinal tract of infected humans. At night, females work their way to the anus and lay their eggs. Their activity tickles a bit and may induce an indiscriminate child to scratch the itch, in which case little fingertips may get contaminated with eggs. If unwashed fingers inadvertently go in the mouth, the eggs are subsequently swallowed. They soon develop and hatch in the small intestine and finally come full circle when they mature in the large intestine. This parasite is more of a nuisance than anything else and is understandably more common in children since they can be notoriously unhygienic. Fortunately for these little tykes, pinworm disease symptoms are minor.

In contrast, one particularly nasty nematode is a scourge to humanity in underdeveloped countries, particularly in the tropics. Several different species of **filarial worm** can, in chronic cases, cause a ghastly disease called elephantiasis. One such dangerous species is *Wuchereria bancrofti*. Growing up to 10 cm, the adults live their lives in the lymphatic system of an infected person, obstructing the flow of lymph back from the extremities. This, in concert with the immune system's response to the infection (inflammation), results in grotesque swelling of legs, arms, genitals, etc., hence the name "elephantiasis."

To pass on this insidious disease, the females release their live young (microfilariae) into the lymph, and thc microfilariae eventually reach the circulatory system. These are tiny enough to be picked up by a bloodsucking intermediate host, such as a mosquito, in the case of *Wuchereria bancrofti*. Within the mosquito, the microfilariae develop into a larval stage and are then injected into a new host when the mosquito bites another person. Once in a new body, the larvae continue to develop and move to the lymphatic system. About a year after infection, they reach adulthood. Fortunately, there are great efforts in several countries to eradicate this disfiguring disease.

There are many other nasty parasitic nematodes, but keep in mind that not all nematodes are bad guys. Many species live unobtrusive lives, consuming microbes and tiny invertebrates in the many different ecosystems in which they inhabit.

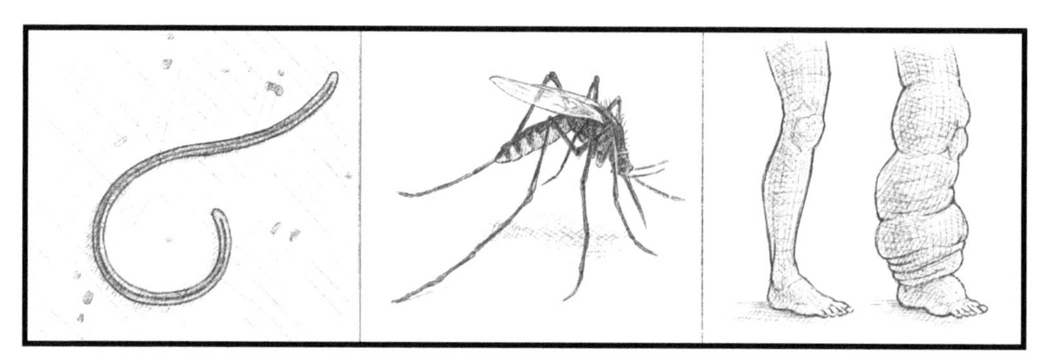

Figure 23.5 Elephantiasis: worm, vector, symptoms

PHYLUM ANNELIDA: THE SEGMENTED WORMS

This phylum are the ringed worms or **segmented worms** (*anellus* is Latin for little ring). This includes the familiar earthworms, leeches, and polychaetes.

If you live near the seashore, you may have encountered a variety of polychaetes in the sand or under rocks in the intertidal zone.

The main feature of Annelids is that they all have a body that is divided up into segments (little rings). Some have fleshy appendages sticking out of their sides for locomotion. Most (except leeches) have bristles (short or long, many or few) sprouting out of various locations along the body or on their appendages if they have them. As usual, it is hard to summarize such a disparate group, but I'll mention a few that span the range.

Earthworms belong to Class Oligochaeta. They are the most familiar representative of this class, but keep in mind that there are thousands of aquatic and semi-terrestrial species, too.

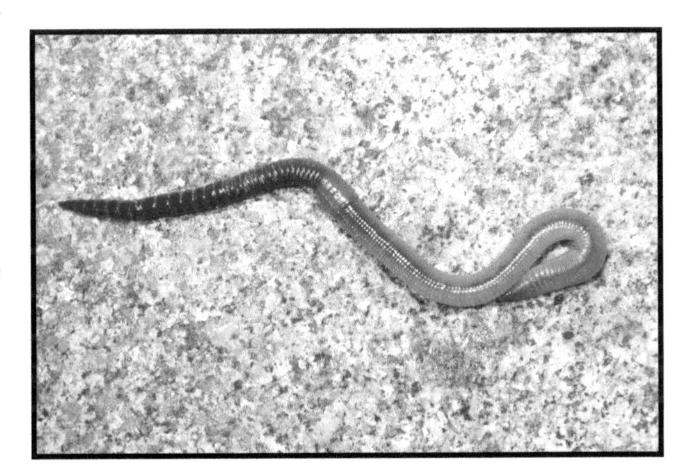

Figure 23.6 Earthworm

Earthworms are not only very useful to us as live fishing bait, but are also a vital part of soil ecology. Collectively, they consume and run through their guts vast quantities of the world's soil. They contribute to the nitrogen supply in the soil when they excrete as well.

Earthworms are God's little rototillers, aerating and mixing the soil by burrowing and feeding. Many earthworms come to the surface and pull decaying plant material into their burrows for food, thus mixing and enriching the soil with organic nutrients. Earthworms have bristles which you can feel if you run your fingers down their sides. (Hence the name "Oligochaeta," which means "few bristles.") These bristles provide traction as the earthworms move in their burrows.

Leeches (Class Hirudinea) are often loathed by people who swim in muddy-bottomed lakes—and for good reason. Certain species of leeches certainly have a nasty blood-sucking habit. But not all leeches are bloodsuckers. Many work for a living by actually preying on smaller invertebrates which they consume whole. All true leeches have both anterior and posterior suckers that enable them not only to suck but also to move in an inchworm fashion. The anterior sucker is on the narrower end

Polychaetes (Class Polychaeta, meaning "many bristles") is the largest group of Annelids. They are mostly found in marine environments and exhibit a startling array of sizes, shapes, habitats, and life histories. One group includes the sedentary **tubeworms** that live in leathery or calcareous tubes which they construct for themselves. Most stay in their tubes but stick out their head to collect food in various ways. Some species of tubeworms have resplendent crowns of feathery tentacles that collect food particles suspended in the water (see Figure 23.8).

Active predatory **clamworms** are wildly different in how they feed. They vaguely look like soft-bodied centipedes when they leave their burrows to scurry about, hunting for prey. The clamworm has sharp jaws mounted on top of a jack-in-the-box pharynx that pops out with lightning speed to seize its victim.

Lugworms live a humble life in U-shaped burrows. They are in the habit of eating muddy sand that is rich in organic material for them to digest and absorb. When they excrete on the surface, lugworms leave squiggly piles of sand called castings that betray their secretive activities below.

Figure 23.7 Leech

Figure 23.8 Feather-duster worm

Figure 23.9 Clamworm

CHAPTER 23: REVIEW QUESTIONS

1. Phylum ______ are the flatworms because they are all dorsoventrally flattened.

2. List the three classes of flatworms (common name of the class is fine).

3. The tapeworms don't need a digestive tract because ______.

4. Which two classes of flatworms have an incomplete digestive tract?

5. Which class of flatworm is parasitic and has a mollusk for a primary host and a vertebrate for a final host?

6. The tapeworms have segments called ______ that detach and leave the host with the feces when they mature and are loaded with eggs.

7. Can these segments crawl on their own?

8. Tapeworms anchor themselves to the gut lining using hooks and or suckers mounted on the head-like ______.

9. Planaria are known, after being cut in pieces, for each piece to ______ the missing parts.

10. The planaria's mouth is located on the end of a hose-like ______ which is positioned in the middle of the underside. Incoming food is brought into its ______ cavity.

11. Roundworms:
    a. have tapered ends.
    b. have a complete digestive system.
    c. are round in cross section.
    d. all the above
    e. only a & b
    f. only a & c
    g. only b & c

12. Roundworms belong to Phylum ______.

13. How does their digestive tract differ from Phylum Platyhelminthes?

14. Many filarial worms cause massive swelling is due to the blockage of ______ coming back from the extremities. The swelling is also aggravated

by the victim's immune response called ______. This disfiguring disease is called ______.

15. Filarial worm larvae are injected into human hosts by a ______, which is the intermediate host.

16. More than half of roundworm species are:
    a. free-living
    b. parasitic

17. True of False. Both free-living and parasitic nematodes live only in the tropics.

18. The segmented worms belong to Phylum ______.

19. List three major classes of segmented worms.

20. True or False. Earthworms are the only kind of oligochaetes.

21. Name three ways earthworms benefit the soil.

22. True or False. All leeches suck blood or body fluids out of their prey.

23. What class of segmented worm is mostly found in marine (ocean water) environments?

CHAPTER 24

PHYLUM MOLLUSCA

THE MOLLUSKS: CLAMS, OYSTERS, SNAILS, SLUGS, SQUIDS, ETC.

As is usual of animals at the phylum level, mollusks manifest a huge array of diversity in size, shape, color, anatomy, behavior, and reproduction. The characteristics they all share are not very obvious at first sight, so it is helpful to have biologists point them out. The few traits that all **mollusks** have in common are 1) a **mantle,** 2) a **mantle cavity,** 3) **gills** or **lungs** within the mantle cavity, 4) a **visceral mass,** 5) a **head-foot,** and 6) a **shell** secreted by the mantle (in many but not all mollusks). As we survey the major classes of mollusks, pay attention to these six features in each. Also, consider how these features are similar (as well as how they are different) in each class.

CLASS BIVALVIA: THE BIVALVES—CLAMS, OYSTERS, SCALLOPS, MUSSELS, ETC.

If you're already familiar with the **bivalves** listed above, then you will know they all obviously sport two shells (or valves) hinged together, each one being more or less a mirror image of the other. There are currently over 9,000 species. They come in all sizes, from the 1-mm seed shell to the giant clam over 1 meter long and weighing up to 500 pounds.

The clam is a good representative of a bivalve, so I'll use the clam to discuss a bivalve's general body plan, locomotion, and feeding. In Figure 24.1 on the next page, the front of the clam is to the left, the back is on top, and the rear is to the right. The bulge on the two valves near the hinge is called the **umbo.**

Just beneath each valve is a sheet of epidermis lining the inner surfaces of the valves but covering the rest of the body like a poncho. This is the mantle and it has the important job of secreting the structurally complex layers of the shell.

Sandwiched between the right and left sides of the mantle is the visceral mass containing the bulk of the organs. The mantle cavity is the space between the visceral mass and the mantle. Protruding from the visceral mass

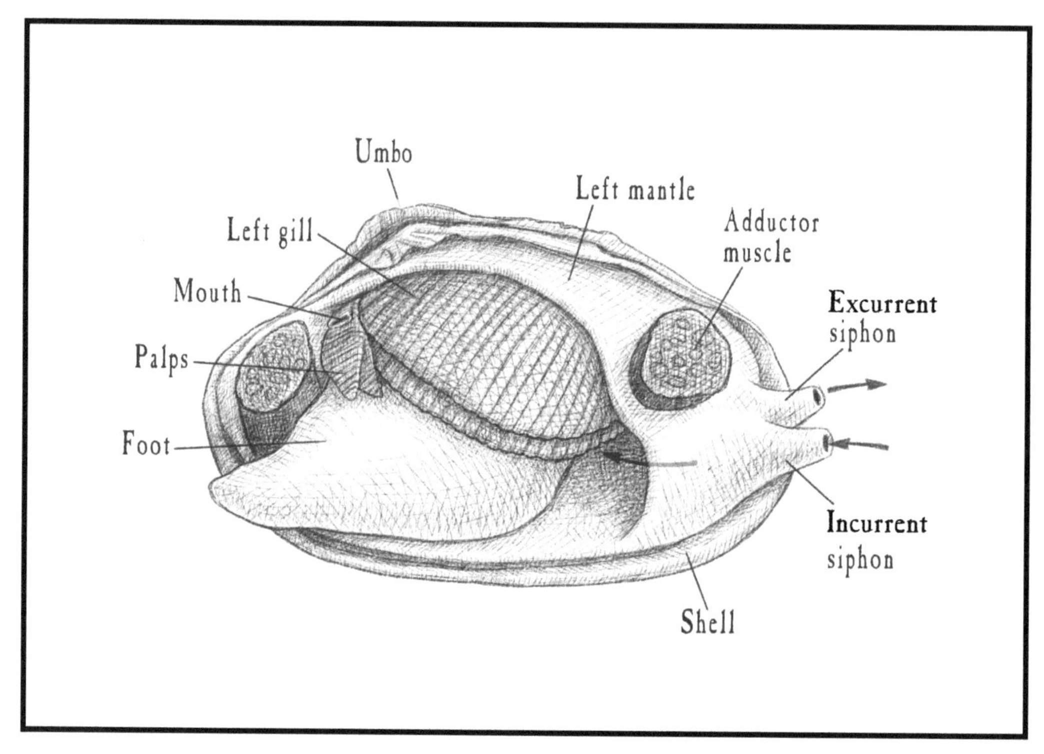

Figure 24.1 Bivalve anatomy (left shell removed)

on the lower left side of the figure is the **foot**, which is muscular and (you guessed it) used in locomotion. The clam moves along by extending the foot, gripping the substrate with a bulge at the end of the foot, and then contracting the foot.

Bivalves are filter feeders. The two sides of the mantle at the rear form two apertures (the **incurrent** and **excurrent siphons**) that allow water flow in and out of the mantle cavity.

On each side of the visceral mass is a pair of leaf-like gills dangling in the mantle cavity. Though not apparent to the naked eye, these gills are hollow and are covered with microscopic pores. Due to the action of cilia on the gills, water is drawn into the mantle cavity through the incurrent siphon along with tiny plankton and other suspended particles. The water is pulled into the interior of the gills through the pores, but much of the plankton is caught on the surface of the gills in a thin layer of mucous. Like a conveyor belt, the cilia on the gill surface then move the food that's stuck in the mucous down to the edge of each gill. At the edge of the gills, the larger, indigestible bits drop off, but the rest of the food is moved onto other ciliated food grooves running along the lower edge of each gill toward the palps, which are also grooved and ciliated. Finally, these palps convey the food to the mouth opening where it is ingested.

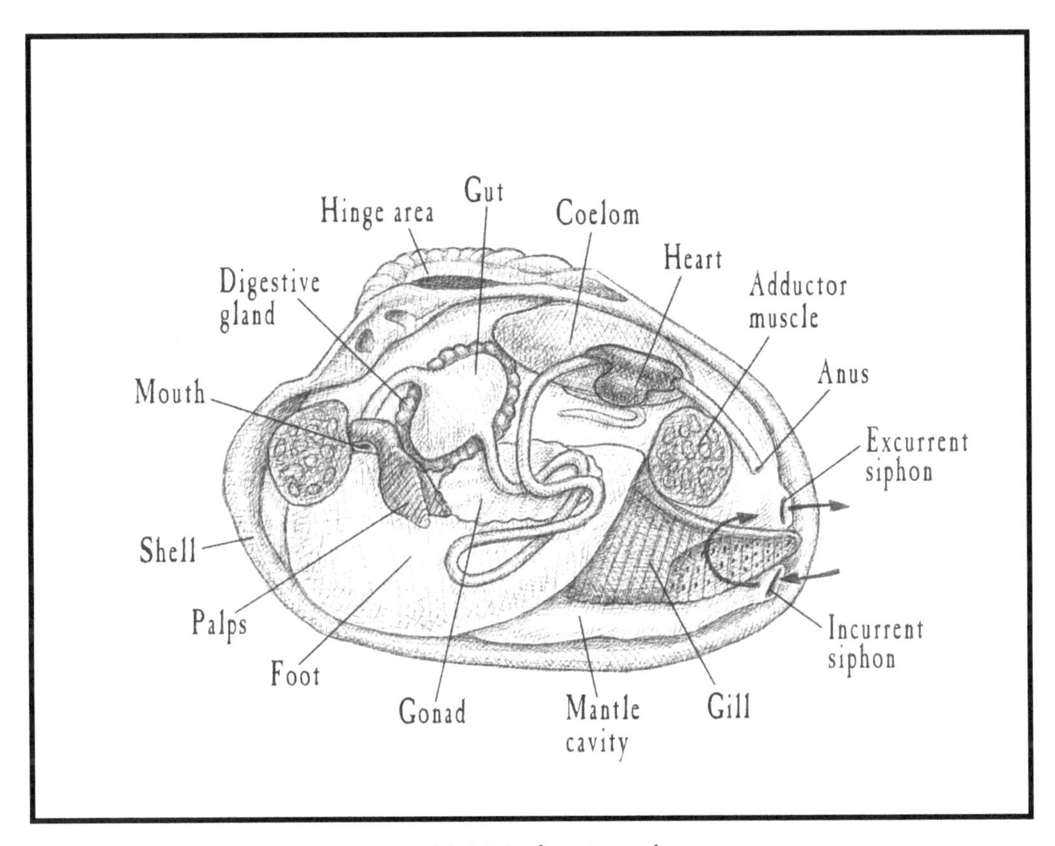

Figure 24.2 Bivalve visceral mass

Meanwhile, the water that entered the gills moves up through the gill's interior and flows into suprabranchial chambers. This conducts the water rearward, where it merges with the excurrent siphon. The food moves down a short esophagus and enters a stomach surrounded by a greenish tissue called the digestive gland. Although some food is digested in the lumen of the stomach, much food is digested intracellularly by digestive gland cells and other phagocytic cells called amebocytes. The intestine conveys waste dorsally to the rectum and out through the anus which is conveniently situated near the excurrent siphon. Waste is then whisked away with the water exiting the excurrent siphon.

Figure 24.3 Diversity of bivalves

This is the general way bivalves feed, but bear in mind that there are many variations on this theme out there. Figure 24.3 shows some bivalve diversity.

CLASS GASTROPODA: SNAILS, SLUGS, WHELKS, CONCHS, NUDIBRANCHS, ABALONES, ETC.

This class is by far the largest class of mollusks: over 60,000 species. Like I've been saying all along, it's difficult to summarize such a diverse group. **Gastropods** range in size from microscopic members to a large marine snail (whose shell is more than a foot-and-a-half long) and a sea hare or nudibranch (which reaches a meter in length). Not only that, but they also range in habitat. There are deep-sea gastropods as well as tree-dwelling snails; there are both saltwater and freshwater inhabitants. Many have gills hidden under their shell but the land dwellers have a lung-like cavity called a **pneumostome**.

Nevertheless, gastropods do have a few things in common. The name gastropod means "belly foot," referring to the fact that they slide about on their "belly" which is really a mucus-producing muscular **foot**. The foot lays down a thin carpet of mucus, and the animal moves by waves of muscular contractions in the foot that propel it over the mucus.

Figure 24.4 Slug pneumostome

With few exceptions gastropods all have the rasping tongue-like **radula**. Some slurp up organic particles in the sediment, some munch on plants, others on algae, and some dine on the flesh of animals.

Gastropods are the only mollusks that have a few land-dwelling species: slugs and land snails. While other gastropods have a huge diversity of sensory organs, the land snails and slugs have two pairs of tentacles. You've probably seen these before. The upper tentacles have eyes perched atop them, and the lower tentacles are used to touch and taste their surroundings.

Unlike the bivalves, if gastropods possess a shell (and the vast majority do), there is only one. Many of them have shells that form a variety of spirals. Beachcombers love to collect gastropod shells for knickknacks because of their beautifully sculpted, colored shells. Some, however, are naked like

Figure 24.5 Diversity of Gastropoda

slugs and sea hares (sea slugs and nudibranchs). These can be very beautiful even without shells.

CLASS CEPHALOPODA: SQUID, CUTTLEFISH, NAUTILUS, AND OCTOPUS

These mollusks are spectacularly complex in their anatomy and behavior. They are much more mobile than the other mollusks

Cephalopod means "head-foot." As the name implies, they have a well-developed head. Instead of a single muscular foot, a number of **arms** and **tentacles** are mounted on the head. These often bear suction cups that aid in grasping their prey and moving the prey to the hard, sharp, horny **beak** inside the head. The beak then tears the prey into manageable pieces. Inside the beak is the radula, which moves the bits of prey back to the esophagus for swallowing.

Figure 24.6 Chambered nautilus

With the exception of the chambered nautilus, cephalopods do not have external shells. Many do, however, have bony or cartilaginous structures embedded in their mantle: cuttlefish have a **cuttlebone**, for example, and squid have a thin, flexible, flat, supporting rod called a **pen**. Octopuses do not have a shell of any kind.

Though cephalopods vary in size, shape, color, habitat, and behavior, they are all predators. They digest and absorb their food in their gut, where the digestive system takes a U-turn and terminates in the anus below the head, near the siphon or **funnel**.

The mantle of a cephalopod forms a sac-like body wall that surrounds the creature's visceral mass. The open end of the mantle surrounds the head like the cuff of your sleeve around your wrist. When the mantle expands, sea water is sucked in around the head and into the mantle cavity. It then washes over the visceral mass, including the gills, which pick up oxygen from the water (the organs in the visceral mass are lined with a thin, transparent epidermis).

Figure 24.7 Hooded cuttlefish

When the mantle constricts, the open end tightens around the head, thus preventing water from exiting the same way it entered. The only exit is a short, tapering tube called a funnel, positioned below the head and pointing forward. The funnel allows the compressed water to quickly escape from the mantle cavity, creating a water jet that propels the cephalopod.

The cephalopod can aim this funnel, somewhat controlling the direction of its movements, but since the funnel is pointed forward, the cephalopod is primarily propelled backwards.

The funnel is actually a multi-purpose opening, providing more than just nifty jet propulsion. Since the anus is near the funnel, feces are shot out with out-going water. Also, attached to the rectum (near the anus) is an **ink sac**. If the cephalopod needs to evade a predator, it excretes ink out of the anus and then

Figure 23.8 Octopus

out through the funnel, creating an ink cloud in the water that serves as a smoke screen to (hopefully) confuse or distract the predator while the cephalopod jets away.

Besides having all these amazing features, cephalopods are also thought to be the most intelligent invertebrates. Some octopuses are problem-solvers and have been known to open screw-capped jars to get at prey trapped inside.

CHAPTER 24: REVIEW QUESTIONS

1. List six characteristics of mollusks (one is possessed by most but not all mollusks).
2. Which class of mollusks are filter feeders?
3. The tongue-like rasping organ in many mollusks is the ______.
4. Name three mollusks that don't have a shell of any kind.
5. In bivalves, what organ collects plankton on its surface and sweeps it toward the mouth with cilia?
6. In bivalves, what organ is the gateway of water into the mantle cavity?
7. What organ is the exit of water out of the bivalve?
8. By expanding and contracting their mantle, cephalopods accomplish at least two important things. List them.
9. Name three types of cephalopods.
10. Name four types of bivalves.
11. Name three types of gastropods.
12. Slugs and land snails have two pair of tentacles. What do the upper ones have at their tips?

CHAPTER 25

PHYLUM ARTHROPODA

THE ARTHROPODS: CRUSTACEANS, ARACHNIDS, INSECTS, ETC.

Of all the phyla in the world, Phylum Arthropoda is far and away the biggest and most diverse. In this textbook, I am covering just nine of the largest, most familiar animal phyla (out of about 36), yet those nine cover 98% of all animals. To give you an idea of the immensity of Phylum Arthropoda, it covers 80% of the total number of animal species. That's a considerable amount, since there are over a million described species of animals.

The name "Arthropoda" means "jointed foot," which is one obvious characteristic of the group. All **arthropods** share the following traits:

1) an **exoskeleton** that is hardened to various degrees,
2) a **segmented body,**
3) **jointed appendages** (hence the name), and
4) a periodic need to **molt.**

The nonliving outer portion of the exoskeleton is called the **cuticle.** Since the cuticle can't grow indefinitely, an arthropod needs to produce a new flexible, folded cuticle underneath the old rigid one. The folds allow the new cuticle to expand to a larger size than the previous one. Once the new cuticle is formed, the arthropod inflates its body, cracks open the old cuticle at its weak seams, and crawls out of it. This is called molting.

The expanding body stretches the new soft, pliable cuticle so there is room to grow. The cuticle then

Figure 25.1 Molting

hardens (and darkens) to its appropriate firmness.

Many arthropods have a more or less rigid exoskeleton, so as to be able to move freely. They were also designed with joints and seams made of flexible cuticle along the body and legs (rather like the joints and seams in a suit of armor), giving arthropods their segmented appearance.

A centipede is a good illustration of the main features of an arthropod.

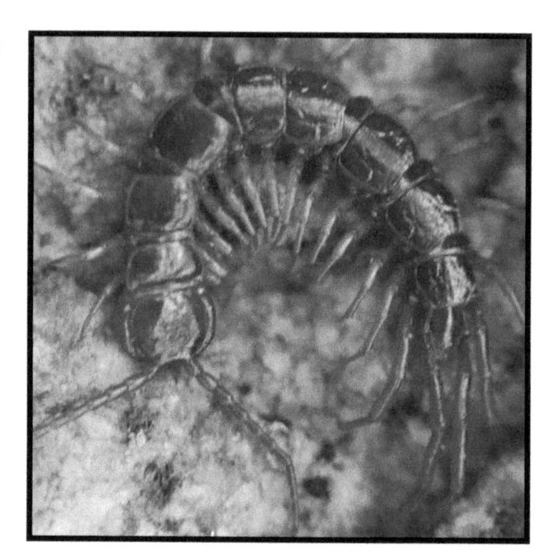

Figure 25.2 Arthropod features

ARTHROPOD DIVERSITY

Because this phylum is so huge, I'll cover groups that span a number of taxa including subphylum, class, and order. New data is constantly changing the ways these groups are sorted, so don't worry about the taxonomic level. Just know what belongs to what group.

Class Trilobita: Trilobites

This amazing group of arthropods is now extinct (as far as we know), but they are still worth mentioning. In their heyday, their diversity was phenomenal: about 17,000 species of all sorts of shapes and sizes. Nevertheless, the general body plan of the **trilobite** is pretty consistent. They had a **head**, a **thorax** (middle region), and a **pygidium** (tail region). The name "trilobite" refers to the fact that they had three distinct longitudinal lobes running perpendicular to the body segmentation. The head had complex compound eyes. Since antennae have been found on a few specimens, it is assumed that most had them. Based on abundant fossil evidence, it looks like trilobites had a broad array of life histories. Many were sea-floor dwellers and some were even swimmers. Trilobites could be predators, scavengers, or filter feeders.

Figure 25.3 Trilobite

Class Diplopoda: Millipedes

Figure 25.4 Millipede

Millipedes are fairly familiar arthropods (if you're in the habit of turning over logs, rocks, or other objects). There are about 10,000 species, with the smallest measuring 2 mm long, but some tropical giants reach the length of almost a foot.

The millipede's body consists of two basic body regions: the **head** and the **trunk**. The head, as usual, contains the sense organs (compound eyes and antennae) and chewing mouthparts.

Except for the first few trunk segments, they have two pairs of legs sprouting out of each trunk segment. Since the number of trunk segments vary from species to species, the number of legs varies as well. Although they can secrete noxious chemicals from glands to discourage predators, millipedes are actually quite mellow creatures and are easy to handle if you're gentle with them.

People might confuse millipedes with centipedes, but this is really odd since millipedes (in my view) don't look nearly as creepy. Their legs are not splayed out in a spidery fashion, but are neatly tucked more or less underneath their cylindrical body. Nor do millipedes have the nasty reputation that centipedes have. They just mosey slowly over the forest floor and eat lichens and detritus (dead plant matter), though some can be a minor greenhouse pest as they feed on living plants.

Class Chilopoda: Centipedes

Figure 24.5 Centipede

There are approximately 8,000 species of centipedes. Now, **centipedes** might be similar in some ways to the slow-moving, herbivorous millipedes (they are roughly the same size), but they are quite distinct in appearance and habits. These are the fast, creepy predators, unlike the mild-mannered millipedes.

A centipede's legs are splayed out on both sides and their body is quite dorso-ventrally flattened. They move in a quick, serpentine manner. Like the millipede, they also have two body regions: the head and the trunk. The head has compound eyes, long antennae, and mouthparts. They have one pair of legs per trunk segment. On the first trunk segment is mounted a pair of **poison claws** which extend forward under the head. These are used to stab and inject venom into their hapless victims. Once the venom kills (or paralyzes) the prey, the dead (or immobile) meal gets passed to the mouthparts on the head, where it is consumed.

Most centipedes prey on small invertebrates, but the Amazonian giant centipede can capture and consume bats, birds, frogs, lizards, and mice.

SUBPHYLUM CRUSTACEA: THE CRUSTACEANS—CRABS, LOBSTERS, CRAYFISH, WOOD-LICE, BEACHFLEAS, BARNACLES, ETC.

Again, this is a very numerous (around 50,000 species) and disparate group of arthropods. The distinguishing features that an arthropod must have to be considered a crustacean are the following: 1) two pairs of antennae, 2) a pair of mandibles and two pairs of maxillae, 3) biramous appendages, 4) calcium salts within its cuticle, and 5) some sort of gills for respiration. (A quick note on biramous appendages. "Biramous" means that the appendage is divided into two branches: the exopod and endopod. This is not a universal trait since a number of appendages on many crustaceans do not exhibit this arrangement. This is where an evolutionist's presuppositions force him to say that the biramous condition was primitive (ancestral) and that if a modern crustacean has uniramous (not branched) appendages, it is because it secondarily lost the biramous pattern on those particular appendages. Whatever the case, biramous appendages are not universal in this group.)

MAJOR GROUPS OF CRUSTACEANS[1]

Barnacles

Barnacles are a very unusual group whose physical appearance doesn't suggest crustacean-hood. Superficially, they act and look more like mollusks. However, upon close inspection, they are obviously true crustaceans both developmentally and internally. They're just good at covering this up by enclosing their bodies with calcareous plates and shields.

1. These groups vary from class, infraclass, to order (plus they change), so I won't emphasize the taxonomic level as much as I will emphasize each group and its characteristics.

As adults, barnacles are anchored firmly to sturdy surfaces such as docks, rocks, shells, and animals. Hence, they're extremely common on the sea coasts that provide lots of rocks or pilings to attach to.

Barnacles go through an early larval stage (where it is called a nauplius), which is clearly indicative of their crustacean status.

Their legs, which are called **cirripeds** or **cirri**, are the only part of their adult body that clearly betrays their crustacean body plan. These legs are thin, wispy, and covered with small hairs (setae). Barnacles use their legs like a net. When covered with water, they open their plates, whip out their cirri, and sweep the water to strain out tiny plankton. The cirri then pull in the catch (just like fish in a net) and transfer it to the mouth.

There are about 1,200 barnacle species, but they come in two basic forms. Sessile barnacles have their hard plates directly glued to the surface. Goose barnacles, on the other hand, have a fleshy stalk which allows the barnacle to sway a bit in strong surf.

Figure 25.6 Barnacle feeding with cirri

Decapods: Crabs, Lobsters, Crayfish, and Shrimp

As the name implies, these crustaceans have 10 walking legs (there are many more appendages). They are the crustaceans we are the most familiar with due to their popularity as seafood. The crayfish (a common decapod) is a good example of a crustacean anatomically, so we'll study its body to get a pretty solid idea of the rest of them.

Look at the figure below. The crayfish's body is divided up into two general regions: the **cephalothorax** and **abdomen**. The cephalothorax, which means "head-thorax," bears 1) the **compound eyes**, 2) two pairs of **antennae**, 3) one pair of **mandibles**, 4) two pairs of **maxillae**, and 5) three pairs of **maxillipeds**. The compound eyes and the two pairs of antennae are, of course, involved in sensory perception, whereas the mandibles, maxillae, and maxillipeds are involved in handling, sorting, and chewing food. To the rear of the maxillipeds are 6) five pair of **walking legs**. Sometimes the first pair is enlarged as pinchers called **chelipeds**.

The cephalothorax appears as a single unit because it is covered by a single exoskeletal plate called the **carapace**. The walking legs have feathery gills attached to their bases and are hidden under the carapace where oxygenated water is circulated. Beneath the segmented abdomen are small, paired appendages called **swimmerets**. These have various functions including swimming (obviously), carrying eggs (female), and creating water currents. Mounted on the end of the abdomen are the paired **uropods** and the middle, single **telson**. These are involved in swimming and egg protection.

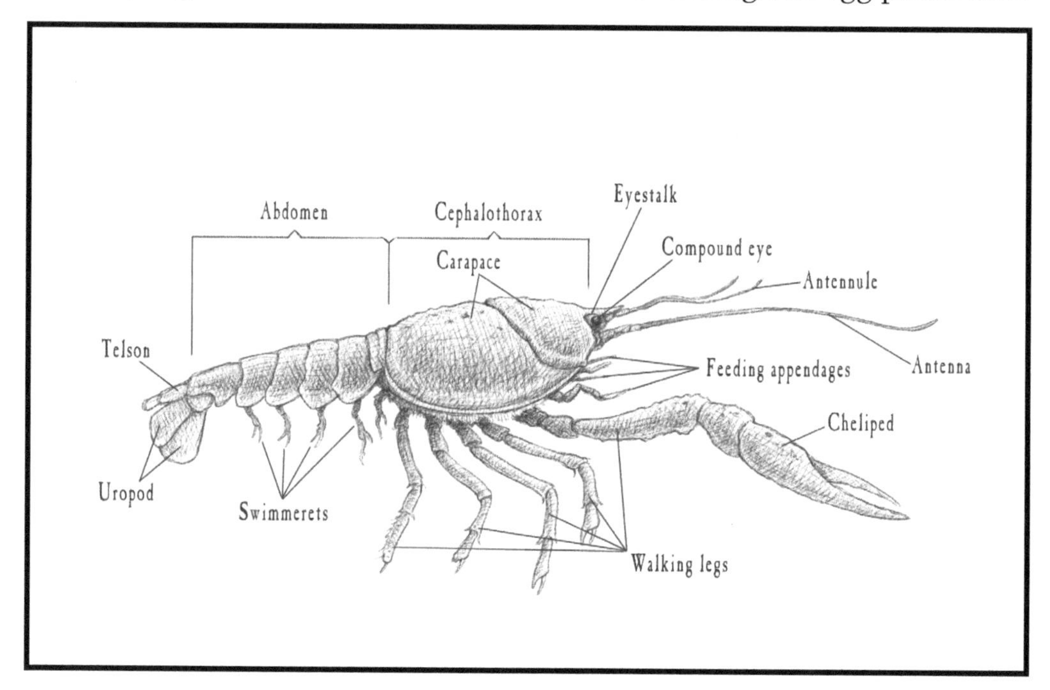

Figure 25.7 Crayfish anatomy

Isopods: Woodlice and Assorted Freshwater and Marine Isopods

The most familiar isopods are the woodlice, simply because these crustaceans are terrestrial and are frequently found under rocks, logs, or other damp, humid retreats. They are also known as sow bugs, pill bugs, and roly-polies.

There are over 10,000 species of isopods (about 500 freshwater, 4,500 marine, and 5,000 terrestrial) and they range in size from less than half a millimeter to a whopping 20 inches. Most, however, are between 1 and 5 cm. They are dorso-ventrally flattened (which means they are wider than they are tall), but they aren't as flat as a tick.

Figure 25.8 Isopod

All isopods have two pair of antennae, mouthparts, and seven pair of legs which are similar in shape and size (which is where it gets its name, isopod, which means "same feet"). They also have trachea-like lungs housed in their rear, page-like appendages called *pleopods.*

The isopods run the gamut as far as feeding habits go. There are herbivores, omnivores, scavengers, carnivores, and parasites, but most of them are either scavengers or omnivores. The familiar woodlice feed on fungus, algae, moss, and detritus. Isopods also occupy a huge range of habitats from deserts to the ocean floor.

Amphipods: Sideswimmers, Beachfleas, etc.

Amphipods have bodies similar to that of isopods, with the obvious difference that they are laterally flattened (which means they're taller than they are wide). Though they have **seven pairs of legs**, amphipod legs are more varied in shape and function; hence the name amphipod ("both kinds of feet"). There are around 7,000 species, and they range in size from 1 mm to 13 inches. Most are aquatic (both freshwater and marine), but those that stray onto land like it nice and damp. Like beach fleas, for example. If you flip a clump of seaweed over, you'll have probably crashed a beach flea party. This great disturbance will send hundreds of beach fleas scampering in all directions.

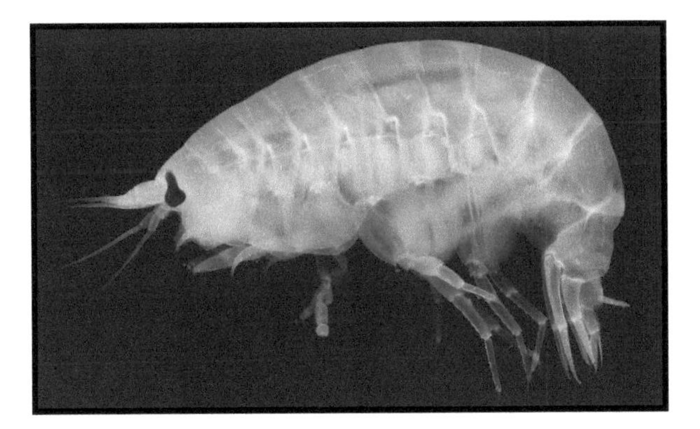
Figure 25.9 Amphipod

Sideswimmers or scuds are small amphipods (2-3 mm) that are common in the shallows of ponds and lakes. One of the deepest-dwelling animals is a lowly amphipod. It lives several miles straight down in certain ocean trenches.

These crustaceans are quite common in aquatic ecosystems, but usually go unnoticed by all but the most observant outdoorsy folks.

CLASS INSECTA: THE INSECTS

Insects are by far the largest group of arthropods. They occupy their own class and are distinct from all the other arthropod groups. The number of described species is mind-bogglingly huge: currently over one million. Beetles alone (just one order of insects) include over 350,000 species—way more than all the other animal phyla *put together.*

The general body plan of insects is easy to grasp: 1) three body regions: a **head**, a **thorax**, and an **abdomen**.

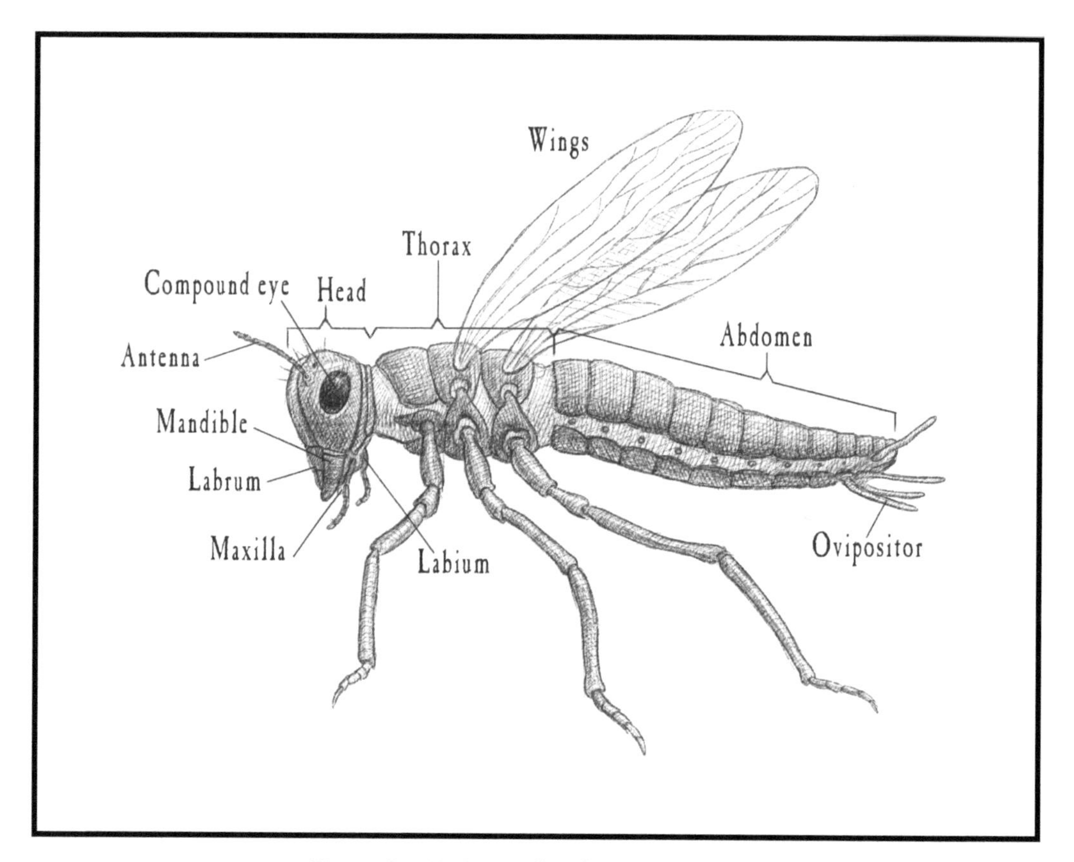

Figure 25.10 Generalized insect anatomy

The Head contains:

- One pair of antennae
- Compound eyes
- Mouthparts: one labrum, one pair of mandibles, one pair of maxillae, and a labium.

The Thorax is composed of three segments: the pro-, meso-, and metathorax, and it contains:

- One pair of legs per thoracic segment (hence, six legs). These would technically be called the prothoracic legs, the mesothoracic legs, and the metathoracic legs.
- One pair of wings on the mesothorax and metathorax; hence, four wings.

The Abdomen contains:

- A variable number of segments
- No or reduced paired appendages. (Exception: cerci, which are rear-end sensory structures like antennae.)
- External genitalia (female/ovipositor; male/aedeagus)

As is true of all arthropods, insects have an exoskeleton made of chitin and protein. Consequently, they must molt as they grow. Many insects don't just molt and re-molt and come out looking the same; instead, they undergo a phenomenal change in body shape called metamorphosis (which I'm sure you've heard of).

No Metamorphosis:
Certain insects do not metamorphose. They just undergo several molts until they are adults, each time becoming a slightly bigger version of the stage before (see the examples on the next page). The stages between each molt are called **instars**. The last instar is the adult. Besides size, the only difference between a juvenile and an adult is that the adult is sexually mature.

Incomplete Metamorphosis:
Many insects exhibit a partial metamorphosis between the juvenile instars and the adult. The obvious difference is that the adult has fully developed wings whereas the nymphs have no wings or wing pads.

Egg → nymph → nymph → nymph → nymph → nymph → adult

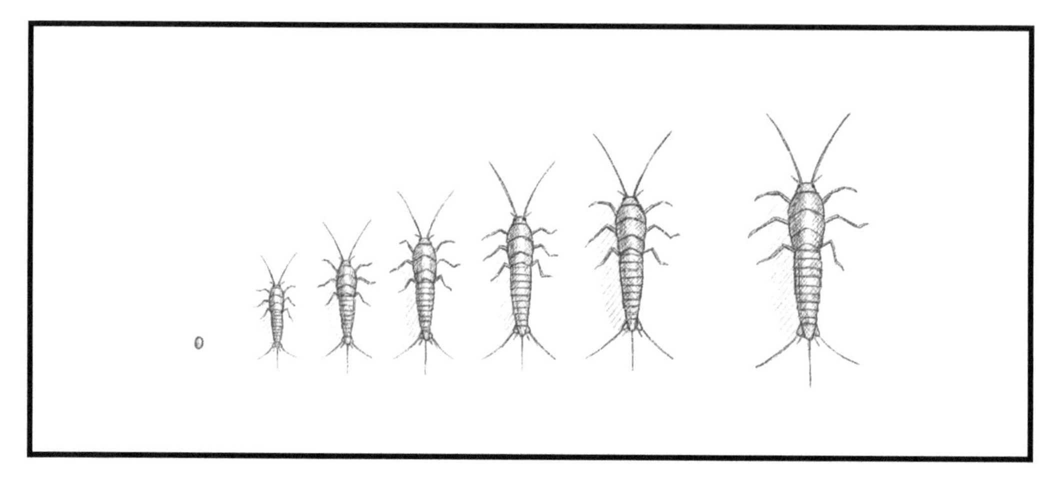

Figure 25.11 No metamorphosis (example: silverfish)

Figure 25.12 Incomplete metamorphosis (example: bug)

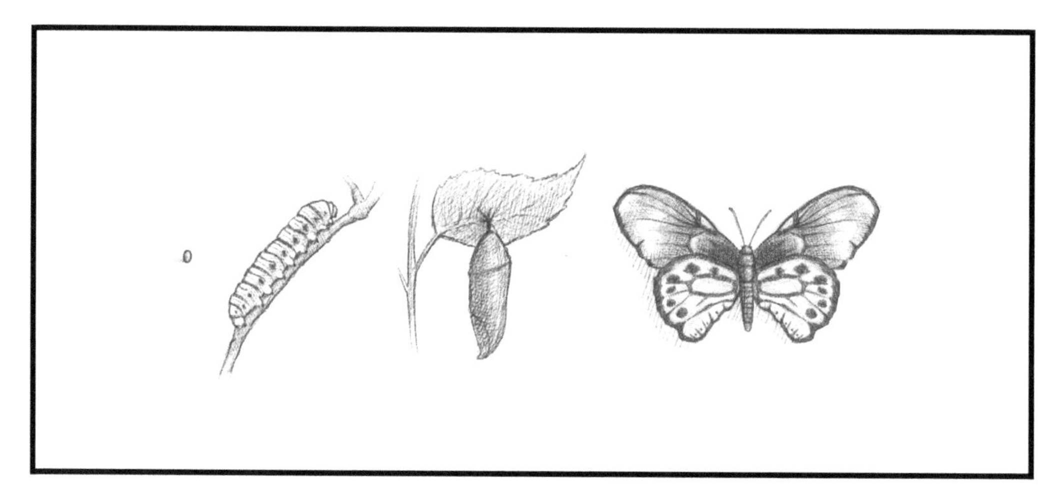

Figure 25.13 Complete metamorphosis (example: butterfly)

Complete Metamorphosis:
This is the kind of metamorphosis we're all familiar with from watching butterflies. In these insects, juveniles (larvae) are radically different from the adult—so different, in fact, that it is necessary to have an inactive instar called a **pupa** to make the huge transition. The names of the larvae have special names in some of the orders. For example, beetle larvae are called grubs, butterfly larvae are called caterpillars, and fly larvae are sometimes called maggots.

Egg → larva → larva → larva → pupa → adult

INSECT ORDERS

There are approximately 30 orders of insects, but I will briefly introduce you to the seven largest and most conspicuous orders.

Figure 25.14 Dragonfly

Order Odonata: The Dragonflies and Damselflies
There are over 5,500 described species of these beautiful and amazing aeronauts. These wonderful aerial predators catch and consume insects on the wing. They have small bristle-like antennae and compound eyes that occupy most of their head. Their six spiny legs are hitched forward on the underside of their thorax and are positioned so as to scoop up hapless flying insects as they patrol the airways around ponds, lakes, and streams. Their abdomen is long and slender. They lay eggs in the water where they hatch and undergo incomplete metamorphosis. They spend their juvenile life as aquatic nymphs. The nymphs are predators, too, but they hunt their small invertebrate quarry underwater.

Figure 25.15 Dragonfly naiad

Order Orthoptera: The Grasshoppers, Crickets, and Katydids

These insects are very familiar to us and they all share a common conspicuous feature: large, saltatorial metathoracic appendages. That's the scientific way to say "big, jumping hindlegs." The name "Orthoptera" means "straight wing" and refers to the straight veins in the forewings of grasshoppers.

Figure 25.16 Wings of grasshopper

The forewings of Orthopterans are called **tegmina**, and are not used for flying, but rather form protective coverings for the membranous hindwings which are folded up like Japanese fans beneath the tegmina.

Most species in this order are herbivores of various tastes, though some are omnivores and detritovores, such as crickets. Some unusual members are even predators.

Figure 25.17 Variety of Orthoptera

Order Hemiptera: The True Bugs

If you thought I've been talking about bugs all along, I haven't been. In order to be considered a true "bug," an insect has to belong to the order Hemiptera. Membership criteria are as follows: 1) piercing-sucking mouthparts, which are shown in Figure 25.19; and 2) two pairs of wings (usually). Keep reading for the specifics.

There was recently some taxonomic reshuffling, but suffice it to say that Order Hemiptera has three suborders: 1) Heteroptera, 2) Sternorrhycha, and 3) Auchenorrhycha. I normally don't go into any details below the rank of order, but since Heteroptera used to be its own order and has a very distinguishing characteristic, I will mention that characteristic: unique forewings called **hemelytra**. The hemelytra are also protective wing covers in which the proximal half is leathery and the distal half is membranous.

The membranous portions overlap; the leathery parts do not. The inner edge of the leathery portion borders the sides of a triangle in the middle of the back. The hindwings are completely membranous. These bugs include stinkbugs, assassin bugs, plant bugs, leaf-footed bugs, etc.

Figure 25.18 Piercing-sucking mouthparts of a hemipteran

In Figure 25.19, the top two pictures are bugs in Heteroptera. Note the hemelytra bordering the sides of the triangle in the middle of their back and the overlapping membranous portions.

I won't describe the differences of the other two suborders, nor have you learn their names. I'll just say that if these insects have wings, they can fly with both forewings and hindwings. The forewings may or may not be membranous, but whatever their texture, they are more or less the same throughout (unlike Heteroptera), and their hindwings are entirely membranous. These bugs include cicadas (the bottom picture of Figure 25.19), leafhoppers, aphids, and scale insects.

Heteropterans can be sap feeders or predators, whereas the other two suborders feed entirely on plant sap. Whether it's plant or animal juice they're after, almost all of them pierce and suck their liquid food with their straw-like mouthparts. All Hemipterans undergo incomplete metamorphosis.

Figure 25.19 Variety of Hemiptera

Order Coleoptera: The Beetles

Like I said, this is an enormous order with over 350,000 described species. This means that about a third of all animal species are beetles![2]

Although beetles vary in size, shape, color, habitat, and feeding habits, they all are

2. For more about the amazing variety of beetles, you can check out this article of mine: "Beetles: Go Anywhere, Do Anything," *Answers in Genesis,* http://www.answersingenesis.org/articles/am/v8/n2/beetles [accessed June 20, 2014].

proud owners of unique forewings called **elytra.** The order name "Coleoptera" refers to these structures; *coleos* means "sheath" and *ptera* means "wing." These elytra do not overlap. Where the two elytra meet in the middle, they form a straight line down their back. That's how you can tell whether or not it's a true beetle.

Figure 25.20
Variety of Coleoptera

The elytra are thickened shields that act as covers for the membranous hindwings. The segment in front of the elytra is the prothorax. Some misguided instructors assume that the elytra correspond to the abdomen and then think that the prothorax is the entire thorax, but remember that the legs sprout out of the thorax, so if you look at Figure 25.21, you can see that only the front legs are mounted on the prothorax. The other four legs are coming out of the meso and metathorax. Now look at a beetle belly (Figure 25.22). All the segments behind the last pair of legs belong to the abdomen.

Some beetles never fly, many occasionally fly, and some do quite frequently. If the beetle decides to fly, the elytra lift up, the hindwings are unfurled, and the beetle takes to the air (Figure 25.23).

Being such a huge group, beetles have extremely variable life histories. They have every conceivable diet, but they all fall under these general categories: omnivores, herbivores, predators, and scavengers.

All beetles undergo complete metamorphosis, and the larvae are usually called grubs.

Most beetles can be easily recognized as such, but some have names that may throw you off—like ladybugs. Their proper common name is actually "ladybird beetle." They have classic elytra that are often brightly colored, as every kid knows.

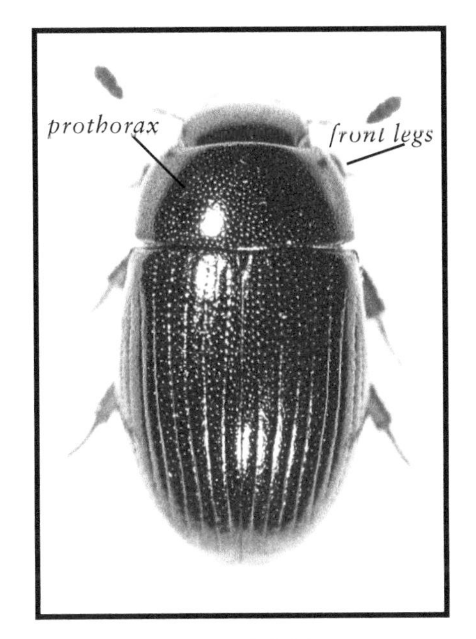

Figure 25.21
Dorsal view of Beetle

Figure 25.22
Ventral view of Beetle

Figure 25.23 Beetle flying

Figure 25.24 Firefly

Another misnomer is the firefly or lightning bug. It's neither a fly nor a bug; it's 100% beetle with elytra. The feature that sets it apart from other beetles is the glow organ on its abdomen which has delighted countless children lunging about in the darkness wherever fireflies dwell.[3]

3. If you want to know more about this amazing beetle, you can read "Lightning Bugs," *Answers Magazine,* http://www.answersingenesis.org/articles/am/v4/n2/lightning-bugs [accessed June 20, 2014].

Order Diptera: The Flies

This is another humongous order (currently around 120,000 described species), though nothing rivals the beetles. As you probably expected, flies come in a huge number of different body sizes and shapes. Life histories are also highly variable. Houseflies, horse flies, deer flies, mosquitoes, gnats, midges, craneflies, and hoverflies are all examples of these dipterans, to give you an idea of how they can vary from each other.

Figure 25.25 Hoverfly halteres

As the name indicates, dipterans have two wings (the forewings or mesothoracic wings). Instead of hindwings, they all have club-shaped gyroscopic organs called **halteres** which vibrate during flight. These tiny structures sense torque when a fly changes direction and rotational movement during flight.

The fly's nervous system processes and responds to stimuli from the halteres. Exquisitely designed, this system enables flies to carry out their aerobatics with superb control—sometimes annoyingly so when they dodge your fly swatter.

Dipterans also undergo complete metamorphosis. Certain groups of larval flies are often called maggots.

Figure 25.26 Variety of Diptera

Order Lepidoptera: The Butterflies and Moths

This order is also huge with an estimated 170,000 species. *Lepido* means "scale" and *ptera* means "wings," making them the "scale-winged" insects. If you zoom in on any butterfly or moth wing with a microscope, you will discover tiny **scales** covering its surface.

The creatures in Order Lepidoptera are known for wings exhibiting some of the most breathtaking patterns in nature. The stunning patterns on their wings come from the particular arrangement of different color scales formed in the same way that different color pixels form a digital photograph; each scale is like a pixel.

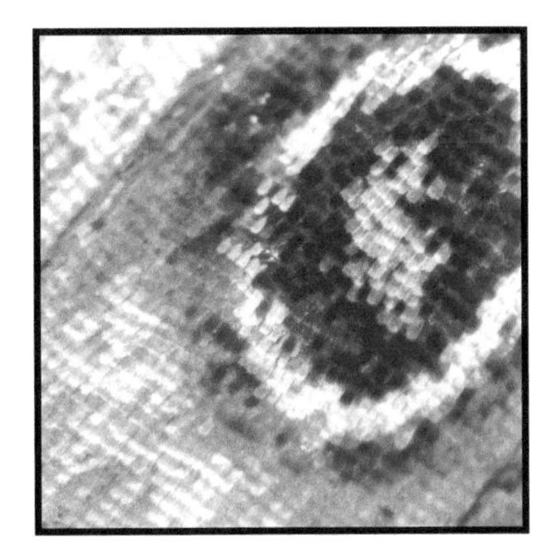

Figure 24.27
Wing scales of butterfly

The other characteristic that all lepidopterans share is a **proboscis** that siphons up liquid food. When not in use, the proboscis is coiled up under the head, but when a lepidopteran feeds, it uses muscles to extend the proboscis, and suck up the juice such as nectar, guano fluids, sweat, etc. (but usually nectar).

Lepidoterans are the most famous example of complete metamorphosis:

egg → several instars of caterpillar (larva) → chrysalis (pupa) → adult

For some species (usually moths), the last instar caterpillar spins a silken cocoon around itself before it molts into a pupa. Butterflies often pupate naked (no cocoon) and their pupae are called chrysalises.

Figure 25.28
Variety of Lepidoptera

Now, there is no clear taxonomic way to separate the moths from the butterflies—mostly because taxonomists can't agree on how to define their differences. At the same time, there are too many exceptions to their differences to stick them in their own suborders. Due to the confusion, moths and butterflies will remain popular groupings, but will never become taxonomically valid.

That said, the general differences are 1) butterflies are diurnal (active during the day) and are usually more brightly colored, whereas moths tend to be nocturnal, fuzzier, and more drab; 2) moths tend to hold their wings in a triangle shape, flat and low, whereas butterflies tend to hold their wings perpendicular to the surface; and 3) moths usually spin cocoons; butterflies usually don't. But, just to keep you on your toes, there are many exceptions to all these differences. (We simply don't have time to get into them.)

Figure 25.29 Moth versus butterfly, at rest

Order Hymenoptera: The Bees, Wasps, and Ants

At about 130,000 described species, this order is in the top four most speciose insect orders along with Coleoptera, Diptera, and Lepidoptera. Order Hymenoptera includes the bees, wasps, tiny parasitic wasps (gnat-sized), sawflies, and ants. They all have chewing mouthparts (some have additional lapping structures) and if they possess wings, they have two pairs of membranous ones.

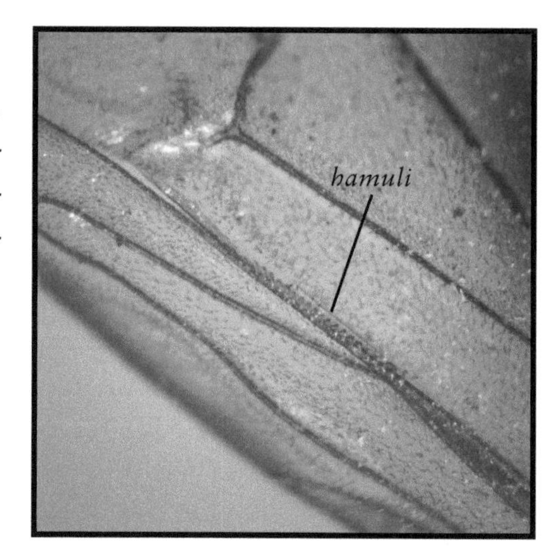

Figure 25.30 Hamuli

The hindwings possess a row of almost microscopic hooks called hamuli that are coupled to the forewings by curling around a vein on the rear edge of the forewings.

The fore and hindwings are effectively linked to each other so that they beat together as a unit, more like one pair of wings than two.

Also, most hymenopterans have a skinny waist, but as usual, there are exceptions—like the sawflies.

Hymenopterans are also very diverse and can't easily be summarized. Feeding habits are all over the map: there are predators, parasites (females lay their eggs into host animals or plants, and their larvae consume the living host's tissues until they pupate), nectar-feeders, pollen feeders, herbivores, etc. They also range in size from less than a millimeter to a couple of inches.

In many larger hymenopterans, females have an egg-layer (ovipositor) that also functions as a stinger. If they are a queen, eggs are laid from the base of the stinger. Stingers are used primarily to immobilize prey, but can also be used quite effectively in self-defense, as most of us know from experience.

Many in this order (mostly bees, wasps, and ants) have complex societies with a very clear division of labor. Various casts such as workers, soldiers, drones, and queens can be found carrying out their tasks instinctively. No one in the colony appears confused as to the job they are cut out for.

Figure 25.31
Variety of Hymenoptera

Class Merostomata: The Horseshoe Crabs

This is a very small group of crustacean-like arthropods, with only four living species. Nevertheless, they can be quite common in certain coastal areas. They aren't crustaceans simply because they don't have two pair of antennae. In fact, they don't have any.

Horseshoe crabs have two major body regions: the cephalothorax and the abdomen. The topside of the cephalothorax is covered by a sturdy carapace with a pair of compound eyes perched on top. On the underside of the cephalothorax, positioned up front, is a small pair of feeding appendages called **chelicerae**. Behind the chelicerae are five pairs of **walking legs** with spiny bases. On the underside of the body is the abdomen that has **book lungs** which extract oxygen from the water. The tip of the abdomen has a long, stiff

Figure 25.32 Horseshoe crab

appendage called a **telson** that comes in handy if the crab ever gets flipped over. It just uses the telson to flip itself back onto its feet.

Horseshoe crabs scavenge on various small invertebrates (worms, mollusks, crustaceans, etc.), some algae, and even small fish. They pick up food with their pincers on the tips of their chelicerae and walking legs, and then pass the food to the bases of their legs (gnathobases). These spiny bases mince up the food and pass it to the mouth, which is conveniently located between the gnathobases.

The lives of horseshoe crabs are shrouded in mystery except when they come ashore to breed. This is where they are often encountered by curious beachcombers.

CLASS ARACHNIDA: THE ARACHNIDS

Arachnids are, to many people, the scariest group of arthropods—if not the scariest animals, period. Arachnids all have two body regions (cephalothorax & abdomen). The cephalothorax has a similar design for every arachnid. At the front of the cephalothorax are mounted the chelicerae which are used for feeding and defense. The second pair of appendages are the **pedipalps** which can be used for feeding and walking. Finally, after the pedipalps, comes the hallmark feature of arachnids: the eight walking legs.

Order Opiliones: The Harvestmen

This group of arachnids is pretty familiar. The proper common name is "harvestmen," but "daddy longlegs" is also frequently used, and no, they technically aren't spiders, though we often think they are simply because of their eight legs This group has over 6,400 species worldwide. If we're in an observant mood, we may see them puttering along on their stilt-like legs over vegetation in our backyards or on a hike in the mountains.

Figure 25.33 Harvestman

Their cephalothorax is broadly joined to their abdomen so they don't have a narrow waist like the spiders; instead, their body is roughly egg-shaped. They also have two sideways-facing eyes on the top-middle of the carapace, and four pairs of long slender legs sprouting out of the cephalothorax. Most have leg spans of an inch or two, but there are some tropical giants that reach seven inches.

These spindly arachnids are omnivores, feeding on small invertebrates, bits of fruits and vegetables, and fungi. They grab their prey with their pedipalps, then pass it to the small, pincer-tipped chelicerae where the prey is crushed. The food is then swallowed.

Unlike spiders, harvestmen can ingest bits of solid food. There is an old wives' tale that says they have the most potent venom in the world, but aren't dangerous simply because they have no way to inject you with it. Although the part about "no way to inject" is true, the venom claim is complete nonsense. Harvestmen don't even have venom glands. And even though they are spidery looking, they don't have silk glands either.

Figure 25.34 Mite

Order Acari: The Ticks and Mites

Although harvestmen can be regarded as a benevolent outdoor curiosity, ticks and mites cannot be considered so lightly. They range in size from extremely minute (less than a tenth of a millimeter) to only about ¾ of an inch long, but many species can be as nasty as they are small.

There are well over 50,000 described species, occupying virtually every conceivable habitat in water and on land. Many are parasites on both invertebrates and vertebrates, many are detritovores in organic debris, and many feed on plants. Due to the diversity of feeding habits, their pedipalps and chelicerae are adapted for biting, sucking, stinging, or sawing'.

Figure 25.35 Deer tick

Although most pose no threat to mankind, there are still many species of ticks and mites that cause all kinds of damage to us by sucking the juices out of plants and animals and, yes, sometimes humans. And if that wasn't enough, many also vector plant, animal, and human diseases. These bad habits are just some of the reasons why acarologists are busy studying the Acari, devoting whole scientific journals to these critters.

Order Scorpiones: The Scorpions

These arachnids are also well known—not because of their diversity (over 1,500 species) but because of their venomous sting and formidable appearance. They range in size from about one-third of an inch to over eight inches. The large, intimidating, pincer-tipped appendages up front are the pedipalps. Nestled up front and between them are the small chelicerae. The cephalothorax seems relatively small (when viewed from the top) and is not segmented. The abdomen, however, is segmented, composed of the wide preabdomen (seven segments) and the narrow postabdomen (five segments). The venomous sting is mounted on the end of the postabdomen. While pedipalps up front are employed in seizing prey, the sting is used for paralyzing and killing. If the prey is weak and defenseless, scorpions don't use their sting. Instead, the pedipalps hand the dead or paralyzed prey over to the chelicerae, which crush and rip it to bits before the scorpion ingests the food.[4]

Figure 25.36 Variety of Scorpiones

Order Araneae: Spiders

To many people, these are the most familiar of all arachnids. They number over 40,000 described species and are all over the world (except Antarctica).

4. Here's another article I wrote if you want to know more about these critters: "Scorpions—Armed and Dangerous," www.answersingenesis.org/articles/am/v8/n1/scorpions.

They range in size from less than half a millimeter to a leg span of about twelve inches.

Spiders have the two typical arachnid body regions: the cephalothorax and the abdomen (see Figure 25.38 on the next page). Although the eye number varies, spiders typically have eight simple eyes on the front of the cephalothorax. Just beneath the eyes are the chelicerae tipped with fangs, which are supplied with venom commensurate for their prey. Regardless of the method of capture (pouncing on, running after, catching in a web, etc.), whenever the spider nabs its prey, the fangs inject the venom which contains digestive enzymes that liquefy the prey's tissues into a nutrient broth. In some spiders, the chelicerae may also chew the prey, which helps mix in the enzymes for chemical digestion. The predigested food is then sucked into the mouth. (For the male spider, one enlarged pedipalp is also a copulatory organ.) Behind the pedipalps are the distinctive four pairs of walking legs mounted on the sides of the cephalothorax. Between the cephalothorax and the abdomen, the spider has a narrow waist. On the underside of the abdomen, depending on the spider, there are either two pairs of openings to **book lungs**, or just one opening to the **tracheae**.

Figure 25.37 Variety of Araneae

Female spiders have a central genital opening between the front pair of legs. When the male prepares for mating, he deposits a bit of sperm on some silk and then loads the sperm silk into the hollow of his copulatory pedipalp. If he succeeds in this dicey courtship ritual, he places his pedipalp in the female's genital opening and deposits his sperm in her seminal receptacle. Later, when she lays her eggs, the sperm fertilizes the eggs as they leave her body and are placed in the silken egg sac.

The book lungs consist of a series of air tubes surrounded by blood chambers. Oxygen diffuses from the air into the blood, which is continually circulated throughout the spider's body. In most spiders, air enters a single opening (spiracle) just in front of the **spinnerets** and goes into a branching system of tracheae. The tracheal system, which isn't as complex and extensive as it is in insects, is a system of air tubes branching throughout the spider's interior and delivering gaseous oxygen to the tissues.

Near the end of the abdomen are several pairs of conical spinnerets (see below), each endowed with many spigots. Large **silk glands** are connected to the spigots and eject the silk in liquid form. The silk hardens immediately when exposed to the air, forming the spider web strands that are so familiar to us. Spiders employ silk in many ways, handling it with awe-inspiring agility. They use it to make an amazing array of web types for prey capture, including the well-known orb webs, the trip lines of trapdoor spiders, and even a single thread with a blob of glue used by the bolas spider to deftly lasso their prey.

Spiders also use silk in a variety of other ways. They swaddle their prey, wallpaper their nests with it, use it to hold their sperm (males), and make egg sacs out of it (females), to name just a few uses.

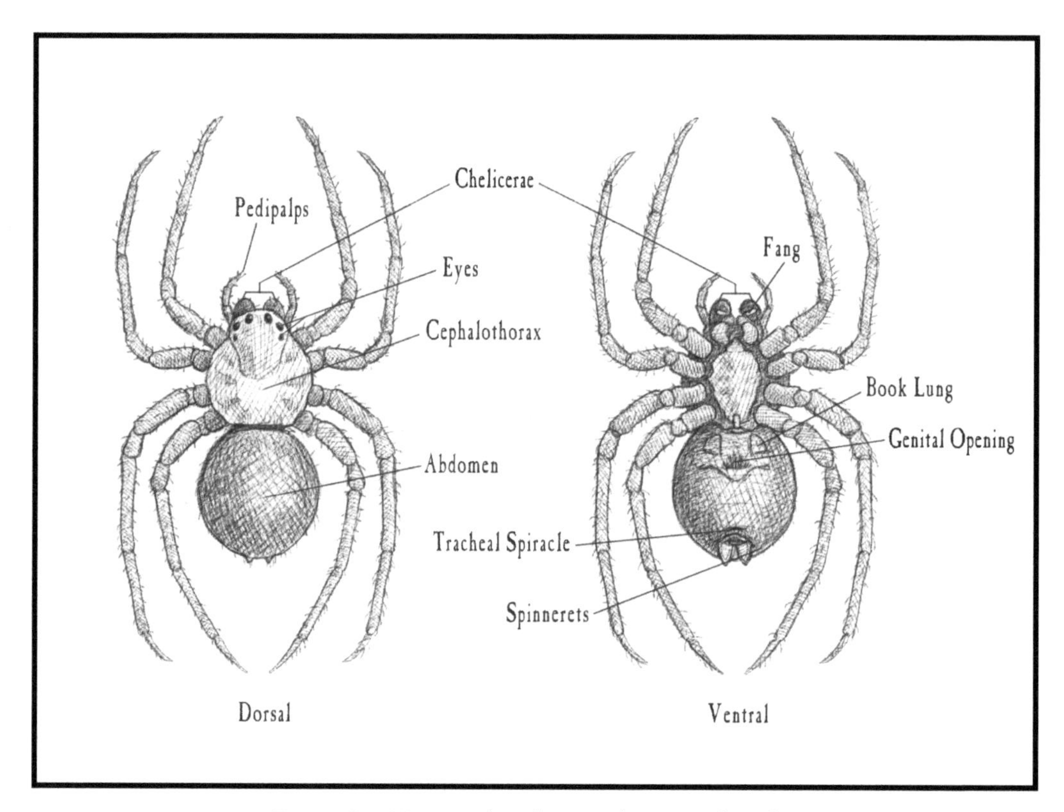

Figure 25.38 Dorsal and ventral views of spider

CHAPTER 25: REVIEW QUESTIONS

1. List four major characteristics of the arthropods.

2. Arthropod means ______.

3. In the molting process, the new cuticle is produced ______ the old cuticle.

   a. underneath

   b. on the outside of

4. An extinct group of arthropods having a head, thorax, and pygidium is the ______.

5. Slow, graceful arthropods that feed on lichens, detritus, and some plants and have two pairs of legs per segment (on most segments) are the ______ and belong to class ______.

6. Fast, creepy predatory arthropods having one pair of legs per segment are the ______ and belong to class ______.

7. The answers to both 5 and 6 have two major body regions; the head and the ______.

8. List five general characteristics of a large group of arthropods called the crustaceans.

9. Sessile or stalked crustaceans called ______ are covered in calcareous plates and use their wispy legs (cirri) to filter feed on plankton.

10. A group of crustaceans, many of which are popular among seafood lovers, that have ten walking legs, is the ______.

11. Be able to label the crayfish with these body parts: carapace, cephalothorax, feeding appendages, walking legs (specify the chelipeds), abdomen, telson, uropods, swimmerets, antennules, antennae, and compound eyes.

12. A group of crustaceans that is dorso-ventrally flattened and has seven pairs of legs is called the ______. List two extremely different habitats in which these crustaceans can be found.

13. A group of crustaceans that is laterally flattened and also has seven pairs of legs is called the ______.

14. The largest group of arthropods (by far) possessing head, thorax, abdomen, ______ legs, ______ wings (if present), and ______ pair of antennae is the insects.

15. Draw and label a generalized insect with these body parts: head, thorax, and abdomen; prothoracic, mesothoracic, and metathoracic legs; fore wings and hind wings; antennae, compound eyes, and mouthparts.

16. The forewings of beetles, comprising the biggest order of insects (order ______) are hardened wing covers called ______.

17. Order ______ are also known as the flies, only have ______ wings. In place of hind wings are gyroscopic organs called ______ needed for balance during flight.

18. Order Hemiptera are also known as the true ______.

19. Butterflies and moths (order ______) have microscopic scales covering their ______ and ______ mouthparts.

20. Beetles, flies, and butterflies, and wasps have ______ metamorphosis because their larval body form is drastically different from their adult body form. The ______ stage is when most of the transformation occurs.

21. True or False. Horseshoe crabs are crustaceans.

22. Arthropods called arachnids have two body regions: the cephalothorax and ______.

23. In arachnids, the cephalothorax has ______ (mouthparts), short sensory leg-like appendages called ______ and four pairs of ______.

24. Which of the following is not an arachnid?
    a. Ticks
    b. Lice
    c. Mites
    d. Daddy longlegs (harvestmen)
    e. Scorpions
    f. Spiders

25. Order Araneae, the spiders, have ______ which produce silk.

26. Spiders may use silk for:
    a. Prey capture.
    b. Prey wrapping.
    c. Making egg sacs.
    d. Lining their nests.
    e. Containing sperm.
    f. All the above.

27. Which of the following are not arthropods?
    a. Insects
    b. Arachnids
    c. Crustaceans
    d. Polychaetes
    e. Centipedes
    f. Millipedes
    g. Horseshoe crabs

CHAPTER 26

PHYLUM ECHINODERMATA

THE ECHINODERMS

Echino means "spiny" and *derm* means "skin," because these are the spiny-skinned animals.

Figure 26.1 Variety of Echinodermata

The unique body plan of this phylum pretty much defies everything we tend to think is conventional for animals. Compared to what we've discussed so far, the arrangement of their organ systems is downright otherworldly. Even when they have stuff that other animals have, like a GI tract, it is arranged bizarrely and does bizarre things.

The major features of echinoderms are the following:

- Numerous spines projecting through the skin (except when they don't). Spines are an extension of an internal chain mail-like network of interlocking ossicles embedded in the skin.
- Radial or biradial symmetry.
- A water vascular system. This is an internal hydraulic system that controls the movement of tube feet.
- Marine habitat. (There are no freshwater species.)

THE BASIC BODY PLAN

The sea star's body has two basic regions: the **central disc** and the **arms**. On the underside of the arms and running to the center of the central disc's underside are the **ambulacral grooves** from which tube feet emerge. Where all the ambulacral grooves meet in the middle, you'll find the mouth.

The Water Vascular System

The **sieve plate** (**madreporite**) is on the upper surface of the central disc and serves as a filtering gateway for sea water to enter the internal **water vascular system.** The sieve plate is connected to the ring canal by way of a short **stone canal. Radial canals** project radially from the **ring canal** along the bottom of each arm or ray, and numerous **lateral canals** branch perpendicularly off these radial canals and terminate in a lower **tube foot** and an upper **ampulla.**

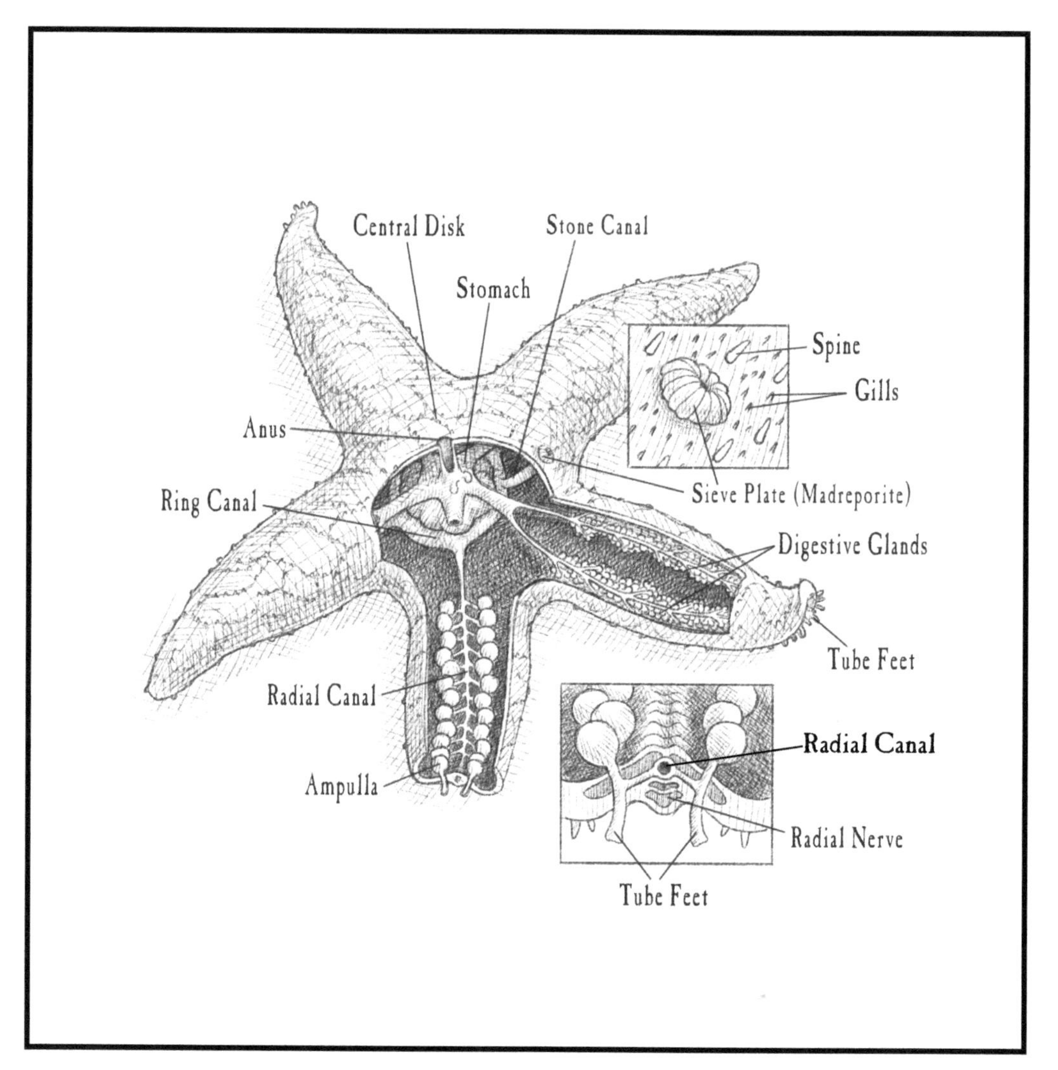

Figure 26.2 Anatomy of echinoderm

When the starfish contracts the ampulla, the water flows into and extends the tube foot. Longitudinal muscles in the wall of the tube foot enable the foot to retract completely or bend in any direction when "walking." More little muscles in the end of the tube foot can also contract, pulling up on the middle of the tube foot's "sole" and creating suction so the tube foot can tightly adhere to a firm surface. (Note: some echinoderms in loose sediment lack this sucker.) The movement of these little tube feet is not synchronous, so when you look at the starfish from the side, it actually looks like a crowd of tiny people walking together across a street.

On top of providing locomotion, tube feet are thin-walled enough to function as a gill for gas exchange.

Feeding

Predatory sea stars use their tube feet to grip the shells of bivalve prey and pry the shells apart. Once the prey is open just a crack, sea stars can extrude their own stomach out of their mouth and in between the shells to grab lunch. Digesting prey using a stomach that's turned inside out and is outside one's own body not only seems straight out of a monster movie, but it also calls for lots of chemical digestion since the prey isn't chewed ahead of time. So how does the sea star manage this?.

In each arm of the sea star is a pair of greenish digestive glands that produce large quantities of enzymes. The enzymes flow to the central upper stomach (called the **pyloric stomach**) and on down to the extruded **cardiac stomach**. The enzymes then digest the prey alive even before it's actually consumed by the sea star. Once the prey has been digested, ingested, and absorbed, digestive waste moves upward from the pyloric stomach through a short intestine and out the anus. The anus exits the sea star on the top and near the center.

Echinoderm odds and ends

Most echinoderms also have thin-walled, fingerlike projections called **papulae** scattered all over their upper surface. Along with the tube feet, these numerous, almost microscopic papulae serve as gills for gas exchange.

Scattered among the papulae or surrounding the spines are the **pedicellariae**, outlandish "housekeeping" structures that are peculiar to echinoderms. These microscopic "tweezers" or "scissors" remove debris, larvae, and tiny animals that may otherwise settle on the echinoderm's upper surface.

CLASS ASTEROIDEA: THE SEA STARS

This group of echinoderms is probably the most familiar to people. There are roughly 1,800 described species of sea stars. Although sea stars are predators and devour their prey in the aforementioned manner, some of them are scavengers feeding on dead animals and algae, others are detritovores consuming organic particles that have settled on the bottom of the ocean, and still others are suspension feeders picking off organic particles and plankton suspended in the water. Sea stars also have the marvelous ability (some are better than others) of regenerating missing arms.

Figure 26.3 Sea star

CLASS OPHIUROIDEA: THE BRITTLE STARS

Ophiuroidea means "snake-like," and they are so named because they move mostly by the writhing motion of their arms (which, as you can see from Figure 26.4, are clearly distinct from the central disc) with very little help from the tube feet.

The bony ossicles are covered by plates that appear to be more like a suit of armor. Although the ambulacral grooves are closed, small holes between these plates on the undersides of the arms allow the brittle star's suckerless tube feet to waggle about on the outside. Brittle stars have five jaw-like plates surrounding the mouth, and emerging from the arms and central disc are spines (the size of which depends on the species).

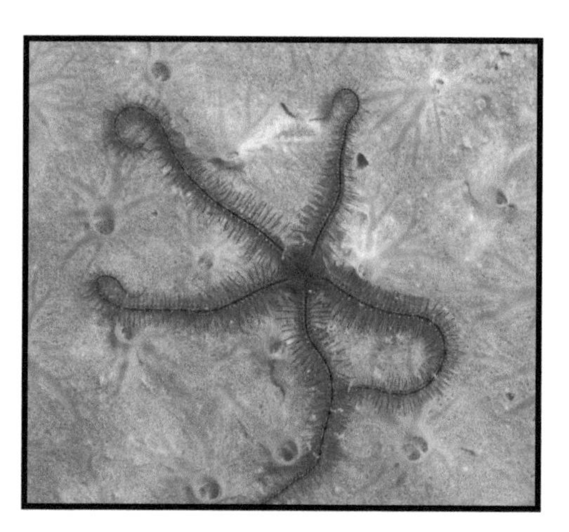

Figure 26.4 Sponge brittle star

Although brittle stars are mostly suspension or deposit feeders, some are scavengers and predators. The suspension feeders (so called because the food is suspended in the water) have strands of mucous like clothes lines stretched between spines of adjacent arms. The mucous collects plankton and detritus. Using cilia or tube feet, the brittle star hauls in the catch and transports it to the mouth on the underside. The deposit feeders (so called because the food is deposited in the bottom sediment) simply browse organic material off the sea floor sediment using their tube feet to collect and pack it into food balls and pass it on to the mouth. Predatory brittle stars generally consume mollusks, polychaetes, and small crustaceans.

As the name implies, these stars act brittle. They jettison their appendages at the slightest nibble, and the detached arm continues to wriggle on its own to distract the predator away from the previous owner. No big loss; the missing arm soon regenerates.

CLASS ECHINOIDEA: THE SEA URCHINS, SAND DOLLARS, AND HEART URCHINS

Most of these echinoderms look like a cross between a deflated ball and a porcupine. In the case of sand dollars, they look like extremely deflated balls and never mind the porcupine (the spines are tiny).

Their body wall is rigid. All the bony ossicles are fused to form a bony spheroid test. The spheroid is perforated in the ambulacral areas so the tube feet (which are quite long) can protrude and do their thing. Their spines, which are also relatively long, are mounted on movable turrets so they can move about and help with locomotion, although the tube feet do most of the work.

Figure 26.5 Sea urchin

On the underside of the sea urchin are five plate-like jaws surrounding the mouth. The feeding apparatus, which includes the jaws, is called **Aristotle's lantern.** Most sea urchins use this feeding machine to consume algae (herbivores), though other small critters wind up as food in the grazing process.

Irregular urchins, sand dollars, and heart urchins have very small spines used both to burrow and to keep their upper surface clear of debris. Most of these creatures are deposit feeders. Sand dollars, for example, use their dexterous tube feet to pick up small food particles in the sediment (including diatoms and bits of algae) and pass the goodies from tube foot to tube foot all the way to the mouth located in the middle of the underside.

CLASS HOLOTHUROIDEA: THE SEA CUCUMBERS

The sea cucumbers deviate from the echinoderm plan in one important way: their skin is leathery, not spiny. If they happen to look spiny, the "spines" are soft and fleshy, not like the bony extensions of the ossicles. Nevertheless, like good echinoderms, they do have a water vascular system with tube feet.

As their common name suggests, these creatures are elongated like cucumbers. In many sea cucumbers, five ambulacral areas run lengthwise like the seams of a football which help them crawl around on one side, walking on three rows while the other two rows are on the top side (see below).

Figure 26.6 Sea cucumber

On the front end, sea cucumbers have **tentacles** which are extensions of the water vascular system and are like branching versions of tube feet that serve to collect food.

Sea cucumbers are suspension or deposit feeders. If they're suspension feeders, they gracefully wave their tentacles about in the sea water, catching organic debris and plankton in the tentacles' mucous coating. After a tentacle has collected enough, it is brought into the mouth where the food is pulled off and swallowed. I have seen a one-year-old boy feed in a very similar fashion. He stuck his hand in his mouth, covered his fist in drool, then smacked the Cheerios on his highchair tray without bothering to pinch them between finger and thumb. He then stuck his hand back in his mouth and removed the Cheerios with the squeegee action of his lips.

As for deposit feeding sea cucumbers, they sweep their tentacles around and basically shovel sediment into their mouths (mud, sand, and all). Any food in the mix is digested and absorbed while the mud and sand pass through and are excreted as castings, rather like in the castings of earth and lugworms.

Sea Cucumber Odds and Ends

Sea cucumbers have a few novel features not shared by other echinoderms. The **respiratory tree** is a system of internal branching tubules for gas exchange. A pair of respiratory trees branch off of the rectum, and oxygenated water enters through the anus, into the rectum, and up the respiratory trees. The oxygen then diffuses from the lumen of the tubules into the fluid-filled body cavity.

Some species of sea cucumbers have a clever anti-predator device: the **Cuvierian tubules.** When disturbed, the animal ejects spaghetti-like Cuvierian tubules out its anus, aiming the sticky mess at its assailant.

While the attacker is thus preoccupied with extricating itself from these bothersome noodles, the sea cucumber seizes the opportunity and makes a getaway at a glacial pace.

What about the sea cucumbers not endowed with Cuvierian tubules? They just practice **self-evisceration.** This anti-predator tactic involves blowing a portion of its internal organs out its anus or mouth—a shocking unpleasantness to the attacker. Losing organs in this masochistic manner may seem life-threatening, but the sea cucumber simply grows them back.

CHAPTER 26: REVIEW QUESTIONS

1. Echinoderm means ______.

2. Name the hydraulic system that all echinoderms share.

3. Which is not part of this hydraulic system?
   a. sieve plate
   b. stone canal
   c. ring canal
   d. pedicellariae
   e. radial canal
   f. lateral canal
   g. ampullae
   h. tube feet

4. Echinoderm walking appendages are called ________ and are extensions of the above system.

5. Give the common name(s) of these echinoderm classes.
   a. Asteroidea: ______

b. Echinoidea: ______
c. Ophiuroidea: ______
d. Holothuroidea: ______

6. Which class is known to have the longest spines?

7. Which of the classes above (#5) is mostly herbivorous on kelp and other seaweeds and uses a jaw-like apparatus called Aristotle's lantern to graze the bottom?

8. Which of the above classes is usually lacking spines and can eviscerate when disturbed?

9. A predatory sea star can extrude its ______ outside its body and insert it into its bivalve prey.

10. Sea cucumbers collect food on their branching ______. Once enough is collected, it is inserted into its mouth and the food is swallowed.

CHAPTER 27

PHYLUM CHORDATA

THE CHORDATES

There are three subphyla within Phylum Chordata: Cephalochordata, Urochordata, and Vertebrata. We'll briefly discuss the first two groups of marine creatures, but since the vast majority of chordates are vertebrates, we'll move on to spend most of our time on them.

The general characteristics of Chordata are:

- A **dorsal nerve cord**
- A **notochord** (a stiffening protein rod which develops into the vertebral column in vertebrates)
- **Pharyngeal slits**

Remember, evolutionists try to get a lot of mileage out of these or, indeed, any similar features of large taxa like kingdom, phylum, class, or order. They see the similarities as undeniable proof of *common ancestry*. Creationists, however, see them as indicative of *common design*. On top of that, it should be noted that further research has unveiled some fundamental *differences* (both genetically and developmentally) in these supposed "homologous" traits.

Figure 27.1 Sea squirts

The Urochordates are affectionately called **tunicates** or **sea squirts**. There are roughly 3,000 species. Though these little blobs of jelly don't seem worthy to be in the same phylum as backboned animals, they are chordates nevertheless because their larvae exhibit all the aforementioned chordate traits. After they finish their larval stage (the free-swimming tadpole-like stage), the adults settle

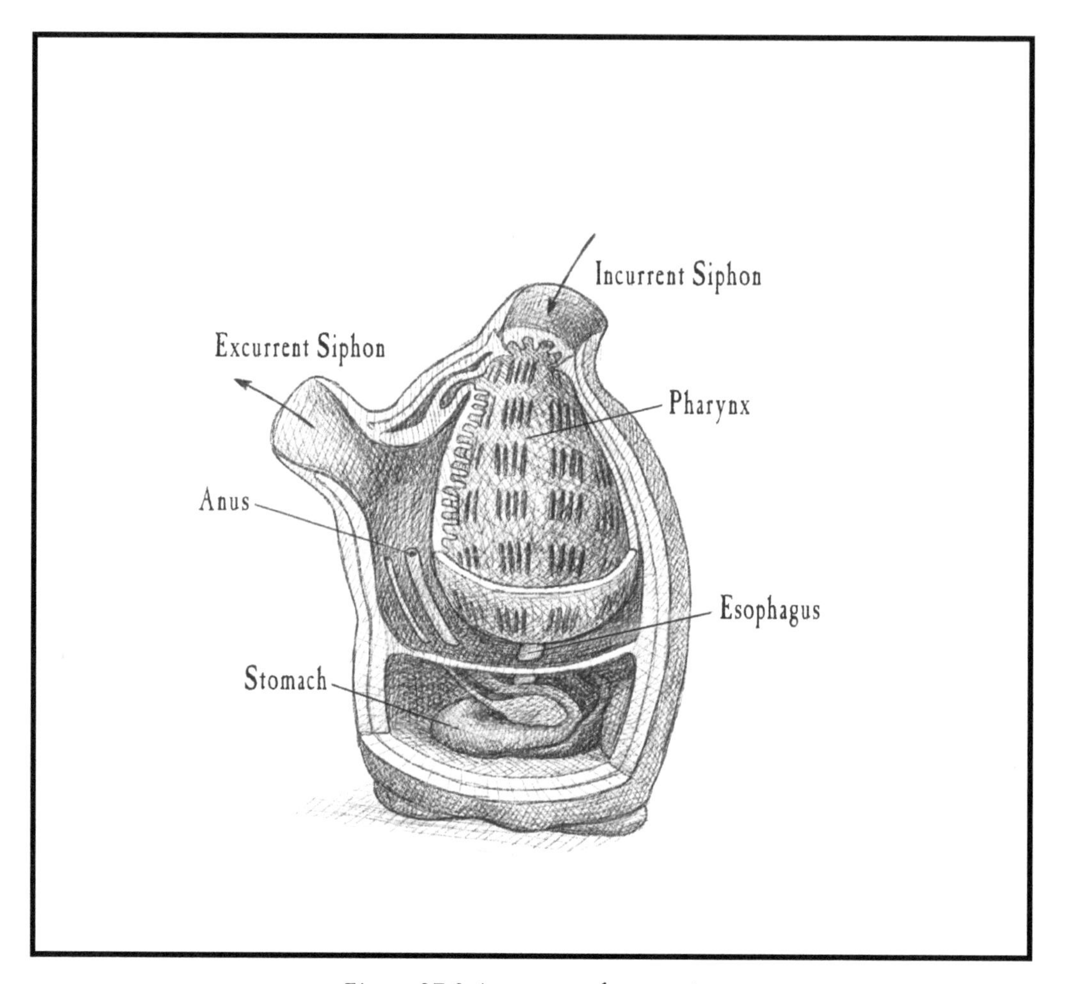

Figure 27.2 Anatomy of sea squirt

down and take up a sessile existence on the ocean bottom, living much like a sponge. They are filter feeders, like sponges, but the apparatus with which they filter water is quite different.

Their pharynx is relatively large compared to the body. Marked with little slits, the pharynx essentially acts like a colander in that it catches food while letting water pass through. The incurrent siphon brings water into the pharynx, flows through the slits, and exits by way of the excurrent siphon. In the process, plankton is caught on a mucous net produced by the pharynx, and cilia on the pharynx pull the mucous sheet (along with its catch) into a mucous strand which is hauled down into the esophagus and then stomach. After food is digested and absorbed, waste exits the anus and is carried out through the excurrent siphon.

Lancelets are good representatives of cephalochordates. These small, fish-like creatures manifest the hallmark chordate characteristics even as adults. Their notochord serves as a stiffening rod, but since it never develops into a backbone, they are not considered vertebrates. Usually around two inches long when fully grown, lancelets partially bury themselves in the sand in tropical and temperate ocean shallows, leaving their front end sticking out.

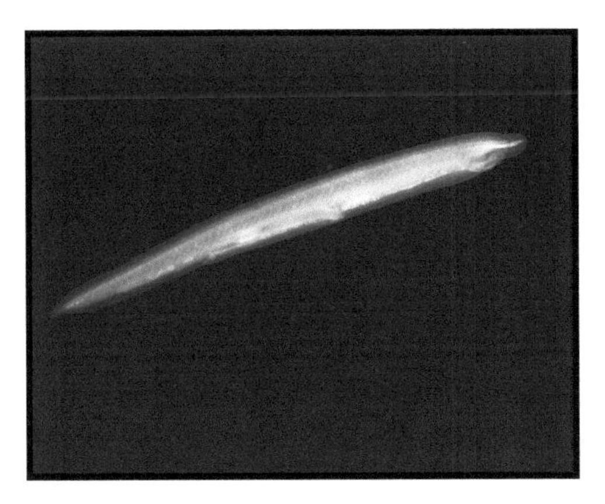

Figure 27.3 Lancelet

There are only a little over 20 species of cephalochordates worldwide. They have **oral cirri** that, besides serving as sensory structures, also filter water for food. The food particles are passed to the pharynx (which is slitted and colander-like, similar to a urochordate's). The pharynx produces a mucous film that catches the food, and then ciliary action pulls the food into the digestive tract. The water passes out of the pharyngeal slits, into an atrium, and then exits the body via the **atriopore** just in front of the anus. Unlike any vertebrate, the cephalochordate can phagocytose food particles using cells that line their **caecum** (a blind pouch off their digestive tract).

Although the pharyngeal slits are often called gill slits, they serve no respiratory function. (Naming is often done with an evolutionary agenda. To give different things the same name implies homology—in this case, implying that the pharyngeal slits in lancelets became gills in fish. These are big, unsubstantiated assumptions). So how do lancelets breath? Oxygen simply diffuses from the water through the skin.

The **vertebrates**, as you probably know, are all the backboned beasts. They include the following:

- Jawless fishes: the hagfish and lampreys
- Cartilaginous fishes: sharks, skates, and rays
- Bony fish: the rest of the fishes not listed above
- Amphibians
- Reptiles
- Birds
- Mammals

The next three groups of vertebrates are collectively called fish. The general field of study that focuses on fish, whether they are jawless, cartilaginous, or bony fish, is called *ichthyology*, from the Greek word *ichthus* meaning fish.

AGNATHA: THE JAWLESS FISHES

Figure 27.4 Hagfish mouthparts

In the past, Agnatha (the name means "no jaw") was considered a class and included hagfish and lampreys, which were grouped together because they had one big thing in common: no jaw. Further study, however, revealed many big differences which warranted the splitting of these two disgusting fish into separate classes. While I acknowledge these differences, for my purposes here I will lump them back together as "jawless fish," since their differences are beyond the scope of this text.

Hagfish are jawless, elongated, eel-like fish, usually a foot and a half long. Ironically, although they are considered a vertebrate because they possess a cartilaginous skull, hagfish don't have a vertebral column of any sort. Instead, they retain their notochord into adulthood. Their mouth has six to eight barbels and teeth-like structures made of keratin on their tongue (see above). They are in the habit of scavenging flesh off of dead or dying fish as well as common invertebrates like crustaceans, mollusks, and annelids. Pinching onto their prey with paired toothed plates on the sides of their mouth, they thrust their rasping tongue forward to tear bits of flesh off their meal—which may still be alive. Hagfish can also tie their body in a loose knot, slide it forward, and brace the knot against the body of their lunch to gain more leverage in pulling off stubborn pieces of flesh.

Hagfish are also loaded with many slime glands along the sides of their body. When harassed, they secrete vast quantities of slime, making themselves nearly impossible to handle.

About a third of the way down their body, hagfish have one pair of external gill openings. Oxygenated water enters the mouth, passes over the gills, and then exits the body through these same openings.

Lampreys, though eel-like and jawless and thus similar in overall appearance to the hagfish, are quite different in the details of anatomy and natural history. They are notorious for their ectoparasitic habits on the skin of freshwater game fish. ("Ectoparasitic" means they are parasites on the outside of the host.) Lampreys have large eyes, one nostril, a cartilaginous skeleton, seven pairs of gill slits, and unpaired fins lying medially on the dorsal and ventral surface.

There are about 40 species worldwide and they range in size from about five inches to a meter long. While some are ectoparasitic as I've already described, a good number of species are non-parasitic and feed only during larval development.

Some species are freshwater and some are marine species. Those that are marine dwellers are **anadromous**, meaning they migrate to freshwater to spawn. To do this, the male hollows out an oval nest on the stream bottom. Once the female is situated in the nest and has deposited her eggs, he latches onto her back and sheds his sperm on the eggs.

Figure 27.5 Lamprey

The fertilized eggs stick to and are covered by sediment until they hatch. Upon hatching, the larvae anchor their bodies in the bottom sediment and filter feed by turning their mouths upstream. Once they metamorphose, they head out to sea as full-grown adults.

As for the parasitic species, they latch onto the bodies of fish with their round, suction cup mouth. The inner surface of a lamprey's mouth is ringed about with keratinized teeth which help the lamprey hang onto its victim.

The horny (keratinized) tongue thrusts forward and rasps away flesh until blood and tissue fluids can be mercilessly sucked out. Anticoagulants penetrate the wound to help prevent clotting and keep the body juices flowing freely. When they have had their fill, they let go, leaving a gnarly hole in the side of the fish which may continue to bleed. Although not always a fatal wound, fish can indeed die from it, particularly if two or more lampreys attack a single fish.

CLASS CHONDRICHTHYES: THE CARTILAGINOUS FISHES

This group of fishes includes the sharks, skates, rays, sawfish, and chimaeras. As their name suggests, they all share a cartilage skeleton. (*Khondros* means "cartilage" and *ikhthus*, of course, means "fish.") As they mature,

Figure 27.6 Lemon shark

the notochord is replaced by a cartilage vertebral column.

Now we're starting to see the features that are unequivocally fishy. Chondrichthyes do have jaws (situated on the ventral side), and unfortunately, as too many a hapless swimmer or surfer has discovered, their jaws are not cartilage; they are hard bone with rows and rows of hard sharp teeth.

The **sharks**, though spanning a considerable range of sizes, have a fairly uniform body plan. A shark's body is covered with small, tooth-like **placoid scales** which give its skin a sandpapery texture. They usually have two medial **dorsal fins**, one median heterocercal **caudal fin** (meaning, the top lobe is longer than the ventral lobe), one medial **anal fin**, one pair of **pelvic fins**, and one pair of **pectoral fins.** Male sharks have **claspers** that extend from the back edge of the pelvic fins. These are copulatory organs that accomplish internal fertilization (unlike most bony fish). Just in front of the pectoral fin bases are five to seven pairs of **gill slits.** The eyes are positioned laterally above the mouth. Just behind the eyes is one pair of **spiracles.** Nostrils are on the sides of the rostrum (nose) near the front.

It is comforting to know that only a handful of the 400+ species of sharks actually have a record of unprovoked attacks on man. These are the undisputed man-eaters: tiger shark, bull shark, oceanic whitetip shark, and, of

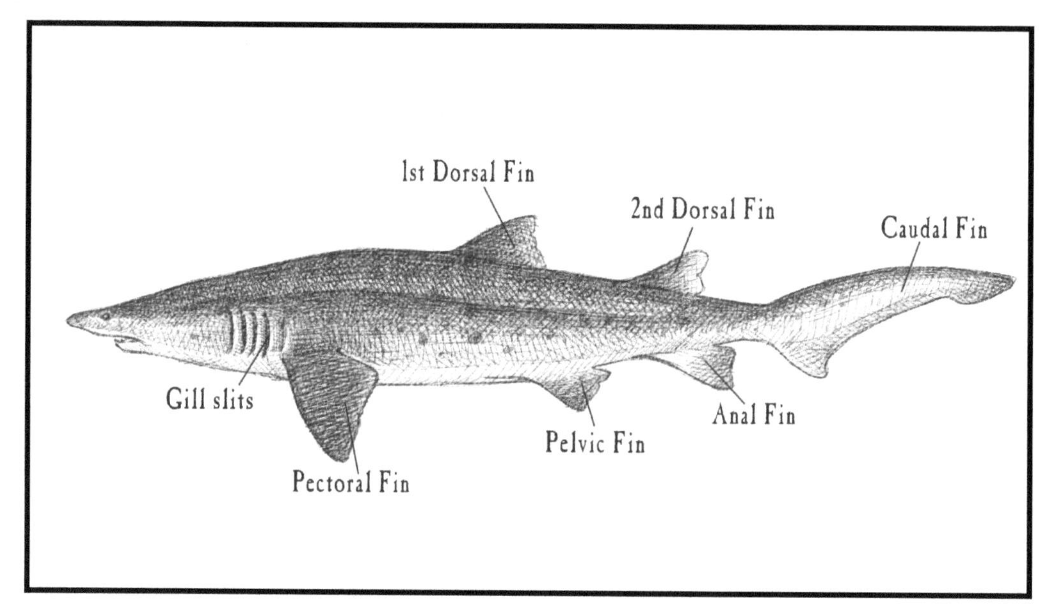

Figure 27.7 Anatomy of shark

course, the great white. Happily, the biggest two sharks (basking shark and whale shark) are harmless, simply filtering plankton out of huge volumes of water with their mouths agape.

Skates and Rays

Skates and rays are also cartilaginous fish and share a number of basic characteristics with the sharks. The differences are that they have a highly dorsoventrally flattened body and greatly enlarged pectoral fins. Gill slits are on the ventral side whereas the spiracles are on the top. The fins behind the pectoral fins are reduced to a greater or lesser degree, depending on the species. Their teeth are small or platelike, designed for crushing prey rather than cutting and slicing as in sharks. Accordingly, their prey consists of small fish, mollusks, crustaceans, and other invertebrate munchables.

Figure 27.8 Skate

Figure 27.9 Ray

Skates and rays have a lot of overall similarities, but I'd like to point out a few noticeable differences between the two:

RAY	SKATE
Viviparous	Oviparous (rectangular egg case)
Thin tail with hollow stinging spines	Fleshier tails with small fins
Larger sized	Smaller sized
Flap pectoral fins like wings	Undulate margins of pectoral fins

Sawfish

These cartilage fish can grow to be quite large and can kind of look like a cross between a shark and a ray. Their unique feature is a long, flattened **rostrum** that is studded with spines on both sides. With it, they can dig in the soft bottom sediment to dislodge buried critters. With a quick swing of the head, they can also knock senseless or even mortally wound their prey, which they then can munch down at their leisure.

Figure 27.10 Juvenile sawfish

Chimaeras

This strange group of cartilage fish looks vaguely like deformed sharks with large heads and long tapering tails. They have a flap called an **operculum** covering the gills (this feature is more akin to the bony fishes). They generally live at considerable depths, though some traffic in relatively shallow water, and they crush their crustacean, fish, mollusk, and echinoderm prey with flat, plate-like teeth. As is typical of Chondrichtyes, their scales are placoid.

CLASS OSTEICHTHYES: THE BONY FISHES

If it's a fish but it's not any of the few we've talked about so far, then it's a **bony fish.** This group includes a vast array of body sizes and shapes, habitats, and life histories. The fish themselves range from typical to very bizarre indeed: trout, eels, sea horses, sturgeon, swordfish, anglerfish, and

Figure 27.11 Variety of Osteichthyes

lungfish, to give you an idea of their disparity. Some bony fish seem more suited to swim around in our nightmares than in our oceans.

We see their obvious differences, but what do most of them have in common?

Bony fish, for starters, have a skeleton made of mostly bone (some have cartilage here and there). They also have an operculum, which is a stiff flap covering the gills unlike the Chondrichthyes which have separate gill slits on the surface with no operculum covering them. The mouth is usually situ-

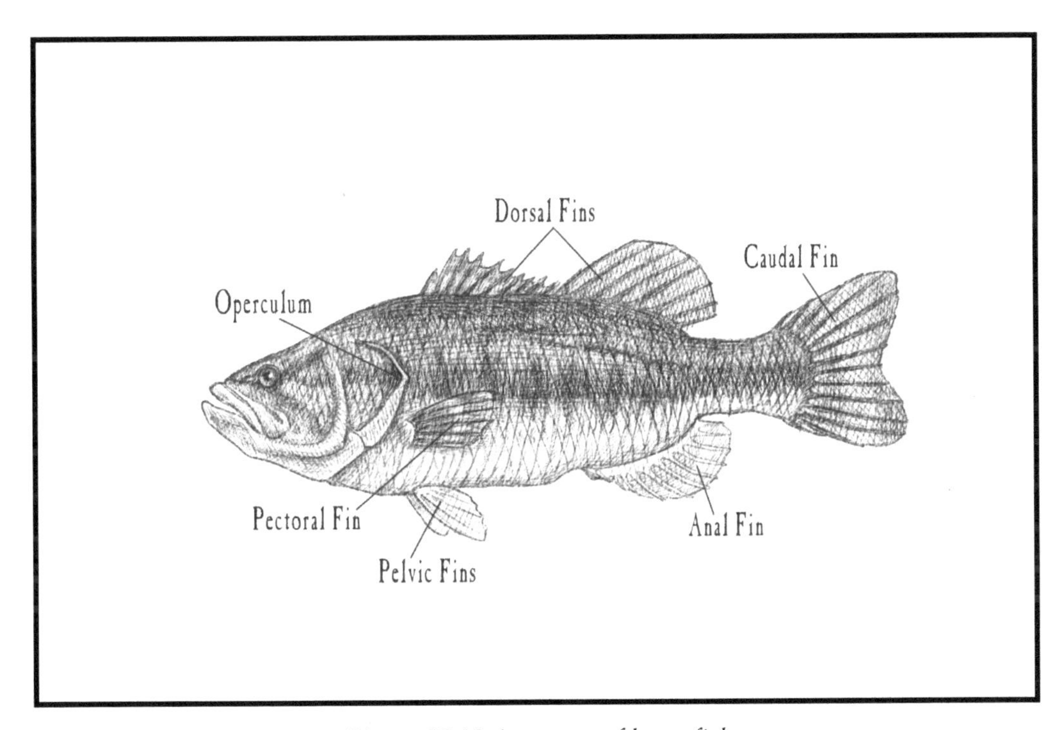

Figure 27.12 Anatomy of bony fish

ated up front rather than on the underside. As for the fins, most bony fish have roughly the same complement of fins as itemized on the representative cartilage fish, the shark: dorsal, caudal, pectoral, pelvic, and anal fins.

That sounds simple enough, but labeling the fins on certain kinds of bizarre fish can be tricky because these fins have unusual sizes or shapes; may be in mounted in odd places or may be missing altogether.

Feeding

While many fish filter plankton out of the water with **gill-rakers** as the water passes over the gills, countless fish are straight-forward predators. They simply catch (via high-speed chase or ambush) and then eat their prey whole or in bits and pieces torn from the body of invertebrates or other fish.

Some parrot fish have hard beaks that can bite off pieces of coral, and they consume the coral rock along with the living polyps. The polyps are digested, but the rock-like coral skeleton is smashed to bits as it passes through the gut and is excreted as fine white sand. Butterfly fish, with their puckered mouths, pluck out the individual polyps, evicting the tenants while leaving the rocky apartment complex in place. Other fish scrape algae off of the rocks.

Reproduction

When fish get down to the business of reproduction, it's called **spawning**. Some fish exhibit **ovoviviparity** (meaning, the eggs hatch inside mother after the embryos are nourished by yolk) or **viviparity** (embryos are nourished directly from the mother's tissues). Both of the above modes ultimately result in giving birth to live young. Most fish, however, lay their eggs (**oviparity**) in some kind of habitat or microhabitat (open water, a depression on the bottom, crevice or burrow, in or on the male's body, etc.). After the eggs are laid, the male sheds sperm on them to fertilize them. The eggs incubate for a certain period and then hatch. That covers the general habits of bony fish, but the details are extremely diverse and depend on the species.

Respiration

Underneath the flap-like operculum are several gill arches with blood vessels running through them. (Refer to the figure opposite if you get lost.) Each arch is fringed with many **gill filaments**. Within each of these filaments there is a tiny blood vessel flowing into it, carrying deoxygenated blood, and a tiny blood vessel (oxygenated) flowing out of it. Many parallel networks of capillaries connect these two blood vessels, which are covered by an exceedingly thin epidermis. As the fish swims, oxygenated water passes in through the mouth, over the gill filaments, and then exits the fish from under the operculum.

The oxygen is less concentrated in the blood inside these capillaries than in the water. Consequently, oxygen diffuses from the water and loads onto the red blood cells as the cells pass through the capillary beds in the gill filaments. It is worth noting that the blood flow is opposite the water flow. This maintains a steeper concentration gradient, making diffusion (for both oxygen and CO_2) quick and efficient. At the same time, CO_2 follows its concentration gradient: it diffuses from the capillaries (high CO_2) and into the sea water (low CO_2). The oxygenated blood leaves the blood vessel in each gill filament and heads back to the heart, where it is pumped to the rest of

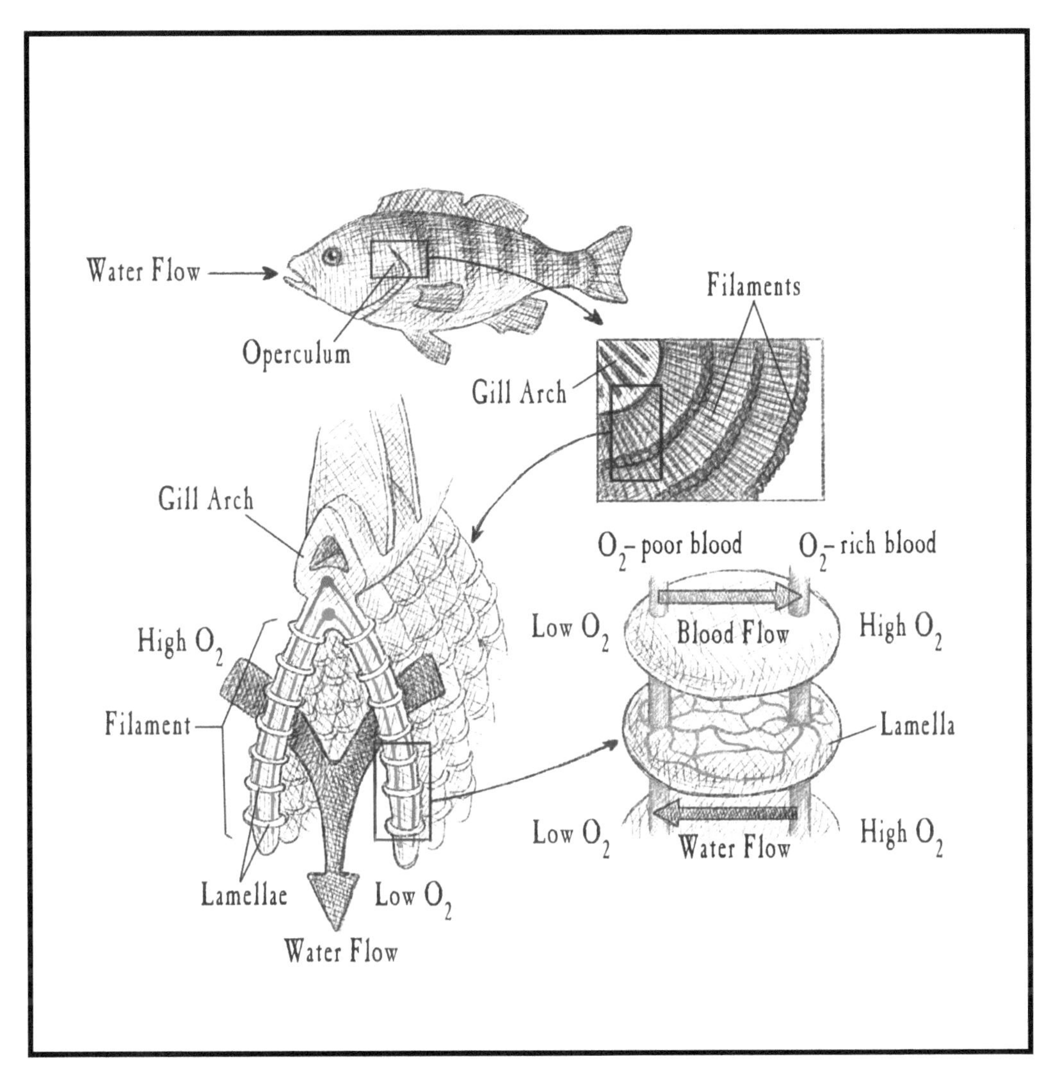

Figure 27.13 Diagram of fish gill respiration

the body. At the body tissues, oxygen is unloaded from the blood and CO_2 is loaded onto the blood (by diffusion again). The blood then circulates back to the gills where it can excrete the CO_2 and receive a fresh load of oxygen.

CLASS AMPHIBIA: THE AMPHIBIANS

The remaining four classes of vertebrates usually have four limbs and are therefore termed *tetrapods* (though there are notable exceptions like snakes, a few lizards, and a group of amphibians called caecilians).

The first class is Amphibia. These include the caecilians, salamanders, and frogs. Features that they all have in common are:

- A thin, moist, glandular skin

- Jelly-coated eggs
- No claws or scales
- Usually two pairs of appendages (four legs)
- Three-chambered heart
- **Ectothermic** (meaning they attain body heat from environment)

Amphibian Respiration

Amphibians' relatively thin, moist skin is perfect for gas exchange. Oxygen can diffuse through the thin epidermis and into the capillary beds that supply the dermis. On the flip side, carbon dioxide (a waste product of cells) diffuses the opposite way from the capillaries, through the epidermis, and out into the water or atmosphere. Because amphibians can breathe through their skin, their lungs are not well-developed; they are more or less simple sacs used for gas exchange. Some amphibians don't even have lungs because their skin is able to absorb enough oxygen.

Larval amphibians have yet another gas exchange surface: they sprout finger-like or feathery gills from their necks that provide a good deal of surface area for gas exchange.

CAECILIANS: ORDER GYMNOPHIONA

There are about 170 species scattered about the moist, tropical regions of the world, but most people don't even know these worm-like amphibians exist, even in places where they are quite common. This is because they live out their secretive lives underground or underwater.

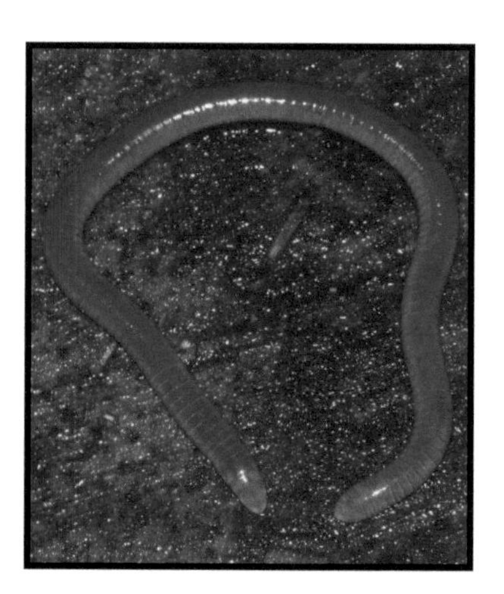

Figure 27.14 Caecilian

At a superficial glance, they look like earthworms (at least the small species do) because they are legless and slimy and their transverse **annular grooves** give them a segmented appearance. They also have blunt tails. But unlike earthworms, they aren't stretchy. They are actually vertebrates with solid skulls, jawed mouths, and relatively long, bony vertebral columns.

Since most lead a fossorial lifestyle, their eyes are small and skin-covered and are poor at image resolution. To aid in sensing their dark, subterranean environment, they sport a pair of small tentacles between and beneath their eyes and nostrils. A few aquatic species have fins on their dorsal and ventral surfaces.

SALAMANDERS AND NEWTS: ORDER CAUDATA

These are the amphibians with well-developed tails (*Cauda* means "tail"). This is a more familiar group of amphibians because they aren't limited to tropical, exotic, out-of-the-way places, but can be frequently found in ordinary, accessible spots. There are over 500 species and they live in both tropical and temperate climates.

Figure 27.15 Variety of Caudata

Superficially, these amphibians are lizard-like because they have four legs and a tail. However, they can be easily distinguished from lizards because they have moist (often slimy) skin, they don't have scales covering their body (although some have warty skin), and they don't have claws on their toes. Also, unlike most lizards, these secretive creatures spend most of their time in moist retreats underground or under leaves, rocks, logs, and other debris. This is important because, like all amphibians, they don't have a waterproof, scaly skin. Consequently, their body moisture quickly evaporates into the air. If left unprotected in a dry environment, they die of dehydration before very long. (I discovered this myself when I was a kid. My pet newt climbed out of its water container and I found salamander jerky the next day in the hallway.)

All salamanders are predators. They usually eat a variety of small invertebrates, although some big salamanders can munch on small vertebrates. Habitats range from deserts to rainforests. Some salamanders are completely aquatic, while others migrate to the water for breeding but spend the rest of their time on land. Most species, however, are completely terrestrial and live and breed on land. Regardless of the habitat (desert dwellers and all the rest), all salamanders must keep their bodies moist.

When most salamanders breed, whether it's in or out of the water, the male uses chemical pheromones and a variety of courtship antics to induce the female to follow him. He extrudes a **spermatophore** (a tiny proteinaceous stalk capped with a packet of sperm) from his cloaca (the common chamber of the reproductive, urinary, and digestive tracts) and places it on the substrate, whether under water or on land. He leads her directly over it, where she halts so that her cloaca is directly over the spermatophore. She then takes the spermatophore into her body with the lips of her cloaca, and the sperm packet is stored in a side pouch off the roof of her cloaca.

After being inseminated, the female lays her eggs. As eggs pass through her cloaca, sperm is released in tiny quantities to fertilize them before they exit the cloaca. (This is called **internal fertilization.**) The eggs then pass out of her body and are laid in various patterns, depending on the species. Some are laid singly, some in various sized clusters. Most salamanders lay eggs in moist habitats on land, though a fair number lay eggs in the water.

Figure 27.16 Salamander gills

Those that lay their eggs on land have offspring that hatch out as juveniles looking like miniature versions of adults; in other words, there is no free-living larval stage. The aquatic eggs, in contrast, hatch as salamander larvae. These are gilled and legless. As I mentioned earlier, here the gills look like feathery tufts sprouting from both sides of the neck.

As the larvae grow, their front legs develop first, followed by the hind legs. During metamorphosis, the gills disappear and the salamander becomes a juvenile which may take to land or remain aquatic, depending on the species.

It would be good to note that salamanders which have aquatic adults are often called newts. However, a number of species called newts have terrestrial adults that only return to the water to breed. Also, some salamanders breed in the water and are not called newts. Consequently, there is no consistent taxonomic or ecological significance to the word "newt."

There are a few exceptions to this spermatophore mode of breeding. In one of these exceptions, a particular family of giant salamanders spawns like certain fish. The eggs are deposited in an underwater nest chamber and the male sheds his sperm on them. (This is called **external fertilization.**) He then guards the clutch from predators and other threats.

FROGS AND TOADS: ORDER ANURA

Last, but not least, is the biggest and best known group of amphibians: the frogs and toads. These amphibians are easily recognized due to their enlarged, jumping hind legs and no tail. (In fact, Anura means "no tail.") Anurans are highly diverse, having almost 5,500 species and coming in a huge range of shapes, sizes, and colors. One species attains a puny adult size of only one centimeter while the Goliath frog can grow to a foot long (and that doesn't include its extended hind legs).

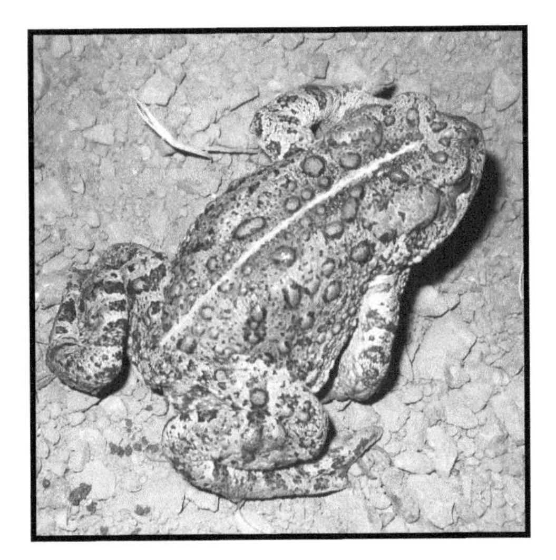

Figure 27.17 Western toad

Frogs dwell in a wide array of habitats—anything from deserts to tropical rain forests. They may be completely aquatic or completely terrestrial. Among the latter, some lead a burrowing lifestyle while others are totally at home in the trees.

Figure 27.18 Tropical tree frog

Reproduction

It's extremely difficult to summarize frog reproduction because they vary so much in where, how, or whether they lay eggs. Their breeding habits may be very typical or jaw-droppingly bizarre. Typical breeding (for North American frogs at least) consists of male frogs calling from their breeding pond (each species has their own distinct call) to woo in the females of their species. When a female approaches, the male climbs on her back and holds on in a position called **amplexus**.

Figure 27.19 Frog amplexus

Eventually, she is stimulated to lay her jelly-coated eggs. As they emerge from her body, they are fertilized by the male when he sheds a bit of sperm on them (external fertilization). The eggs are usually deposited in clusters or strings near the surface of the water. The frog embryos undergo some development until they hatch as tadpoles. Tadpoles swim around freely and graze mostly on algae with a rasping, sucker-like mouth while they continue to develop.

Development

Tadpole gills are small, finger-like growths sprouting from the neck region. Shortly after hatching, these gills are covered by a growing fold of skin called an operculum. During metamorphosis, which occurs gradually, both

Figure 27.20 Frog development

forelegs and hind legs begin to develop early, but the forelegs are hidden along with the gills under the operculum.

Since the forelegs are hidden, the hind legs appear first, followed eventually by the enlarging front legs as they break through the operculum. The last major step of development is the resorbing of the tail. At this point, jaws also develop and major changes occur in the digestive track since the tadpole has to transition from an herbivore (tadpole) to a carnivore (frog).

I would be remiss to not mention several bizarre reproductive modes in frogs. Female Darwin frogs in South America lay eggs on the forest floor. When the babies hatch as tadpoles, the male gobbles them up and stores his kids in his vocal sac, where they continue to develop. Once they are fully developed froglets, they hop out of dad's mouth.

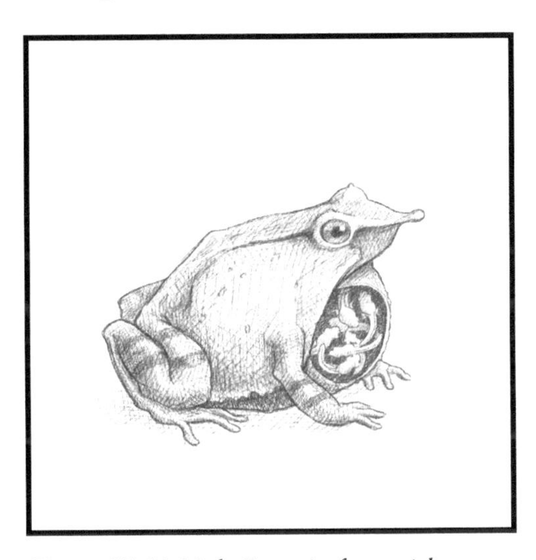

Figure 27.21 Male Darwin frog with young

The poison dart frogs (there are over 20 species, all having different but wildly psychedelic color patterns) also lay eggs on the forest floor. When each tadpole hatches, it wriggles up onto mom or dad's back and holds on with its mouth. They get a piggyback ride up into the canopy of the rain forest and are then dropped into a small pool of water within a bromeliad plant growing on the branch of a large jungle tree. There they are cared for by the parents, who feed the tadpoles with unfertilized eggs.

Figure 27.22 African bullfrog eating mouse

The male marsupial frog watches over eggs that were laid on the ground. When they hatch, the tadpoles squirm up into pouches of skin in his hip region. There they develop, eventually emerging from the pouches as froglets.

Feeding

As I mentioned, adult frogs are predators (one species eats fruit). Because frogs are relatively small, their menu consists largely of invertebrates (mostly insects). Some of the bigger species can hunt down and eat small vertebrates (including mice, lizards, snakes, and fledgling birds).

CLASS REPTILIA: THE REPTILES

Reptiles are usually grouped with amphibians in a common field of study called **herpetology** (*herpeton* is Greek for "creeping creatures"). Although herpetology could include many other creatures, the modern scientific discipline has limited it to just reptiles and amphibians.

Reptiles are an amazingly diverse group having over 8,200 species. Reptiles include turtles (~300), lizards (~3,800), snakes (~2,900), tuataras (2), and crocodilians (~23). Although it is quite easy to tell these groups apart, the characteristics that unite them are still pretty obvious.

Figure 27.23 Green iguana

- Scaly skin – Reptiles have skin wholly or partly covered in epidermal scales (no hair, fur, feathers, or moist glandular skin).
- Four limbs – The exceptions to this would be snakes and some lizards.
- Ectothermic (cold-blooded) – Reptiles obtain their body heat from the environment.
- Internal fertilization – Their eggs are always fertilized inside the female.
- Three-chambered heart (two atria; one ventricle) – The exception would be crocodilians, which have a four-chambered heart.
- Shelled eggs – Snakes and a few lizards are the exceptions as they are live-bearing.

Reptile Respiration

Because most reptiles have relatively thick, scaly skin, the amount of gas exchange through their skin is greatly reduced. Terrestrial reptiles breathe almost entirely through their lungs. Consequently, reptile lungs are considerably more developed with more alveoli to increase gas exchange surface area. Surprisingly, many aquatic reptiles can also do a fair amount of gas exchange through their skin, mouth lining, and cloaca.

TURTLES: ORDER TESTUDINES

This group is very distinctive and easily distinguished from all other reptiles. It includes turtles, terrapins, and tortoises. They all have an upper shell called a **carapace** and a lower shell called a **plastron**. The carapace is composed of fused, bony, dermal plates called **osteoderms**, which are, in turn, fused to both the vertebrae and rib cage. The plastron is a set of ventral osteoderms fused to the sternum. Together, the carapace and plastron form a very protective suit of armor.

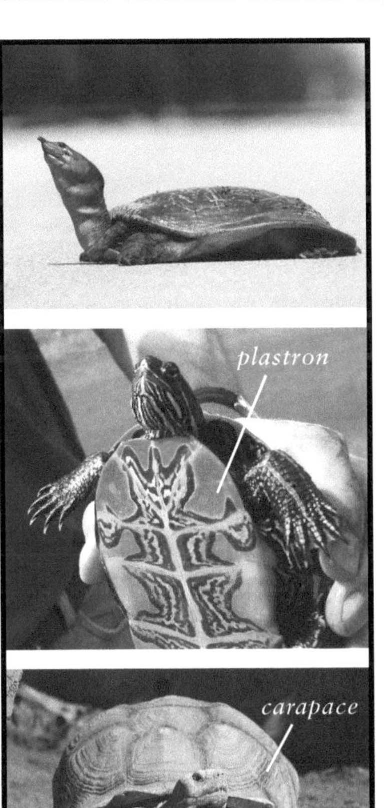

Figure 27.24 Variety of Testudines

Turtles, unlike all other four-limbed vertebrates, have hip and shoulder bones within their rib cage, which allows the limbs to be mostly or even completely withdrawn into the shell as a defense against predators.

The epidermis (which is largely composed of highly keratinized scales called scutes) overlays the bony carapace and plastron. Some turtles, however, have soft leathery skin covering reduced osteoderms.

Turtles have an impressive array of sizes. They range from the diminutive speckled cape tortoise at just over three inches long (fully grown) to the leatherback turtle reaching up to eight feet long and weighing over 1,400 lbs.

Habitat and Feeding

Turtles have a wide range of habitats as well. Some are extremely adapted for desert living. Others tramp about on prairies and in woodlands. Still others are semiaquatic, dividing their time between water and land. The most aquatic of all are the sea turtles, and only the females come ashore to lay eggs.

Turtles can be herbivores, omnivores, or carnivores. The tortoises are quintessential herbivores. They browse on plants of various kinds, depending on the kind of tortoise and the plants available. Good examples of omnivorous turtles are the box turtles. They eat a wide assortment of fruits, fungi, and small invertebrates (and an occasional vertebrate).

Alligator snapping turtles are sit-and-wait ambush predators that use their pink, wiggling tongue to lure small fish into their gaping jaws.

Reproduction

Unlike lizards and snakes, male turtles have a single penis. All female turtles are oviparous and lay shelled eggs. Exactly where they lay them depends on the species, but even the most aquatic sea turtles have to lay them on land. Most turtles dig a hole with their legs, deposit their eggs, and cover them over. The eggs incubate for a certain period (often 2 or 3 months) until they hatch, at which time they are totally on their own. No parental care for these hatchlings.

These reptiles also exhibit **temperature-dependent sex determination.** In other words, the temperature of the nest determines the sex of the

Figure 27.25 Sea turtle

Figure 27.26 Alligator snapping turtle

Figure 27.27 Eastern box turtle laying eggs

hatchlings. Higher temperatures generate females and lower temperatures generate males. The threshold between male- and female-producing temperatures depends on the species.

SNAKES AND LIZARDS: ORDER SQUAMATA

Lizards: Suborder Lacertilia

This group is usually easily recognizable: if a creature is scaly, not a fish, turtle, snake, or crocodilian, then it belongs to this group. This is an exceedingly diverse group in shape, size, habitat, feeding, and reproduction. The creatures range in size from a tiny gecko on a few islands in the Caribbean that can curl up on a dime, to the Komodo dragon reaching 11 feet.

Figure 27.28 Komodo dragon

Within this group are lizards that dwell in the deserts, swamps, trees, and on the sea shore. Some herbivores, such as the marine iguana, graze algae in the shallow waters around the Galapagos Islands. Some are omnivores while still others are carnivores, like the monitors.

Some notable lizards have spectacular equipment designed by their Maker. The chameleons, for example, have an extremely protrusible tongue with which they snap up their prey. Another example: most geckos have amazing toes covered with millions of microscopic hairs called setae covering thin flaps of skin (lamellae) that form strong molecular attractions with most surfaces. These setae enable the lizards to scamper upside down across ceilings like it was a stroll in the park. These strong bonds are easily broken; the lizard simply peels its toes away from the surfaces. And for a final example, the

Figure 27.29 Chameleon tongue

Draco lizard has expandable ribs shrink-wrapped in skin. When they flare their ribs, the lizard can jump off of a tree and glide up to 30 feet.

Reproduction

Male lizards have paired reproductive organs called **hemipenes**. During mating, only one is used to inseminate the female.

Most lizards are oviparous (egg-layers), but a few are ovoviviparous (live-bearers; embryos nourished by yolk) or viviparous (live-bearers; embryos nourished directly from maternal tissues). Those that lay eggs either lay them in a chamber dug by the mother, or barely cover them in leaf litter.

Snakes: Suborder Serpentes

Snakes are very familiar to nearly everyone. These legless reptiles are famous for their forked tongue and lidless eyes.

Snakes come in all sorts of shapes and sizes. Snakes can be either extremely slender and long or quite short and stocky. The smallest is the Barbados threadsnake at 3.9 inches long and the longest is the Reticulated Python at over 32 feet (record length).

Figure 27.30 Rattlesnake

They live in an incredible array of habitats: deserts, swamps, and underground. Some sea snakes are completely aquatic and even give live-birth in the water. Others are excellent burrowers. Others are excellent tree climbers. The flying snake, quite at home in the trees, can glide like the Draco lizard. It launches itself into the air, flares out its ribs, and slithers during its gliding descent.

Feeding

All snakes are predators and consume a vast array of creatures. Generalist snakes aren't picky eaters; they just prey on what's available. Specialists, however, seek out one type of prey, like the crab-eating or snail-eating snakes. They swallow their prey whole, with one exception: the crab-eating snake seizes the crab, tears off its legs, and swallows its legs, leaving the dismembered body uneaten. The tiny thread snake eats tinier insect larvae, while the gigantic pythons can swallow fairly large prey like antelopes (and one tragically swallowed a young teenage boy).

There's even the egg-eating snake that swallows bird eggs whole. Once the egg is in the snake's esophagus, the snake cracks the shell, using bony projections on the ventral side of its vertebrae. The shell is regurgitated after the contents are squeezed out and swallowed.

The familiar forked tongue is used to sample the odor-rich environment. Odor molecules from the air, ground, or water adhere to the flicking tongue, which is then pulled in and wiped on the **Jacobson's Organ** on the roof of the snake's mouth. The Jacobson's Organ "senses" the type of odor and is often used to detect the presence of prey or predators. Some snakes are also equipped with infrared sensors called **pit organs** on their face so they can detect warm-blooded prey in complete darkness.

Snakes can kill their prey in three basic ways: grab-and-swallow, constriction, and envenomation. The first needs no explanation. Constriction involves a deft combination of a swift bite, several wraps of squeezing coils, and the suffocation of the prey until it's dead.

A great number of snakes are venomous. The venom, ranging from mild to lethal, is used both in self-defense and in killing prey. Venomous snakes can either have short, fixed front fangs (which can't fold up) or longer front fangs that are hinged and can fold up against the roof of its mouth. When a snake with hinged fangs bites, the fangs swing forward and stab the prey.

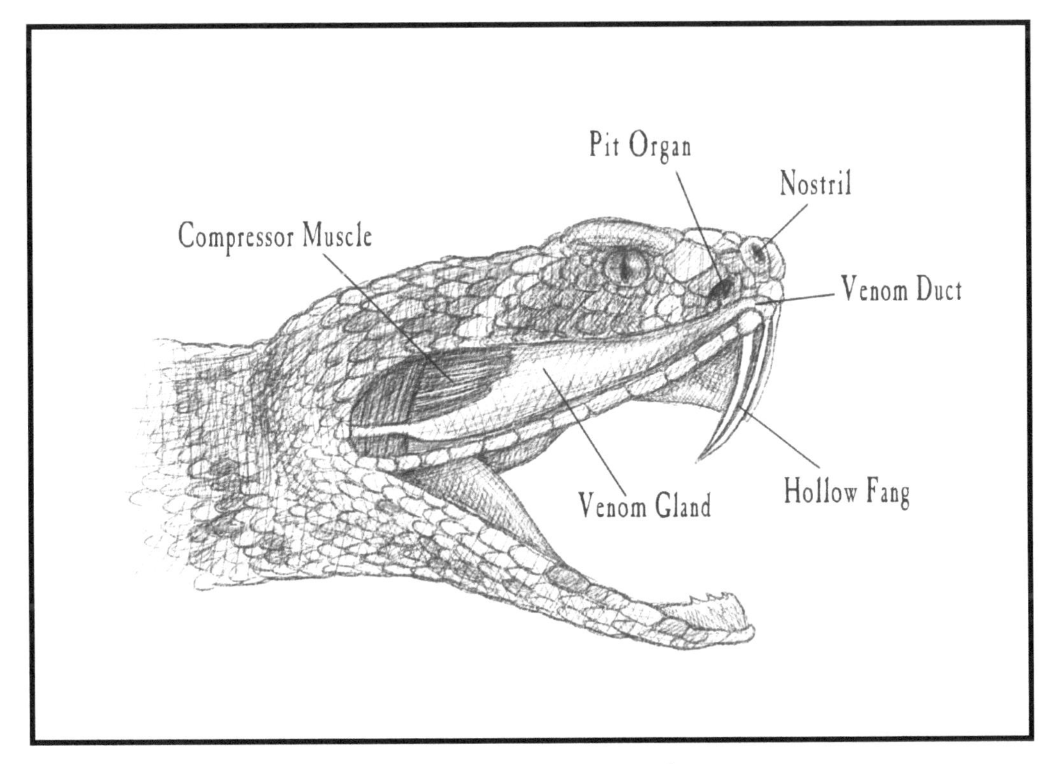

Figure 27.31 Venom apparatus of pit viper

As the fangs pierce the body, the venom is injected through hollow, hypodermic needle-like fangs. The rear-fanged snakes usually have milder venom, but it works perfectly well on their intended prey.

Reproduction

Snakes, like lizards, have paired hemipenes and use them in much the same way. Most snakes are oviparous but there are a good number that are live-bearers (both ovoviviparous and viviparous). Both lizards and snakes can have elaborate courtship rituals that help ensure that the chosen male is worth his salt.

TUATARAS: ORDER SPHENODONTIDA

Figure 27.32 Tuatara

There are only two species of these very lizard-like reptiles. To the lay person, they look like lizards, but since their skeleton and other anatomical details are sufficiently different, experts have classified them in a distinct order. Living on some islands off the coast of New Zealand, they grow to about two-and-a-half feet long and prefer to be active at cooler temperatures than most other terrestrial reptiles. They feed mostly on arthropods, but happily consume seabird eggs or hatchlings and lizards. They are egg-laying reptiles, but unlike lizards and snakes, the males don't have hemipenes. Instead, sperm is transferred into the female when the male presses his cloaca against hers.

CROCODILIANS: ORDER CROCODYLIA

These large reptiles have successfully penetrated popular culture due to their large size, monstrous countenance, and dragon-like scales. In all, there are twenty-three species, and they include the alligators, caimans, crocodiles, and gharials.

Since crocodilians are semiaquatic, they all live where there are permanent bodies of water in a tropical or subtropical climate. Depending on the species, preferences range from freshwater to brackish water to saltwater—or even all three. Certain freshwater species prefer the flowing water of rivers while others prefer the standing water of lakes, ponds, or swamps.

The smallest crocodilian is Cuvier's dwarf caiman at a little over five feet long. The largest is the saltwater crocodile which can grow to over twenty feet long and is a confirmed man-eater. All crocodilians have very protective armor on their back side (some have it on the belly as well). This armor is composed of closely spaced osteoderms overlaid with a tough, keratinized epidermis. These animals have a longish skull, robust body, and a laterally flattened tail that's great for swimming. They are also known for their distinctive serrated dorsal scales that give them a dragonish look.

Figure 27.33
Variety of Crocodylia

Feeding

All living crocodilians are ambush predators that seize their prey in shallow water or at the shoreline. Prey include mollusks, fish, amphibians, reptiles, birds, and mammals. While most crocodilians are not fussy and simply eat whatever's available, a few are true specialists—like the gharials, which feed almost exclusively on fish.

Reproduction

Male crocodilians have a single penis as opposed to the paired hemipenes of lizards and snakes. All crocodilians are oviparous. Their eggs are usually laid in a pile of dirt and decaying vegetation which has been shoved into a mound by the female, who uses her body as a bulldozer. If nesting material is sparse, some resort to digging a nest hole for the eggs.

The females (and sometimes males) often show a great deal of parental care by guarding the nest. This care can even extend to digging up hatchlings, gently cracking the eggs to assist in the hatching process, and ferrying the babies from the nest to the water.

Temperature-dependent sex determination (nest temperature determines sex) appears to be the rule in this order as well. However, it is opposite of the pattern found in turtles. Higher temperatures generate males and lower temperatures generate females. In a few species, an even more complicated pattern occurs. Males are produced at medium temperatures while females are produced at high and low temperatures.

CLASS AVES: THE BIRDS

This very familiar group is comprised of about 10,000 species with (you're getting the hang of this now) *incredible* diversity of form, plumage, size, habitat, behavior, and flying ability. They range from large, heavy, flightless birds (like the ostrich and emus) to tiny, light aeronauts (like the hummingbirds). Or just look at the delightful penguins that are completely alien to the atmosphere, so endearingly clumsy-looking as they waddle about on land, but that rival fish in their swimming skills.

Despite this immense variety, all birds share the following hallmark features:

- Feathers
- Epidermal scales on legs
- Endothermic (warm-blooded) bodies: they generate heat internally through metabolic processes.
- Hollow (pneumatized) bones
- Specialized lungs: there is one-way flow of air over the gas-exchange area.
- Beaks

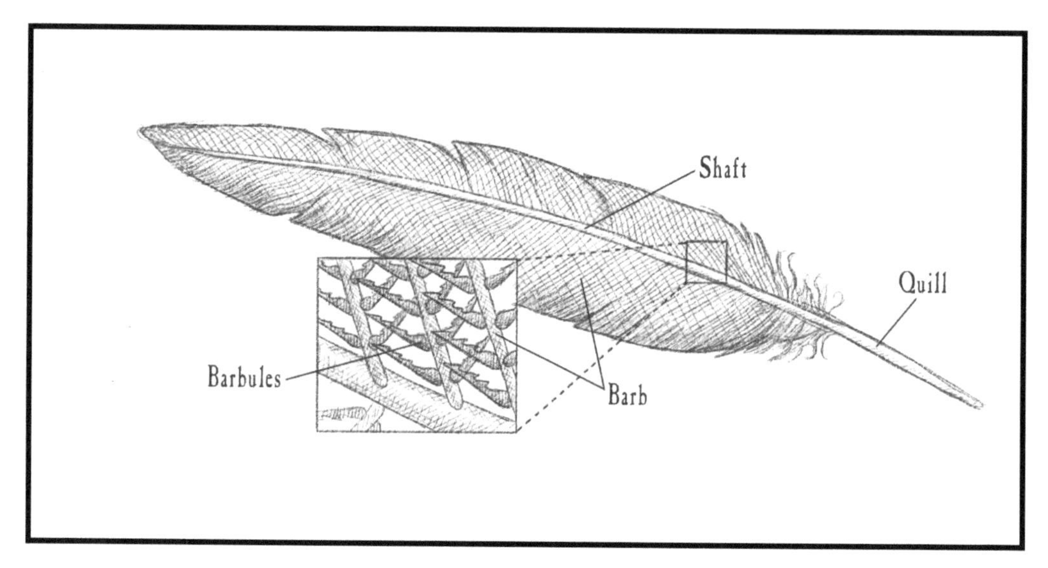

Figure 27.34 Diagram of feather

- Four limbs: their front limbs are wings used for flying, swimming, courtship, balance, etc., while their back limbs are for perching and sometimes for snatching prey.
- Keeled sternum
- Four-chambered heart
- Claws on hind feet
- Oviparous: they have brittle-shelled eggs

The unique feature that sets birds apart from all other living vertebrates is the **feather**. It is exquisite in its micro- and macroscopic structure and (contrary to evolutionist suppositions) cannot be considered homologous to the scales of a reptile.

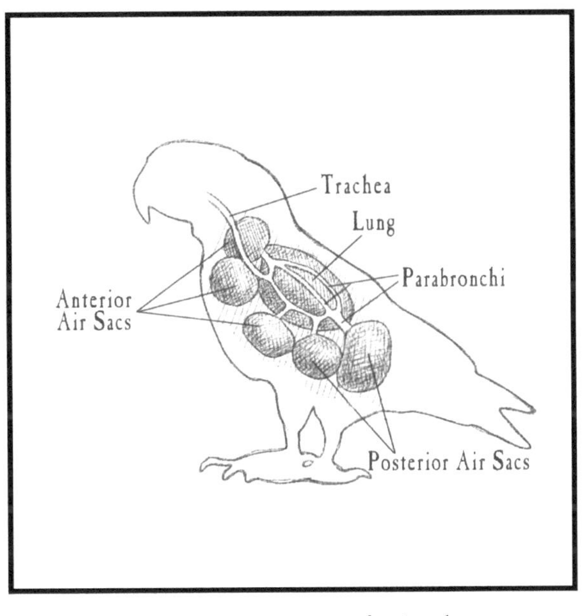

Figure 27.35 Diagram of avian lung

The **quill** is rooted in the skin follicle and protrudes from the skin. The extension of the quill that forms the central axis of the feather is called the **shaft**. Parallel **barbs** project from each side of the shaft and are connected to each other by tiny **barbules** containing microscopic hooks. Hooks on adjacent barbules interlock, thus connecting all the barbs together and forming a vane. The differing sizes, characteristics, and location of these feather parts determine what role the feathers will play on the bird's body. Some are for insulation (down feathers) while others (called contour feathers) are for general covering, outward shape, and color patterns needed for mate attraction, camouflage, etc. Long contour feathers on the wings and tail are called flight feathers.

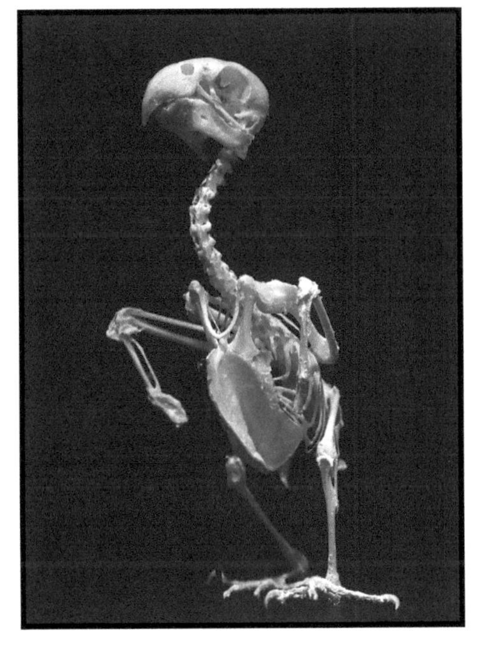

Figure 27.36 Avian skeleton (parrot)

Another unique feature of birds is a set of lungs that provides a continuous air flow over a system of tubes called **parabronchi** which serves as a gas-exchange area instead of dead end sacs called alveoli. This divine design serves the high demand for oxygen needed for flight. When the bird inhales, most of the incoming air bypasses the lung (parabronchi) and flows directly into several posterior air sacs. When it exhales, the posterior air sacs (filled with fresh air) expel their air through the parabronchi where gas exchange occurs, while the anterior air sacs expel their spent air to the outside. During the next inhalation, air moves from the parabronchi into the anterior air sacs while a new batch of fresh air is inhaled into the posterior air sacs. In this way, a constant flow of oxygenated air is flowing over the parabronchi.

Yet another unique avian feature is **pneumatized** (hollow) **bones**. These bones are strong yet lightweight due to the many air spaces contained within. This, of course, is a great design feature because less energy is expended to keep birds airborne.

The unique, keeled sternum is also a great asset to a bird. This enlarged ridge running down the middle of the sternum provides more surface area for the enlarged pectoral muscle attachment used in flight. This also goes for swimming birds like penguins that "fly" through the water.

Figure 27.37 Variety of Aves

Reproduction

Reproduction begins with a male bird successfully attracting a mate. As you can imagine, bird diversity is so great that the various types of courtship boggle the mind. Suffice it to say that there is a lot of song and dance involved: complex songs, elaborate dance routines, flamboyant display of beautiful plumage, gift-giving (food or nesting material), head bobbing, etc. If a male is successful, a female will pair with him and they will soon mate.

Because most male birds lack a copulatory organ like a penis, the birds' cloacas are pressed together and sperm is quickly transferred from the male's cloaca to the female's. The sperm must fertilize the egg inside her oviduct before the shell is laid on (an example of internal fertilization). All birds are oviparous.

Before the eggs are laid, the parents set about constructing a nest. Where, when, and how the nest is built and which building materials are used depends, of course, on the species. Materials include twigs, grass, bird excrement, holes drilled into a tree or sedimentary cliff, bird mucous, leaves, bare ground, or even a small ledge on a cliff. Emperor penguins have to use the tops of their feet since they're breeding in the middle of the Antarctic winter.

In most cases, both parents continue working as a team in incubating the eggs and feeding the chicks once they hatch.

There are approximately 10,000 species of birds, grouped into almost 30 orders. It is way beyond the scope of this text to adequately describe each order separately, so I will list in a table almost half the orders of birds and some familiar examples of each.

ORDER	EXAMPLES
Sphenisciformes	penguins
Struthioniformes	ostriches and emus
Passeriformes	typical birds (sparrows, wrens, robins, crows, warblers, etc.)
Falconiformes	hawks, falcons, eagles, vultures, etc.
Strigiformes	owls
Galliformes	chickens, turkeys, pheasants, grouse, etc.
Anseriformes	ducks, geese, swans, etc.
Piciformes	woodpeckers
Pelecaniformes	pelicans
Psittaciformes	parrots and parakeets

ORDER	EXAMPLES
Apodiformes	swifts and hummingbirds
Charadriiformes	gulls and plovers
Columbiformes	doves and pigeons

Feeding

Along with the great variety of bird shapes, sizes, and habitats comes a wide range of feeding habits. Different birds (along with every other animal group) are designed to exploit different types of food. This allows the bird diversity that we see. If all the species needed the same food, the world would soon be in short supply and the weaker competitors would die off. Refer to Figure 27.38: A bird's "dinnerware" (type of beak) is a major key in determining the type of food it can obtain.

A generalized bill, like the crow's, is handy for an omnivorous diet. The hooked beaks of the birds of prey are designed for tearing flesh.

The woodpecker's jackhammer-like beak, complete with a shock-absorbing cushion at its base, is great for drilling holes into wood to penetrate the galleries of wood-dwelling insects. They can extend their long, stiff yet flexible, barbed, sticky tongue deep into woody galleries beneath the bark to harpoon the insects dwelling there.

Flamingo bills lined with lamellae are designed to filter brine shrimp and blue-green algae from muddy water. The mud is ejected and the food ingested.

Hummingbird beaks and tongues are designed to lap nectar from flowers. Many finches have beaks that serve as miniature seed-crackers.

Many water birds like herons and egrets use their long beak as a fishing spear.

Emperor Penguins may not have fancy beaks, but they can dive to extraordinary depths (1,755 feet is the record) in search of fish, krill, and squid, and can hold their breath for up to 18 minutes. It isn't surprising that these flightless birds have solid bones which prevent damage from the extreme pressure at those depths.

The body, feet, claws, legs, wings, head, and plumage also wonderfully equip each particular kind of bird to be well suited for its particular habitat. If a bird species migrates (and many do), it must also have the instinct to successfully navigate to the correct destination (sometimes thousands of miles away) and back again, and must be equipped to survive in a variety of different habitats that it encounters during its round trip.

Figure 27.38 Variety of bird beaks

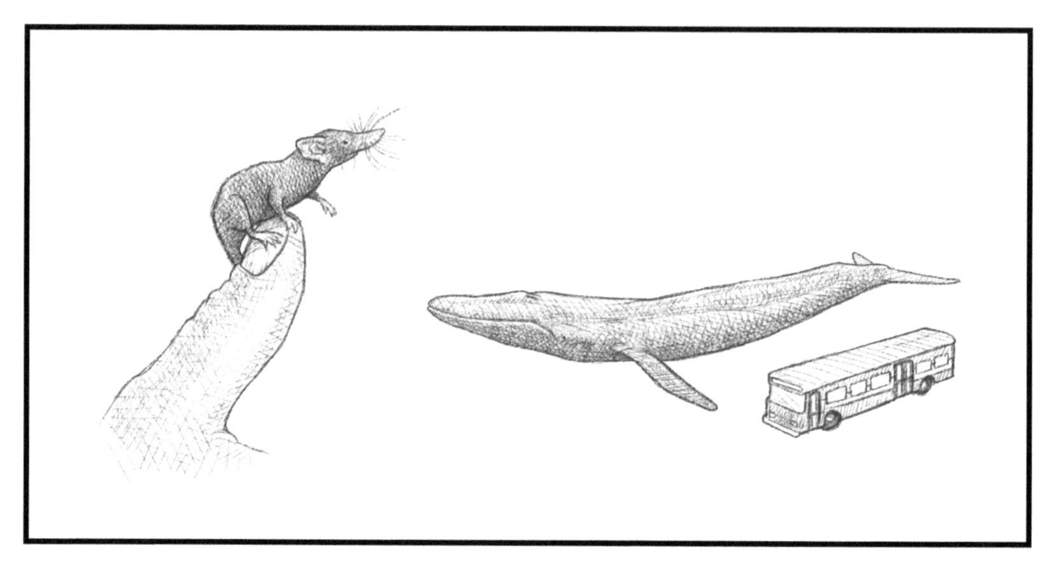

Figure 27.39 Etruscan shrew versus blue whale

CLASS MAMMALIA: THE MAMMALS

Unless you own a bird or a reptile for a pet, this group of vertebrates is probably the most familiar of all. The current tally is about 5,500 thousand species divided among over 20 orders. The smallest mammal is the Etruscan shrew weighing in at 1.3 grams and a length of 4 cm (without the tail). This is a far cry from the mighty blue whale with a mass of up to 190 metric tons and a length of 109 feet.

Notwithstanding the huge disparity in shapes, sizes, feeding habits, habitats, behavior, metabolism, anatomy, and physiology, all mammals share the following features:

- Fur or hair
- Mammary glands (milk-producing glands to nurse their young)
- Sweat glands
- **Sebaceous glands** (oil glands)
- Claws, nails, or hooves on all feet (absent in whales)
- **Heterodont teeth** (different teeth with specialized functions)
- **Endothermic** (warm-blooded): they generate heat internally through metabolic processes.
- Normal bellow-like lungs (many more alveoli for more surface area compared with reptiles).
- Four limbs (used for walking, swimming, digging, grasping, or—in the case of bats—flying; hind limbs absent in whales).
- Internal fertilization
- Four-chambered heart

- Viviparous (live-bearing) – two exceptions: the duck-billed platypus and the echidna, which lay eggs.

Although mammals have these features, not all the above traits are unique to mammals. For example, birds are also endothermic. Reptiles and birds also have claws. Amphibians, reptiles, and birds usually have four limbs.

But a few features are unique to mammals. Just as feathers are to birds, so **fur** or **hair** is the *sine qua non* of mammals; they are not shared with any other class of vertebrates.

Evolutionists would have us believe that certain reptiles had random mutations that led to an epidermis that stopped making scales and started making weird skinny fibers sticking out of their bodies which eventually evolved into hair . . . by accident. This is no accident. If you study the details of hair structure and development, you will see just how complex and intelligently designed it is. Genetic programs orchestrate how, when, and where the cells in the epidermis divide and also dictate how much keratin fills the hair cells. The end result is a cylinder of densely packed, highly keratinized cells growing out of a pore in the skin. This hair or fur can be sculpted into many different hair or fur types depending on the kind of mammal, its function, and where it is on the body. They can be dense and fine, forming a fur coat to insulate and protect a mammal from the cold, or sparse and coarse like the hair on a domestic pig. Hair can be very specialized for a certain job, the way vibrissae (whiskers) on the snout of many mammals are highly sensitive to touch. Hair is sometimes programmed to fuse together, forming a hard, sharp, and nicely sculpted horn. Or hair can be thick, sharp, and barbed like a porcupine quill. The list could go on. The point is hair and fur could only have been designed—never evolved by chance.

Another structure unique to mammals are the **mammary glands**: specialized epidermal glands that form on the chest and abdominal region of all mammals. It may seem strange, but all mammals—even some of the most unusual ones like the egg-laying, duck-billed platypus and aquatic whales—suckle their young. Female mammary glands are designed to produce milk at the time when she gives birth. The newborns instinctively find the mammary glands, latch on, and begin to suckle. This allows the young to have home-cooked meals without the mother having to constantly forage or hunt to bring home food for her young.

Like I did with birds, I will simply list over half the orders of mammals and provide familiar examples of each to give you a good idea of the variety.

ORDER	EXAMPLES
Monotremata	egg-laying mammals
Marsupialia	pouched mammals; e.g., kangaroos, koalas, opossums, etc.
Rodentia	mice, rats, beavers, squirrels, gophers, agoutis, gerbils, etc.
Lagomorpha	rabbits, hares, and pikas
Cetacea	whales, dolphins, and porpoises
Carnivora	cats, dogs, bears, weasels, raccoons, wolverines, etc.
Chiroptera	bats
Soricomorpha	moles and shrews
Artiodactyla	even-toed ungulates; e.g. deer, sheep, goats, cattle, antelope, giraffes, pigs, hippos, etc.
Perissodactyla	odd-toed ungulates; e.g., horses, rhinos, and tapirs
Pilosa	anteaters and sloths
Proboscidea	elephants
Sirenia	manatees and dugongs
Primata	lemurs, bushbabies, monkeys, and apes

Most of you have an idea of what many of the examples above look like, but I'll go ahead and mention a few structural, physiological, and behavioral features in some of these mammals to highlight their radical differences, as well as to show how they differ from other classes of vertebrates.

The duck-billed platypus and the spiny anteater (Order Monotremata) are not just atypical; they are bizarre. They are mammals that lay eggs. Though the female doesn't really have distinct nipples, her breast produces milk which the hatchlings consume.

The sloths (Order Pilosa) are extremely slow-moving leaf eaters with a very low metabolic rate compared to other mammals.

On the other extreme, the Etruscan shrew (Order Soricomorpha) has a completely carnivorous diet. Its heart rate is about 1500 beats per minute and consumes up to twice its body weight per day.

Figure 27.40 Three-toed sloth

The cheetah (Order Carnivora) can reach speeds of up to 75 mph for short distances, whereas the sloth tops out at about six feet per minute.

Bats (Order Chiroptera) have forelimbs with arm and finger bones functioning as wing supports. Thin skin forms a membrane between fingers, arms, body, and hind legs, and serves as airfoils. One large group of bats has a tiny voice-box which produces rapidly pulsating high-frequency sound waves, that, coupled with the bat's very discriminating ears, serve as an echo-location device. These bats pick up the echoes and thus detect the location, size, direction, and speed of prey (flying insects) while at the same time avoiding many obstacles (trees, etc.) in almost total darkness.

Baleen whales (Order Cetacea) can engulf huge amounts of food (often krill) along with hundreds of gallons of sea water. To avoid swallowing the seawater with their food, they forcefully expel most of the water through their baleen (a filter-feeder inside their mouth which acts like a strainer or colander). The food is trapped behind the baleen and then swallowed. The whale's blowhole is on the top of its head so it can inhale more easily when it surfaces. And since its respiratory system is more separated from their digestive system than that of humans, it doesn't send food down its windpipe as we sometimes do.

Elephants (Order Proboscidea) are so familiar to us that we sometimes forget what extraordinary creatures they are. The most conspicuous feature is their trunk. No other mammal has such a wonderful multipurpose organ. It serves as a nose to smell, a hose and nozzle to shower, a hand to grab, an arm to reach or lift objects, and a horn to bugle. The trunk is loaded with a highly complex array of muscles that enable it to do these and many other things.

Rodents (Order Rodentia) are the largest order and come in a host of sizes and shapes, but one distinguishing feature they all share are their large chiseling incisors that make them expert gnawing machines. These come in handy for all sorts of work whether it is felling a tree, nibbling nuts, or crafting a home.

Figure 27.41 Rodent skull

Marsupials (kangaroos, koalas, opossums, etc.), at least to those not living down under, are almost as magical as the duckbilled platypus simply because they are equipped with a curious pouch (marsupium) to house their youngsters (called joeys). But the pouch is not what the young are born into. Marsupials give birth to tiny naked babies that are blind and reminiscent of baby mice. They exit the vagina and crawl through their mother's fur, instinctively homing in on the nipple which is located in (or out) of the pouch. It takes several months of living in the pouch for joeys to fully develop. As the joeys grow, they become increasingly independent of the pouch, spending more and more time outside.

Moles (Order Soricomorpha) spend most of their time underground, using their heavily clawed, shovel-like forelegs to create their extensive system of tunnels. These nearly blind burrowing mammals use their highly sensitive sense of smell and touch to quickly home in on their prey: soil-dwelling arthropods and earthworms. Moles' eating speed gives new meaning to the term "fast food." The star-nose mole can find, grab, and gobble down a worm in less than a half a second. Eating fast, after all, is a necessity. Like the shrews (and like some teenage boys I know), moles must consume a huge amount of food per day (relative to their body size) to supply their immense metabolic demands.

Figure 27.42 Star-nosed mole

Apes and monkeys (Order Primata) can swing through the branches of a tropical rainforest with the agility and speed that would be the envy of world-class gymnasts.

Figure 27.43
Variety of Mammalia

NO FREE LUNCH

We've already covered how evolutionists like to emphasize the similarities shared by all creatures at every level of classification, arguing that these similarities indicate that all members within a order, class, phylum, or even kingdom evolved from a common ancestor. But take a minute to ponder all the tremendous differences we just saw. Could these differences be produced by random mutations and natural selection from a common ancestor that did not have many of these specialized structures, functions, or behaviors?

In my brief survey of these various groups of bacteria, protists, fungi, animals, and (in the next chapter) plants, I have had to leave out countless other unique structures and functions. But you can already see that the more details you learn about any one group, the more obvious it is how distinct they are from each other, and how none of these differences could be explained by mutation and natural selection.

CHAPTER 27: REVIEW QUESTIONS

1. Sea squirts belong to:
   a. Urochordata
   b. Cephalochordata
   c. Vertebrata

2. Lancelets belong to:
    a. Urochordata
    b. Cephalochordata
    c. Vertebrata

3. What is unique about the mouth of lampreys and hagfish (the agnathans)?

4. What is unique about the skeleton (except the jaw) of all sharks, skates, rays, chimaeras, and sawfish?

5. Sharks, skates, rays, etc. belong to the class ______.

6. Class Osteichthyes are the ______ fish. Give three examples that highlight some of the extreme variety in this group.

7. The gill covering called the operculum is a feature of ______.
    a. Bony fish
    b. Hagfish
    c. Lampreys
    d. Chondrichthyes

8. What type of fertilization do most frogs and toads (order Anura) exhibit?
    a. internal
    b. external

9. What is the order or common name of a legless group of tropical amphibians?

10. Which amphibian order employs a spermatophore to inseminate the female resulting in internal fertilization?

11. What is the common name for order Testudines?

12. Most amphibians can breathe using both lungs and ______.

13. True or False. All frogs are oviparous (lay eggs).

14. List two main groups of order Squamata.

15. Name one feature that is unique to order Squamata (other reptiles don't have it).

16. Name one feature that is unique to order Testudines (other reptiles don't have it).

17. Name two general characteristics of *all birds* that would be considered synapomorphies by evolutionists, in that the presumed reptilian ancestor didn't have them?

18. Match the following to the correct order.

a. Mallard duck ______	1. Order Passeriformes
b. Sparrow ______	2. Order Falconiformes
c. Penguin ______	3. Order Galliformes
d. Ostrich ______	4. Order Sphenisciformes
e. Turkey ______	5. Order Struthioniformes
f. Hawk ______	6. Order Anseriformes

19. What two chordate (vertebrate) classes are endothermic?

20. Name two general characteristics of *all mammals* that would be considered synapomorphies by evolutionists, in that the presumed reptilian ancestor didn't have them.

21. Name two general characteristics of *all reptiles* that would be considered synapomorphies by evolutionists, in that the presumed amphibian ancestor didn't have them.

22. Match the following to the correct order.

a. Fruit bat ______	1. Order Rodentia
b. Sperm whale ______	2. Order Marsupialia
c. Beaver ______	3. Order Chiroptera
d. Horse ______	4. Order Artiodactyla
e. Cougar ______	5. Order Perissodactyla
f. Deer ______	6. Order Cetacea
g. Kangaroo ______	7. Order Carnivora

23. Which of the following are not vertebrates?
    a. Lamprcys and hagfish
    b. Cuttlefish
    c. Cartilage fish
    d. Bony fish
    e. Amphibians
    f. Reptiles
    g. Birds
    h. Mammals

CHAPTER 28

KINGDOM PLANTAE

PLANTS

Plants are ubiquitous. We see them every day all around us: our lawn, our gardens, our house plants, trees that line our street, and vegetation that blankets the countryside. The familiarity of plants often causes us to take them for granted and keeps us from really considering how much they beautify our environment, materially bless us, and—last but not least—keep us alive. They produce much of the oxygen we breathe and much of the food we eat (bread, fruits, and vegetables). Sure, you might prefer meat, but even so, meat is ultimately derived from the nutrition from plants. (What do you suppose cattle eat, anyway?) Plants clothe us (cotton and flax) and provide wood for our homes and furniture. When we fully consider the plant creation, we have much to thank God for.

So what defines a plant? The following is a list of features that most plants share though some are not unique to plants.

- Eukaryotic cell structure
- Autotrophic or photosynthetic (although some plants are parasitic and do not photosynthesize)
- Multicellular (composing many tissues and few organs)
- Cell walls (composed mostly of cellulose)
- Cell plate formation during cytokinesis
- Alternation of Generations (a life cycle characteristic to plants)

I described the magical process of photosynthesis in Chapter 7, so I won't reiterate it here. Suffice it to say that chloroplasts in plant cells manufacture glucose from thin air. With the help of a host of enzymatic pathways, coupled with small amounts of nutrients taken from the soil, plants can construct the rest of their body starting with glucose.

In this section I will spend time discussing some of the major groups (phyla) of plants, along with their basic structure, reproductive anatomy, and life cycles. The four major phyla are:

- Phylum Bryophyta (Mosses)
- Phylum Pterophyta (Ferns)
- Phylum Coniferophyta (Conifers)
- Phylum Anthophyta (Angiosperms or flowering plants)

Before I start, I want to outline the curious life cycle shared by all plants: the **alternation of generations**. With it comes some strange new terms so bear with me.

As the name of the cycle states, there are two distinct generations. One is called the **gametophyte** generation, the other is called the **sporophyte** generation, and—you guessed it—they alternate. The structure of these generations differ greatly from phylum to phylum, but the pattern of the cycle and the terminology remains largely the same. So once you learn this general cycle, you'll have the basic pattern and most of the terminology for the life cycles of all four plant phyla.

ALTERNATION OF GENERATIONS LIFECYCLE

In this life cycle, I will arbitrarily start at the spore, which is haploid or 1N (follow along below, and review meiosis in Chapter 13 if you need to).

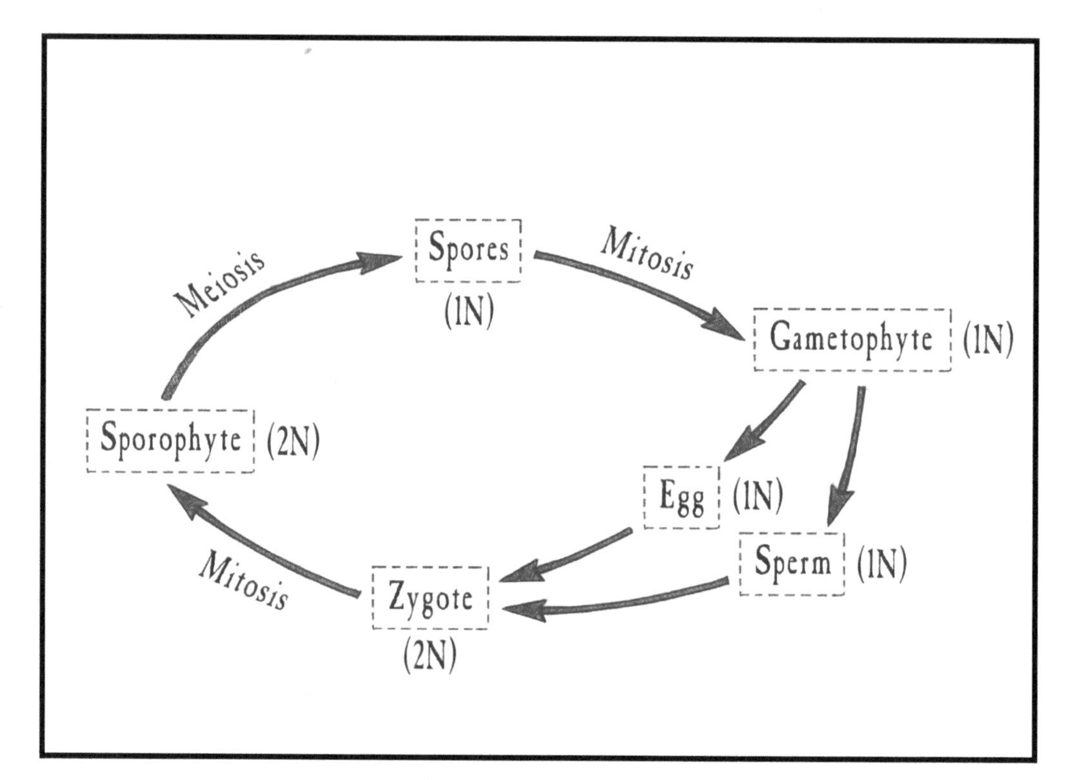

Figure 28.1 Alternation of generations life cycle

Plants are unusual with regard to the purpose of meiosis. In animals, meiosis produces sperm in males and eggs in females. Plants, on the other hand, use meiosis to produce spores. The spore divides by mitosis and differentiates into a multicellular plant or tiny blob of tissue called a gametophyte. *Gameto* means "gamete" (sperm or egg) and *phyte* means "plant." Simply put, **gametophyte** means "gamete plant"—a plant that produces either sperm or eggs or both. Since spores are already haploid, the gametophyte can't do meiosis, nor does it need to. If something is already haploid, then mitosis is all that is needed to produce haploid gametes.

Within the gametophyte, certain structures form. Antheridia form in male gametophytes and archegonia form in female gametophytes. Both antheridia and archegonia form in bisexual gametophytes. By mitosis, cells within these structures develop into haploid sperm (in the antheridia) or eggs (in the archegonia). At a certain stage the haploid sperm are released. If successful, sperm meets egg and fertilizes it to produce the diploid zygote.

The **zygote** then begins mitosis and develops into a diploid sporophyte. *Sporo* means "spore" and *phyte* (as we just discovered) means "plant," so **sporophyte** means "spore plant," or a plant that produces spores. At a certain point in its development the sporophyte develops a structure called a **sporangium**. The cells within it undergo meiosis and become haploid spores.

We have now come full circle. Learn this basic life cycle well; it will help when you learn the distinctive features of specific life cycles in Kingdom Plantae.

THE MOSSES: PHYLUM BRYOPHYTA

One of the most delightful denizens decorating rocks, soil, and trees of moist woodlands are the mosses. They can often be found in town on shady rock walls and roof tops. These cushy carpets are not only an ecologically important part of the forest; they also beautify the ground wherever they grow. There are about 12,000 species of mosses. Small species stand about ½ inch tall, but there are some that reach a whopping four inches tall.

Mosses don't produce flowers, cones, or seeds; instead, they reproduce themselves by spores. Here's how. The familiar velvety green carpet is composed of many individual gametophytes growing close together (some form branching mats). Many moss species have separate male and female gametophytes (leafy shoots) with root-like **rhizoids** loosely anchoring them to the substrate.

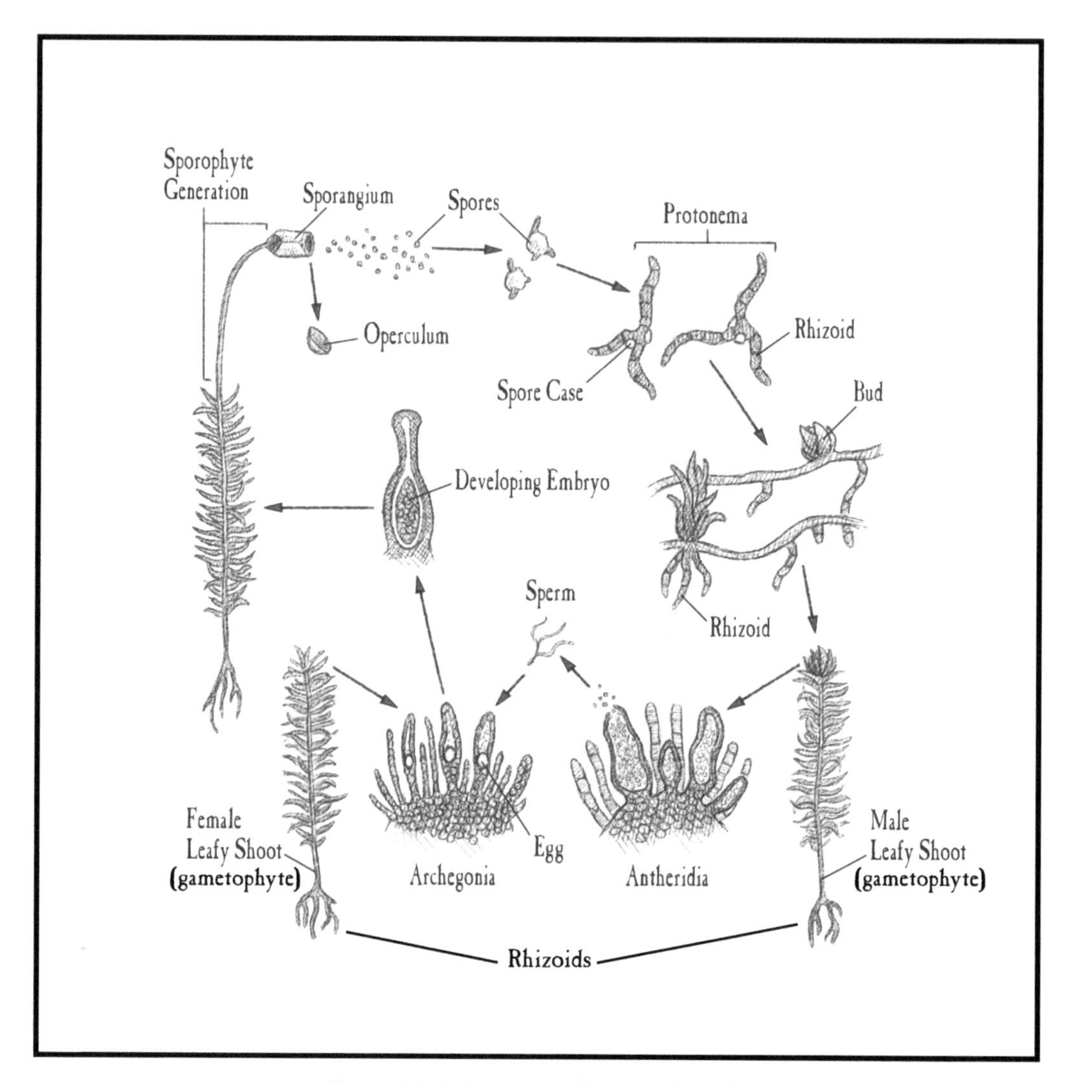

Figure 28.2 Diagram of moss life cycle

On the tips of male gametophytes, groups of **antheridia** grow and produce sperm equipped with flagella for swimming. When it rains, mature antheridia are ruptured by raindrops and release their sperm into the water.

On the female gametophytes, **archegonia** can be found clustered on the top or other parts of the shoot. In each archegonium rests a single egg, like a marble in the base of a single flower vase.

Thousands of flagellated sperm swim through the water film covering the moss carpet. Some successfully swim down the neck of the archegonium and fertilize the egg producing a diploid zygote.

The zygote then begins the new sporophyte generation. It divides by mitosis, producing an elongated embryo that begins growing out of the archegonium. Soon the growing sporophyte becomes a thin slender stalk that protrudes from the female gametophyte. (It remains dependent and attached to the gametophyte generation.) The tip of the sporophyte enlarges into a oval knob called a sporangium. If you inspect a moss carpet at the right time of year, you will see many sporophytes sticking out of the gametophyte carpet.

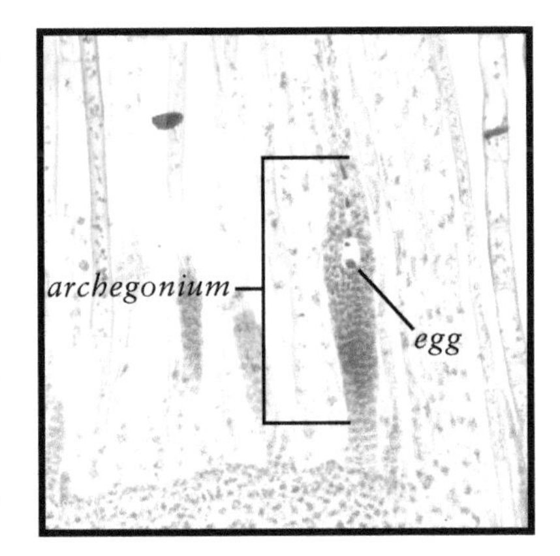

Figure 28.3 Moss archegonium

In the picture to the right (Figure 28.4), the sporophyte stalks are brown; sporangia perched on top are green.

Figure 28.4 Moss gametophytes and sporophytes

Certain cells within each sporangium undergo meiosis, producing haploid spores. This begins the gametophyte generation. As the spores are being formed within, a cap forms at the end of the sporangium. When the spores are ready, the cap falls off and the spores sprinkle out. Peristomal teeth curl in and out of the sporangium, helping to disperse the spores.

The spores are microscopic and can travel by air for miles. If they chance to fall on a moist, suitable surface, the spores germinate by mitosis into algae-like threads called **protonema.**

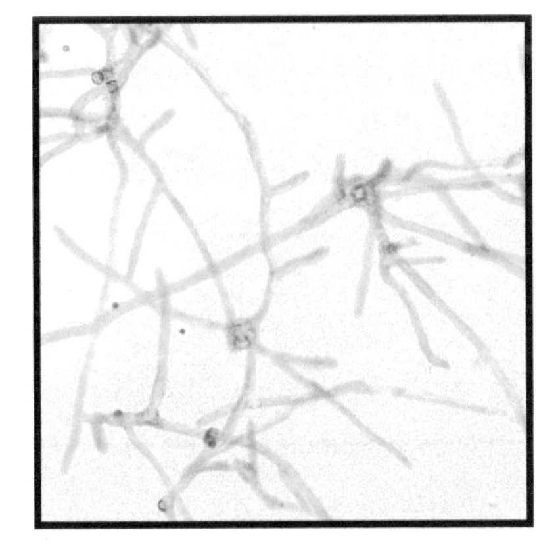

Figure 28.5 Moss protonema

Eventually the protonema form buds that grow into mature gametophytes with antheridia and archegonia.

We have now come full circle. Next time you're in the woods, find a mat of moss and marvel.

THE FERNS: PHYLUM PTEROPHYTA

There are about 12,000 species of ferns. Like moss, they reproduce by spores and don't produce flowers, cones, or seeds. Ferns are typically most common in moist, verdant forests, but they also can be found in the water, open plains, and in arid rocky crags of the desert. These familiar yet comely plants are a beautiful addition to the resident undergrowth and are picturesque growing out of the cracks on rocky cliffs.

In this group of plants, the theme of alternation of generations remains unchanged, but the appearance of each generation is vastly different. For starters, the sporophyte is the dominant generation; it is the generation we are familiar with and see growing in our yards and woods.

Figure 28.6 Fern anatomy

The structure of the fern sporophyte is more complicated than the moss sporophyte, is much larger, and grows independently in the soil. It has a horizontal underground stem called a **rhizome** from which roots grow to anchor the plant to the soil and absorb water and nutrients. The photosynthetic part of the fern consists of clusters of leaves called **fronds** that grow from the rhizome. The **blade** of a frond is divided into many **leaflets** (pinnae) arranged on both sides of the frond's central axis. The stalk of each frond is called a **petiole.**

Figure 28.7 Fern sori

As is to be expected from the life cycle, sporophytes produce spores within sporangia. This is true of ferns as well as moss. During certain seasons (depending on the fern species), an orderly arrangement of spots develops on the undersides of the leaflets. Each spot is called a **sorus** (pl. **sori**).

Numerous sori are usually arranged in two rows running the length of each leaflet. If we zoom in on the sorus (side view) microscopically, we can distinguish individual sporangia and see the spores within.

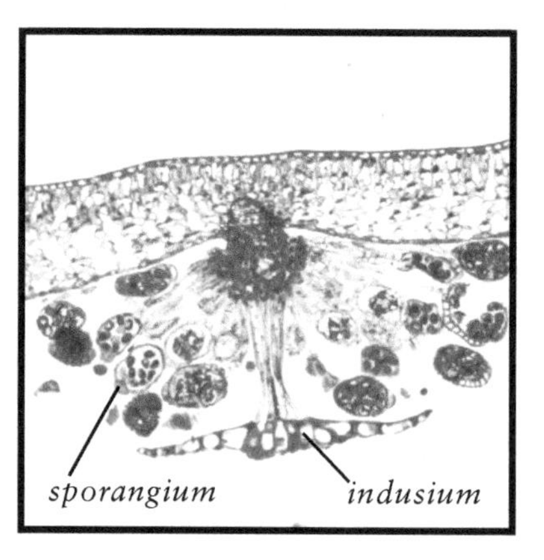

Figure 28.8
Fern sorus with indusium

Fern sporangia have been designed with a built-in catapult called an **annulus.** It is a ring of thick-walled cells that forms a belt

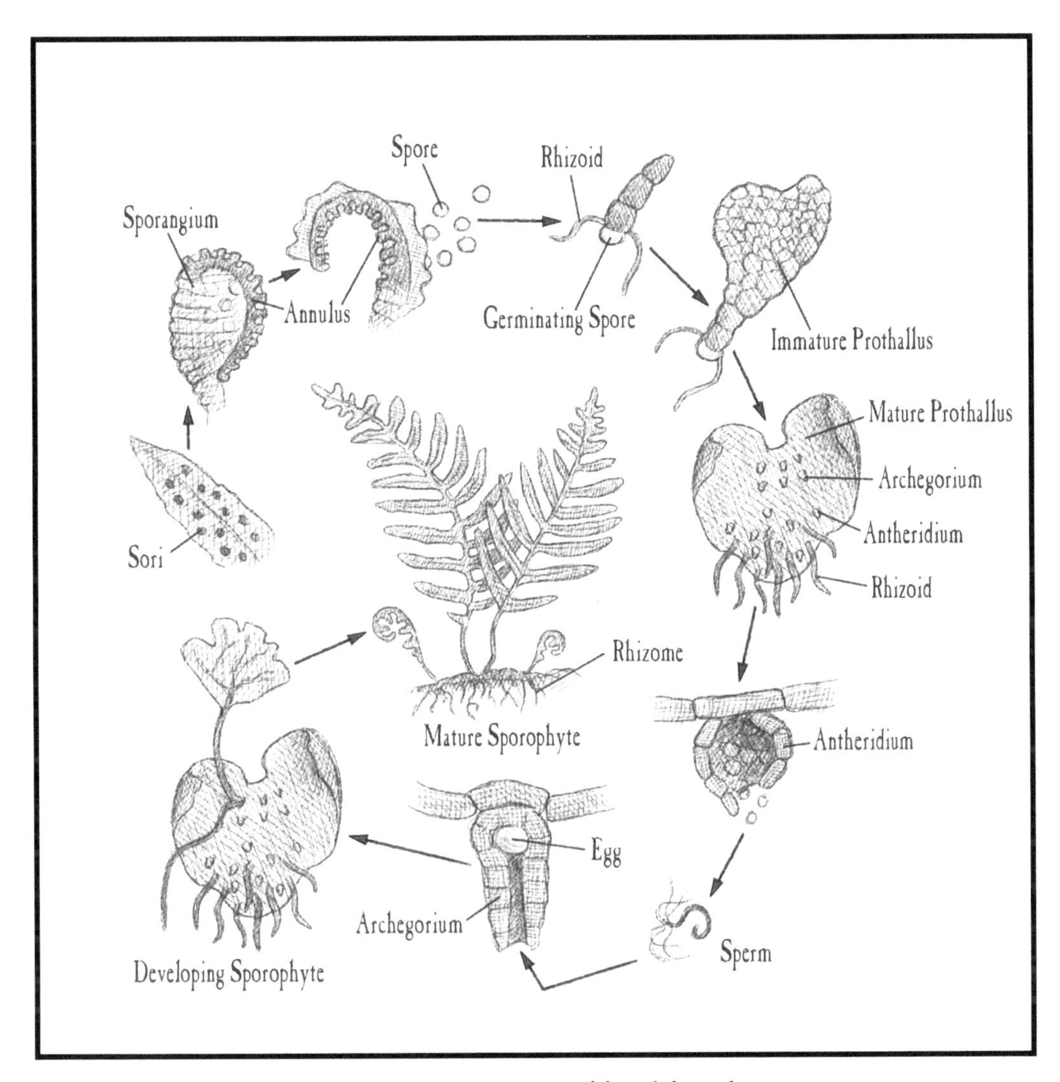

Figure 28.9 Diagram of fern life cycle

around the sporangium. The cells in the sporangium undergo meiosis, producing haploid spores.

After meiosis is complete and the spores are ready for release, the annulus breaks open and slowly bends the opposite way, tearing open and turning the sporangium inside out. The annulus is essentially cocking itself. Once cocked, it snaps forward catapult-like, flinging its tiny load of spores violently from the open sporangium.

If the spores chance to land in a suitable patch of moist soil, they germinate by mitosis. And if you know the life cycle, then you know what happens next. A germinating spore grows into a haploid gametophyte. Unfortunately, you aren't likely to find a fern gametophyte in the woods. Even

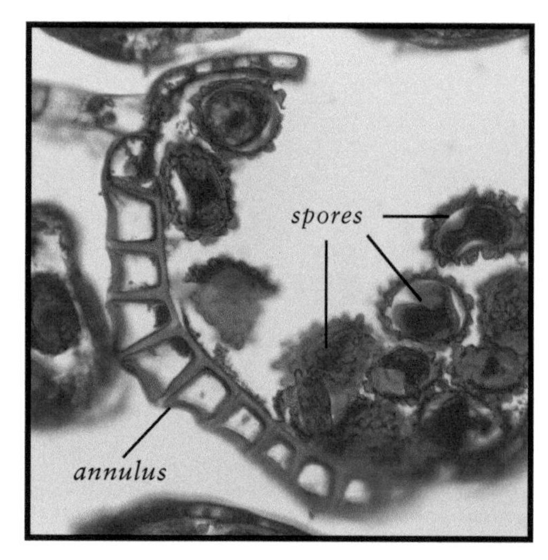

Figure 28.10 Fern sporangia with annulus

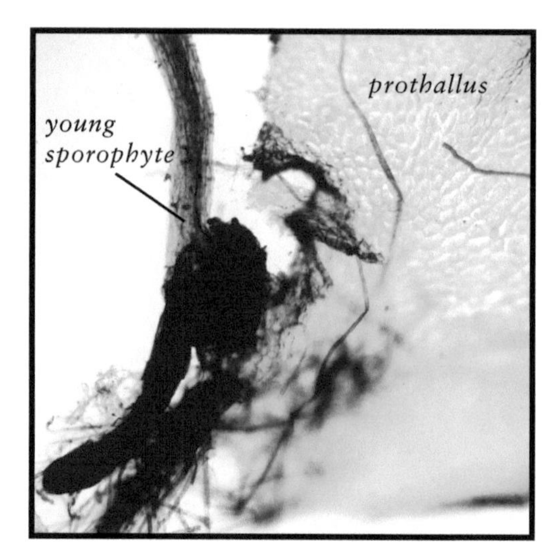

Figure 28.11 Fern prothallus with young sporophyte

fully grown, it is a skimpy speck of cells about the size of a flake of dandruff (1 or 2 mm wide and very thin).

In ferns, there is only one bisexual gametophyte (called a **prothallus**) that develops both antheridia and archegonia.

Again, the antheridia produce haploid sperm by mitosis. The flagellated sperm are released and make their way to the archegonia on the same (or different) prothallus, where they fertilize the egg, thus producing a diploid zygote. The zygote begins to grow into an embryonic sporophyte and emerges from the prothallus.

As the sporophyte grows and takes root, the parent gametophyte disintegrates. Eventually it develops into a mature sporophyte with roots, rhizomes, and fronds.

THE CONIFERS: PHYLUM CONIFEROPHYTA

The conifers are often called **gymnosperms** as well as evergreens, though it should be noted that not all evergreens and gymnosperms are conifers. The name "Evergreen" comes mainly because most of them stay green all year-round. Gymnosperm means "naked seed" because the seeds lie "naked" on the cone scales and are not surrounded by a container.

These trees typically grow into Christmas tree-shapes (indeed, many species are used as Christmas trees), though a few of them are low, spreading shrubs. All conifers are woody and produce cones for sexual reproduction. (In fact, the word conifer means "cone-bearing.") Although they are a relatively small group (over 600 species worldwide), they cover millions of square miles and huge, continuous chunks of entire continents. And because so many of thc trccs arc large, they are of enormous economic importance, producing much of the world's wood and wood products.

Conifers include the pines, firs, Douglas firs, spruces, cedars (old and new world), junipers, larches, sequoia, redwoods, hemlocks, and cypresses. The majestic sequoia and redwood forests are among the most awe-inspiring forests in the world.

Figure 28.12 Conifer forest

Figure 27.13 Pine stem cross section

Just like for the fern, the dominant generation (the tree or shrub) is the sporophyte generation. However, the sporophyte is even more structurally complex with trees: woody stems and roots, leaves (needles or scales), and cones (male and female).

I will use the pine tree for the representative life cycle, focusing on its cones since that's where the life cycle action occurs. The **female cones** are the most familiar to us; they are what we call "pine cones." (Technically, pine cones are only on pines; fir cones on firs, spruce cones on spruces, etc., but pretty much everyone just says "pine cone.")

Figure 28.14 Female early cone

As previously mentioned, sporophytes produce spores, so in the case of conifers, the spores are produced inside each **ovule** (immature seed). On the upper surface of each **ovuliferous scale** (the familiar scales on pine cones), there are two ovules.

These scales are arranged spirally around the central axis of the female cone. Inside the center of each ovule there is a diploid cell (diploid like the

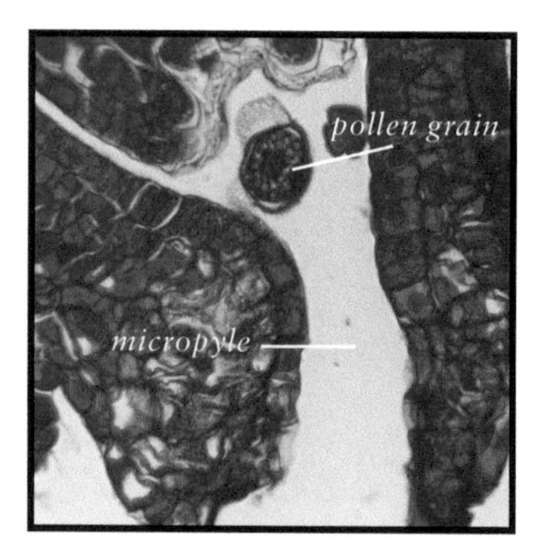

Figure 28.15 Pine pollination

rest of the tree) that's destined to undergo meiosis. According to the basic life cycle, meiosis produces four haploid spores. Now, in moss and ferns the spores are released, but that's not the case in conifers. Instead, the spores remain within the ovule.

In this more elaborate cycle, the female cones produce bigger spores which are consequently called **megaspores**. Of the four megaspores, three die. Again, according to the life cycle, the haploid spores divide by mitosis and grow into a haploid gametophyte. In this case, the one remaining megaspore divides and grows into a **megagametophyte**. (This is still within the ovule which is still attached to the scale of the female cone; everything is growing together.) The megagametophyte produces archegonia (2 or 3), each containing one egg. Now the stage is set for fertilization.

The **male cones** are much smaller and not woody. They are less familiar, but you can probably recall seeing them (Figure 28.16). Male cones have thin scales growing spirally from the central axis of the cone. Each scale bear two sacks called **microsporangia**.

Figure 28.16 Male and female cones

The cells within the microsporangia are destined to go through meiosis to produce haploid **microspores**. (Male cones produce smaller spores; hence the name *micro*spores.) These microspores aren't released from the male cone either. Each microspore (and there are many in one microsporangium) goes through a couple rounds of mitosis, producing a tiny four-celled **microgametophyte**, also called a **pollen grain**.

Once the pollen grains are mature, each microsporangium ruptures and releases thousands of pollen grains into the air. There are thousands of male cones per tree and hundreds of microsporangia per cone, so the number of pollen grains released is enormous. Unlike most flowering plants, conifers rely on the wind and air currents to transport the pollen to its intended destination. Because so much pollen is released, this "shotgun" method works, even though most of the pollen falls on land, water, other plants, etc., and they die. I remember in 1984, my blue Toyota Tercel turned yellow because I parked it under a large Ponderosa Pine just before it dumped most of its pollen.

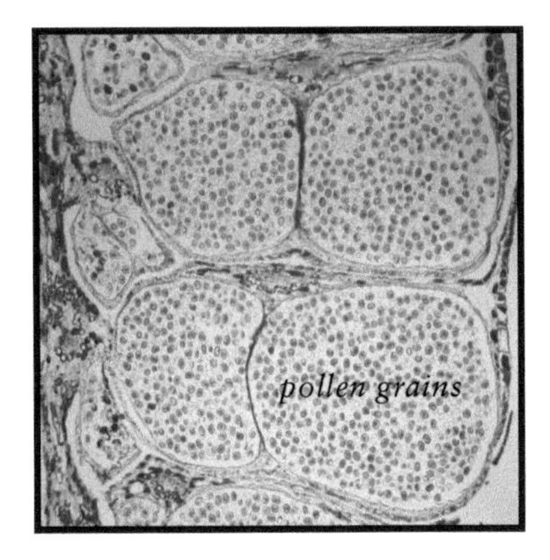

Figure 28.17 Male pine cone (pollen sacs)

Only a tiny fraction successfully land by a **micropyle** of a female cone of the correct species; this is called **pollination** (see Figure 28.15). The pollen grain germinates, resulting in pollen tube growth from the micropyle to the archegonium. A certain cell within a pollen grain produces sperm that move through the pollen tube, are released into the archegonia, fertilize the eggs, and produce diploid zygotes. Even though more than one egg is usually fertilized per ovule, most of the time only one embryo develops completely. Remember that all this is still happening in the ovule which is still attached to the female cone. The dominant diploid sporophyte embryo grows out of the archegonium (while the megagametophyte serves as food for the growing embryo).

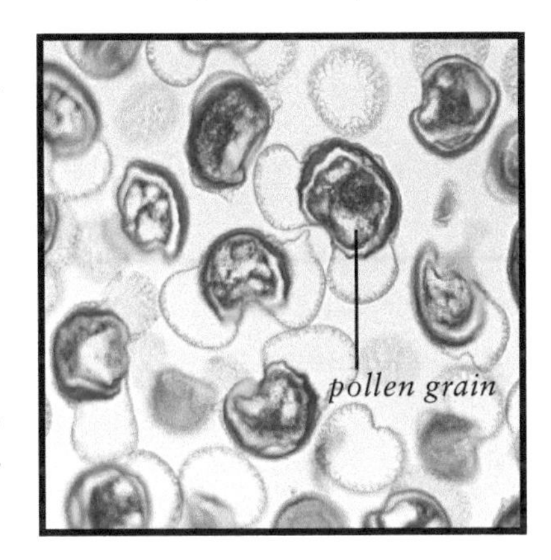

Figure 28.18 Pine pollen

Eventually, the pine embryo is arrested in development, and we now have a pine seed, and the outer **integument** hardens into a **seed coat.** The pine seed is an amazing little package composed of three generations. Think about it—the seed coat (2N) is maternal tissue of the female cone and thus part of the adult sporophyte generation. Inside the seed

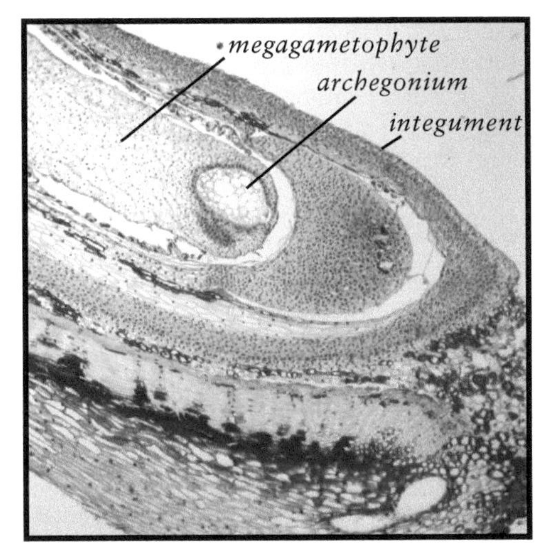

Figure 28.19 Pine megagametophyte with archegonium

coat is the megagametophyte (1N), and inside the megagametophyte is the embryonic sporophyte (2N).

(Cool fact: large pine seeds are called pine nuts. You can buy them at certain grocery stores and they make a great snack.)

Pine seeds are **winged** (the seed coat has an extension on it that serves as an air foil) and when the female cones are mature, they spread their scales (some require fire to open up) and the seeds flutter out. On a windy day, the seeds can ride on the wind for miles.

Figure 27.20 Pine seedling

If it lands on a suitable patch of soil, it will germinate into a pine seedling which will slowly grow into the adult sporophyte, a giant among plants.

THE FLOWERING PLANTS OR ANGIOSPERMS: PHYLUM ANTHOPHYTA

The flowering plants are an immense group which includes typical, showy flowers we all enjoy: lilies, tulips, roses, irises, carnations, daffodils, daisies, etc. But it also includes a vast array of herbaceous plants, woody shrubs, and trees that many people typically don't think of as flowering plants because their flowers are so small, inconspicuous, or lack bright coloration. This group has well over 250,000 species and includes the diminutive duckweed (tiny bright green discs that float on the water) and the massive eucalyptus trees (which can tower over 100 meters tall). It includes the rushes, sedges, cattails, grasses, and many of the familiar broad-leafed trees and shrubs that decorate our cities and towns, even though they don't have

Figure 28.21
Maple flower blossoms

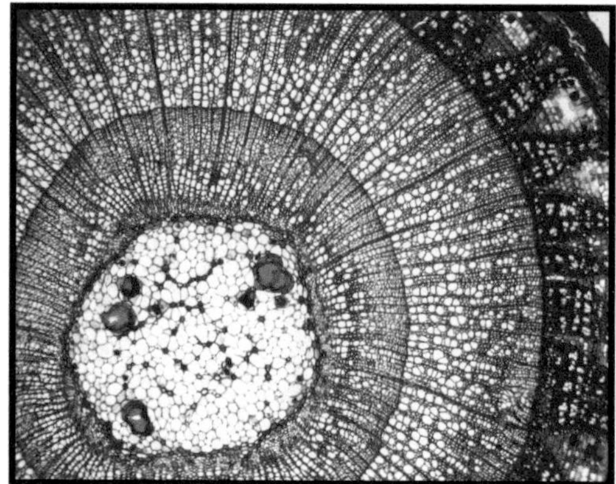

Figure 28.22
Two-year-old woody stem of Tilia

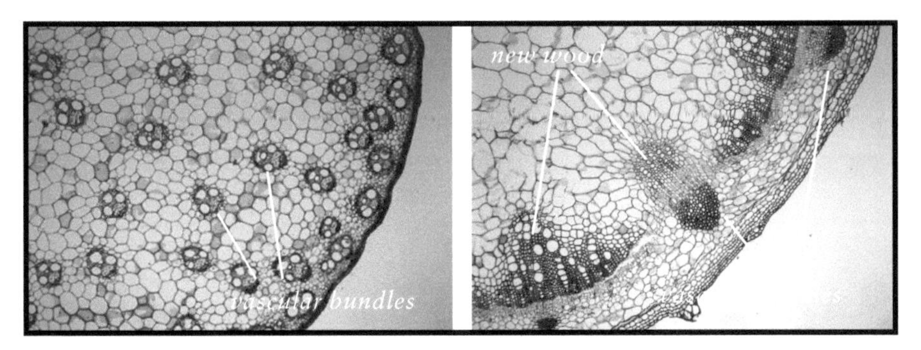

Figure 28.23 Monocot and dicot stems

showy flowers. Basically, plants that are not mosses, ferns, or conifers fall in this group (with very few exceptions).

The structure of the angiosperm sporophyte is highly variable, but the major organs are roots, stems, leaves, and flowers. Roots are for anchoring the sporophyte to the substrate and also for absorption and transport of water and nutrients. Leaves are the major site of photosynthesis. (For details on leaf structure, revisit the section on photosynthesis in chapter 7.) Stems (woody or herbaceous) function to support the plant, transport water and nutrients throughout the plant, and to position leaves where they can catch some rays from the sun. (The figure to the right shows some leaf arrangements you might find in the woods.) Flowers are for reproduction.

Figure 28.24 Leaf arrangement

The cross section of a woody angiosperm stem is similar to the conifer cross section we looked at earlier. Many angiosperms stay herbaceous or at least have a herbaceous stem prior to developing wood. Figure 28.23b is a stem that is just beginning to make wood, but you can still see the **vascular bundles,** which are composed of **xylem** and **phloem.** These cells look round or oval in cross section, but keep in mind that they are actually long cylindrical cells placed end to end (like water pipes in a home) so that water and minerals (in xylem) and photosynthate (in phloem) can be transported where needed.

Figure 28.25 Parts of a leaf

The external anatomy of an herbaceous stem consists of sections of stem called **internodes** interrupted by **nodes** where one or more leaves are located. The leaf consists of a stalk called a **petiole** and a **blade** (Figure 28.25). The blade may be **simple** or **compound.** If compound, it is divided up into **leaflets.** Compound leaves are most commonly pinnately or palmately compound (Figure 28.26).

Figure 28.26 Leaf morphology

Lateral (or axillary) **buds** are located at **leaf axils** which is the upper surface where the petiole meets the stem. When these buds grow, they produce another stem (branch) that follows the same pattern just described. Some leaves have paired leafy growths on both sides of the petiole's base called **stipules.**

The angiosperms are divided into two classes: the **monocots** and the **eudicots.** I will briefly note the major distinctions between the two groups and mention a few familiar examples of each. *Eu* means "true" and *dicot* is short for "dicotyledons." Hence, *eudicots* means "true dicotyledons." A cotyledon is an embryonic or seed leaf (usually fleshy), and eudicots have two of them in each of their seeds. Monocots ("one cotyledon") have just one cotyledon in each of their seeds.

There are other structural differences between eudicots and monocots besides the number of cotyledons in their seeds. Eudicots have netted venation (pattern of vascular bundles) in their leaves whereas monocots usually have parallel venation. Eudicots also have a circular arrangement of vascular bundles in their herbaceous stems when viewed in cross section, while monocots have a scattered arrangement in their stems. Many eudicots can also produce wood; monocots, though some can become trees (palms), produce strong fibrous stems but never make wood. Another difference is that eudicots make floral parts in multiples of fours or fives. Monocot floral parts are in multiples of three.

Figure 28.27 Whole flower

Some examples of monocots are the grasses (including all cereal grains like corn, wheat, barley, etc.), rushes, sedges, tulips, lilies, daffodils, irises, orchids, onions, and palm trees. Eudicots include all the rest of the flowering plants: all woody trees and shrubs, crops (excluding cereal grains), cactus, and any herbaceous wildflower having the eudicot characteristics mentioned above.

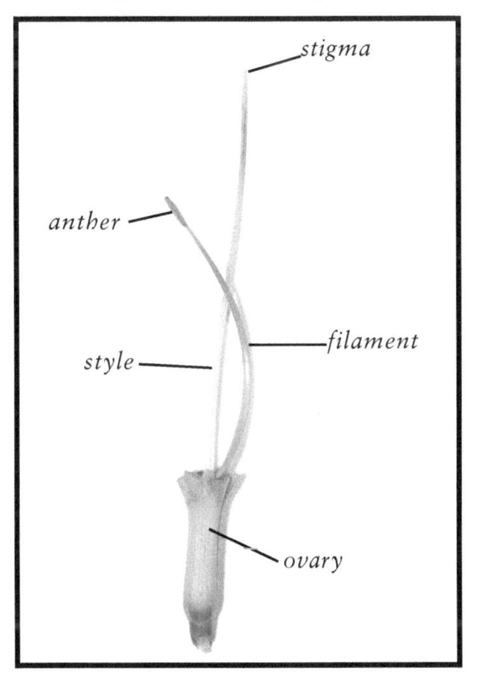

Figure 28.28 Anatomy of flower

As is the case in conifers, the dominant generation in angiosperms is the sporophyte. In other words, the plant that you see is the sporophyte. The gametophyte generation is microscopic and even smaller than the one in conifers. However, similar to the conifers, the gametophyte forms in the ovule and never grows independently, but remains embedded in sporophyte tissue within the ovule (seed coat).

Before I get into the nitty-gritty of the angiosperm life cycle, I need to set the stage and discuss the hallmark characteristic of the flowering plants:

the flower. The outermost parts are leafy structures called **sepals.** The familiar **petals** are next in line. In flowers that we use for decorations and special occasions, the petals are large and showy. Besides being beautiful, the bright colors of petals attract their pollinators: insects, birds, etc. Just to the inside of the petals are the male reproductive structures called **stamens.** Stamens are composed of two parts: the stalk (called the **filament**) and the **anther** which produces and releases the pollen. The central **pistil** (or carpel) is the female portion of the flower and is composed of a swollen base called the **ovary.** (By the way, "angiosperm" means "seed-container" and refers to the ovary as the structure that contains the seeds.) The ovary contains the **ovules** (immature seeds) and within each ovule is an egg. The chimney-like structure atop the ovary is the **style** and at the end of the style is the **stigma.**

Of course, there is tremendous variation in the size, shape, and color pattern of flowers. They can be solitary or grow in clusters. They can be just male (staminate) flowers with only stamens or just female (pistillate)

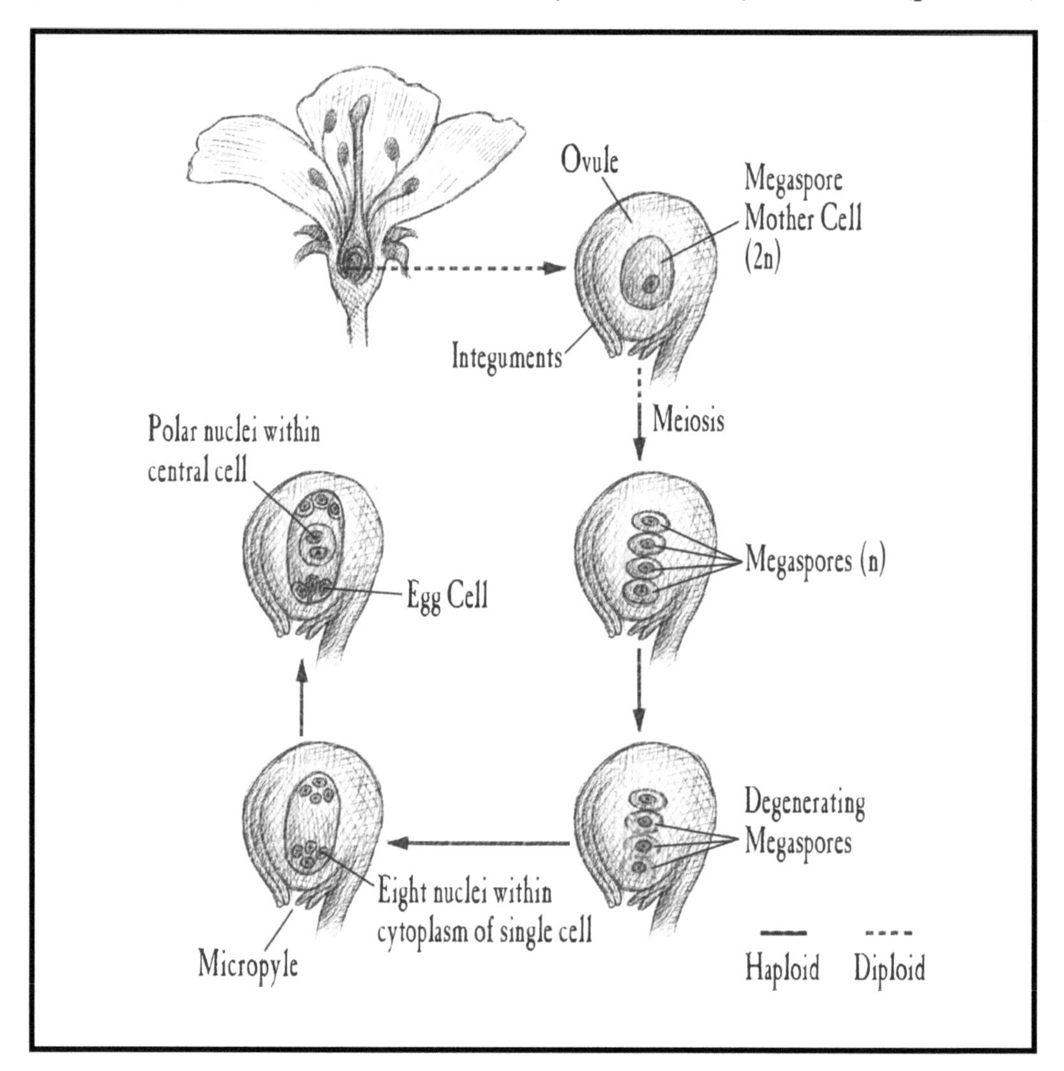

Figure 28.29 Development in the ovule of flowers

flowers with only pistils. They can be missing sepals, petals, or both. They can be brightly colored or very drab.

Now we can discuss the life cycle (refer to Figure 28.29). As already mentioned, the visible plant is the sporophyte. So where are spores produced?

I'll start with the female. Within each ovule (inside the ovary) a certain cell undergoes meiosis to produce four haploid spores. Since the female spores are larger than the male spores, they are called **megaspores.** Of the four megaspores, three die and one remains. So far, this is similar to conifers. Now, according to the basic life cycle, spores grow into gametophytes, which is the case here. The remaining megaspore divides by mitosis three times to produce a **megagametophyte.** At first no cytokinesis happens, so eight nuclei are suspended in one largish oval cell. The eight nuclei arrange themselves so that three nuclei are at each end and two are in the middle (polar nuclei). Then cell membranes (and walls) form around each nucleus—except around the middle two. These two polar nuclei wind up together in the **central cell.**

The mature megagametophyte now has seven cells with the central cell having two **polar nuclei**. One of the three cells at the micropyle end of the ovule is the egg. This megagametophyte is so stripped down there isn't even an archegonium to house the egg.

In an immature anther, cells within the four **pollen sacs** undergo meiosis.

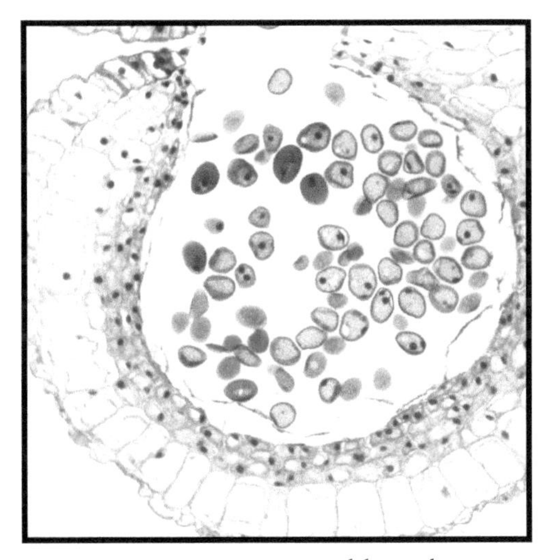

Figure 28.30 Mature lily anther (one pollen sac)

Each cell doing meiosis will produce four haploid **microspores.** This is why the anther can also be called a microsporangium. The microspores, rather than being released, stay put. Each microspore divides once, producing a two-celled haploid **microgametophyte** (also called the **pollen grain**). The two cells are the **tube cell** and the **generative cell.** At the appointed time, the pollen sacs split wide open, exposing the pollen grains to the outside.

The generative cell's nucleus divides to give rise to two sperm. Sometimes the sperm form before pollen release, sometimes after.

Now the stage is set for pollination. Pollination is simply the transfer of pollen to a receptive stigma; a pollinator is the animal that does the job. A variety of critters are employed by the flower for this task, but it isn't done for free. Many flowers were designed to be attractive restaurants with a good menu. They are bright and colorful and offer good food (nectar and pollen) to attract their pollinators. They are highly successful in attracting various insects (bees, wasps, flies, beetles, etc.), birds, mice, bats, and even lizards to pollinate. The pollinators used depend on the plant species.

As the creature visits the flower, their body brushes up against the anthers and is dusted with a bit of pollen. When it visits another flower of the same species, some of the pollen is inadvertently scraped onto the wet and sticky stigma. Some non-showy flowers (grasses) use wind to pollinate other flowers.

Figure 28.31 Bean pod (fruit or ripe ovary)

In any case, after the pollen grain lands, it imbibes the stigma's fluid and germinates. The tube cell produces a pollen tube that grows through the stigma, down through the style, and along the inside of the ovary's wall. Usually the ovary has a lot more than one ovule, so quite a few separate pollen tubes can be growing into separate ovules in the same ovary. Each pollen tube targets a micropyle and grows up to it.

Figure 28.32 Bean (eudicot) germination

Meanwhile, the two sperm follow the tube nucleus down the pollen tube. When they

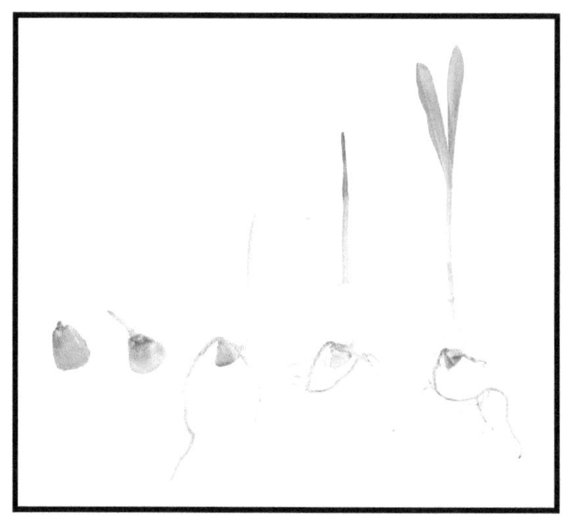

Figure 28.33 Corn (monocot) germination

arrive, one haploid sperm fertilizes the haploid egg becoming a diploid zygote (1N + 1N = 2N). The other sperm fuses with the two polar nuclei (1N + 1N + 1N = 3N). This is called triple fusion and results in a triploid cell. The zygote (2N) divides by mitosis to form the **embryonic sporophyte** while the triploid cell divides by mitosis to form the triploid endosperm. The **endosperm** serves as food for the developing embryo. At a certain point, the embryo ceases growth, dries up, and becomes dormant. It is now a **seed**.

Meanwhile, the ovary, in which all this is occurring, is growing and developing into a **fruit** (apples, bananas, oranges, grapes, watermelons, cantaloupes, peppers, etc.). If it's not a conifer cone and it has seeds in it, it's a fruit—even if it's not juicy and you thought it was a vegetable. ("Vegetable" is more of a culinary term. Botanists use strict definitions of things like roots, stems, leaves, fruits, etc., and a "vegetable" could be any of those four listed.)

The size of the fruit often dwarfs the other flower parts (styles, stigmas, stamens, petals, and sepals). In addition, those parts often shrivel up and fall off. Consequently, it's news to some that the ovary of a flower actually becomes a fruit that they buy in the grocery store. Some fruits are dry like peanuts or sunflower seeds (both in a shell). When you crack the shell, you are cracking open the fruit wall. Peppers and pea pods and beans pods are also fruits.

In one way or other, the seeds are liberated. Many fruits are tasty and attractive, so they get eaten—along with its load of seeds. Now, getting eaten may seem like a rough start to the plant embryos tucked away in the seeds, but it is actually a wonderful design feature. For some seeds, the complete journey through the animal's GI tract is necessary for the seeds to germinate, and when they finally exit they are surrounded in fertilizer.

Depending on the species, seeds may require other conditions before they germinate. Many temperate plants require a certain period of time exposed to cold temperatures. Others need an extremely heavy rain or a highly roughed-up seed coat. Whatever the case, when the conditions are right, the seed germinates and grows into the adult sporophyte.

CHAPTER 28: REVIEW QUESTIONS

1. Which of the following is *not* a characteristic of Plantae?
   a. autotrophic
   b. multicellular
   c. chitin cell walls
   d. cell plate formation in cytokinesis
   e. contains chloroplasts

2. In the alternation of generations life cycle, sporophytes produce ______ within a structure called a sporangium, through a cellular division called ______.

3. What is the ploidy of the gametophyte generation?
   a. Diploid
   b. Haploid

4. What is the generation indicated by the upper bracket in the moss to the right?

5. a. What are the visible spots on the undersides of fern pinnae called?

   b. What is each spot composed of?

   c. What structure in fern sporangia fling the spores abroad in a catapult fashion?

6. Which phylum of plants has a more conspicuous or dominant gametophyte generation?
   a. Flowering plants
   b. Conifers
   c. Ferns
   d. Mosses

7. Pine, spruce, fir, and cedar belong in the phylum ______.

8. Male cones of conifers are made up of many tiny microsporangia which release microgametophytes which are also known as ______.

9. Female cones of conifers have many woody ______ scales, each of which bears two ovules on its upper surface.

10. In conifers, successful pollination is achieved when pollen grain(s) of the correct species lands near the ______ (opening in the integument) of the ovule.

11. List four main differences between the two main classes of flowering plants, the eudicots and the monocots.

12. Flowering plant pollination is simply the transfer of pollen to a receptive ______. Name two very different creatures (from different phyla) that can serve as pollinators.

13. In flowering plants, sperm comes from within the ______.

14. In flowering plants, the egg is within the ovule which is within the ______.

15. Draw a simple longitudinal section of a complete flower. With a clear, neat line trace the growth of the pollen tube. Also label the pistil, composed of the stigma, style, ovary and ovule, and stamen, composed of filament and anther.

CHAPTER 29

THE BASICS OF ECOLOGY

Ecology is a term that we hear quite a bit, but what is it? Most folks understand that ecology has something to do with the environment, but let's get more specific. *Eco* is derived from the Greek word *oikos* meaning "home" (habitat). In short, ecology is the study of the interactions between living creatures and their home, their *environment*, which includes other living creatures as well as the nonliving surroundings. A key aspect of **ecology** is how these interactions affect survival and reproduction.

Ecology may seem intimidating because of the terminology. Don't let the big words scare you. The more you study a particular species—where it lives, why it lives there, what it eats, who eats it, and who competes with it for the same territory or food—the more you can grasp the basics of ecology. It can get pretty abstract and quantitative, but that's just because ecologists are attempting to mathematically describe what's going on in nature. When the abstract, quantitative, and mathematical aspects take a backseat and we emphasize qualitative, accurate, detailed observations of creatures in their natural habitat, it's usually called **natural history** rather than ecology (and it's more fun to study). Of course, this distinction between ecology and natural history isn't hard and fast (words never are), but it may clarify things if you've heard both terms referring to the environment.

It's good to note that many ecological themes were already woven into the survey of life we just finished. Why? Because I don't want you to think that ecology is a sterile set of concepts distinct from the creatures we just discussed. I want you to understand that ecology is best understood and appreciated in the context of the animals and plants that inhabit a particular environment. Trying to grasp ecological concepts without knowing much about the types of creatures in an ecosystem is like trying to understand a car without knowing its parts, how they fit together, and how they interact.

BASIC ECOLOGICAL TERMS

A **population** is composed of all members of the same species at the same place and at the same time. The boundaries of that area are usually set by the researcher. They can be natural boundaries or they can be arbitrarily marked. Population ecology seeks to collect data about a population. This includes the population size, population density, sex (male/female) ratio, movement patterns, growth rates, age structure, and so on, to name a few. For example, when I studied the eastern box turtle I had flagged the boundary of my research site in the Black Water Creek Natural Area. All the box turtles within the boundary defined the population I was studying.

The **population estimate** is an attempt by researchers to figure out the population size. This involves labor-intensive searching, counting, marking, and releasing all individuals caught. Only God knows how many there are, since animals don't register themselves with the government. But the mark-recapture method can allow the researcher to get a ballpark idea. Using one of several formulas, one can compute a population estimate based on the ratio of marked individuals to the total number caught (including marked and unmarked).

This is an oversimplification, but let's say I wanted to get an idea of how many box turtles are in my study site. First, I survey my entire site and capture 20 turtles. I mark them and then release them where they were caught. I wait until the marked turtles have mixed well with the rest of the population. I then do another survey through the site. Let's say I capture twenty-five turtles on the second survey. Of these twenty-five turtles, five of them were marked (20%). Although it is not certain, it is reasonable to assume that the 20% approximates the same percentage of twenty marked turtles (first survey) out of the unknown total. So if twenty turtles are 20% of the total, then the total is approximately one hundred turtles. The more turtles marked in this method, the more accurate it becomes.

A **community** consists of all the populations in a given area (which may involve hundreds to thousands of different populations). Of course, it is impossible to exhaustively study any community in its entirety, so community ecologists usually explore some relationship or interaction occurring in a community. For example, a predator-prey relationship or a symbiotic relationship like mutualism, commensalism, or parasitism could be studied in depth. It may include competition for resources within members of the same population (same species) or competition between different species.

An **ecosystem** is a naturally defined area comprised of all the living and all the non-living factors of that environment. The *eco* refers to the environment and the *system* refers to the fact that its components function as an integrated whole (like the parts of an engine). Two fancy words make the definition of ecosystem even more concise. **Biotic factors** refer to the living portion of the ecosystem (the community) and the **abiotic factors** refer to the physical, nonliving portion of the ecosystem. Some examples of ecosystems would be pond, bog, meadow, mangrove swamp, rain forest, coral reef, river, sagebrush-grass prairie, deciduous forest, etc.

If we did a quick review of a swamp ecosystem, the abiotic factors include water chemistry, soil type, temperature, humidity, seasonal climate changes, topography, etc. of that swamp. The biotic factors include all the different kinds of animals, plants, fungi, protists, and bacteria that are residents of that particular swamp.

Studies of ecosystems often seek to find out the causal relationship between the abiotic factors and biotic factors. In other words, what are the physical reasons why those particular plants, animals, etc., can live there, but others cannot? Because the study of ecosystems involves a thorough knowledge of the living and nonliving factors being considered, ecology can be a very complex and interdisciplinary science drawing from other biological sciences and physical sciences to inform its research—such as genetics, physiology, chemistry, geology, hydrology, and meteorology.

Where a creature naturally lives is its **habitat**. However, even a single habitat can be quite complex, like a tropical rain forest or a coral reef. Each general habitat offers a huge smorgasbord of different and distinct places to hang out.

Many creatures are choosey and prefer certain places over others. These subsets of the habitat are called **microhabitats**. For instance, in a rain forest, some microhabitats include the ground, underground, cracks on the main tree trunks, epiphytes (smaller plants that grow on the branches of the tree), and the canopy (the foliage-covered branches at the top of the large trees in or near the sunlight). All these different microhabitats can even be further subdivided as well.

The **ecological niche** of a particular organism is basically its entire way of life. The niche isn't just where it lives; it also includes many factors in its habitat or microhabitat: the particular food it eats, the temperature it prefers, the shelter it chooses, the soil it grows in, the amount of light it needs, whether it is nocturnal or diurnal, whether or not it migrates, the moisture level it needs, its oxygen needs, and the substrate it resides on (or in)—whether it be soil, rock, water (still or running; salty or fresh), plants, or even animals. And this is *not* a complete list. Each organism has a set of particular requirements that enable it to survive in a fluctuating environment, to grow, and to reproduce. Its way of life and all the factors that contribute to that way of life is its niche.

COMMUNITY INTERACTIONS

Some ecologists are keen in figuring out the abiotic factors that shape an organism's niche. For example, why do trees cease to grow above the timberline? The answer to that question will be largely temperature (an abiotic factor).

Figure 28.1 Predator and prey

As important as these factors are, they don't provide as much drama as do the interactions between living things. **Predator-prey relationships** are almost impossible to count. Whether it is a crocodile taking down a wildebeest or a ladybug pouncing on an aphid or an owl swooping down on field mouse, predator-prey interactions are fascinating as well as important ecologically. The prey provides food for the predator and the predator keeps the prey population in check.

Figure 29.2
Lichen—algae and fungi

Symbiosis simply means "living together." The organisms involved in a symbiotic relationship are called **symbionts**. The three basic types of symbiotic relationships are **mutualism, commensalism**, and **parasitism**.

As we've already seen, mutualism is the most harmonious and friendly. Both symbionts benefit from the relationship and can be symbolized as +/+. Some of my favorite examples are:

- Lichens: In this relationship the algal and fungal symbionts are so intimate that the two seem like one organism.
- Coral and zooxanthellae
- Clownfish and sea anemones

Figure 29.3
Clownfish and sea anemone

- Bullhorn acacia and ants

Figure 29.4 Bullhorn acacia and Pseudomyrmex ferruginea *ants*

Commensalism occurs when one symbiont clearly benefits but the other neither reaps benefits nor is it adversely affected. A classic example of this is the shark and the remora. The remora rides on or cruises alongside the shark and feeds on the scraps of flesh left over from its partner's meal. The shark isn't hindered or deprived in anyway by the remora's presence, but neither is it blessed by it. It is symbolized as +/0.

Parasitic relationships are unfortunately quite common and, more often than not, quite gross. The Phyla Nematoda and Platyhelminthes are loaded with villainous members that live within and feed on their host's tissues or ingested food (**endoparasites**), causing varying degrees of harm from mild to severe. Some examples (I hate to say "*good* examples") are the tapeworms, liver flukes, and filarial worms. Parasites that reside on the outside of their host are called **ectoparasites**. Unpleasant and familiar examples are fleas, ticks, lice, and leeches that suck blood from their hosts. This kind of relationship is symbolized as +/-.

Figure 29.5 Shark and remora

Competition occurs when two or more species are after the same resources (food, territory, sunlight, etc.) that form part of each species' niche (**interspecific competition**). An example would be several grazing antelope species competing for the grass and other plants in the same area. Speaking of antelopes, lion and cheetah menus overlap considerably and where both cats are found, interspecific competition results. If competition for

Figure 29.6 Engorged tick

resources occurs between individuals of the same species, it is called **intraspecific competition.** Examples of the latter would be male deer (bucks) locking antlers to attract mates (does). An example from the plant kingdom would be two adjacent trees of the same species competing for optimal light and good soil. There are many more examples as well as different forms of inter- and intraspecific competition. If you're interested in more details, you can check out an introductory ecology text.

POPULATION GROWTH

Population ecology often requires some knowledge of how fast the population is growing. The **intrinsic rate of increase** is calculated by subtracting the death and emigration rates from the birth and immigration rates. Once calculated, the rate can be graphed with the y-axis representing numbers of individuals and the x-axis representing time (see below). Theoretically, if we assume no limits to resources (e.g., no limits to adequate food and space) and no accumulation of factors that hinder reproduction, then all populations enter into **exponential growth.**

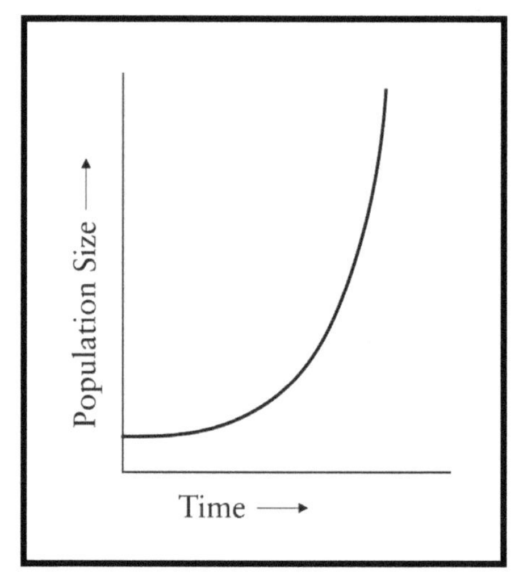

Figure 29.7 Exponential growth curve

This may be useful for comparative purposes, but it does not actually occur in nature. Something is always going to ride the brakes and put limits to population growth. This may be **abiotic factors** that limit growth (not enough water, not enough light, not enough minerals in the soil, etc.), or it may be any number of **biotic factors** (competition, parasites, and/or predators). Any combination of these may put a lid on population growth.

Whatever the case, populations in a highly stable environment manifest **logistic growth.** The maximum number of individuals that a particular environment can sustain is called the **carrying capacity.** As the population approaches

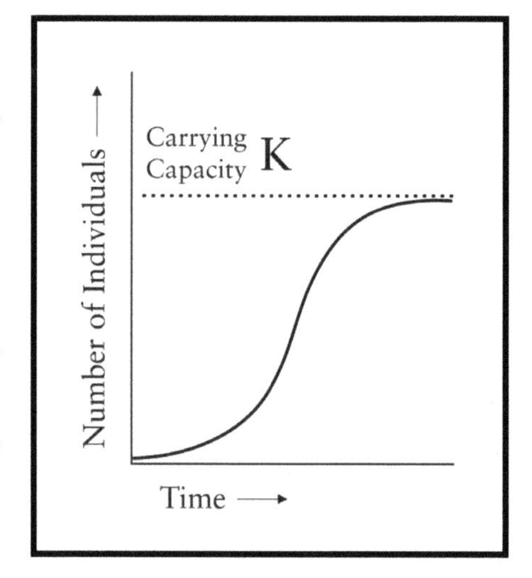

Figure 29.8 Logistic growth curve

the carrying capacity, the rate of increase slows down until it plateaus at carrying capacity.

Although logistic growth is closer to reality than exponential growth, it still inadequately represents the dynamic nature of ecosystems. Why? Partly because biotic and abiotic factors of ecosystems are almost always in a state of flux for many reasons, but mostly because weather patterns change from season to season and year to year. When weather fluctuates, it impacts a multitude of biotic and abiotic factors, which in turn affects population growth. Consequently, growth curves are highly dynamic and tricky to predict.

FOOD CHAINS AND FOOD WEBS

We know that plants capture energy from the sun, enabling them to manufacture themselves with the raw materials from the soil, water, and air.

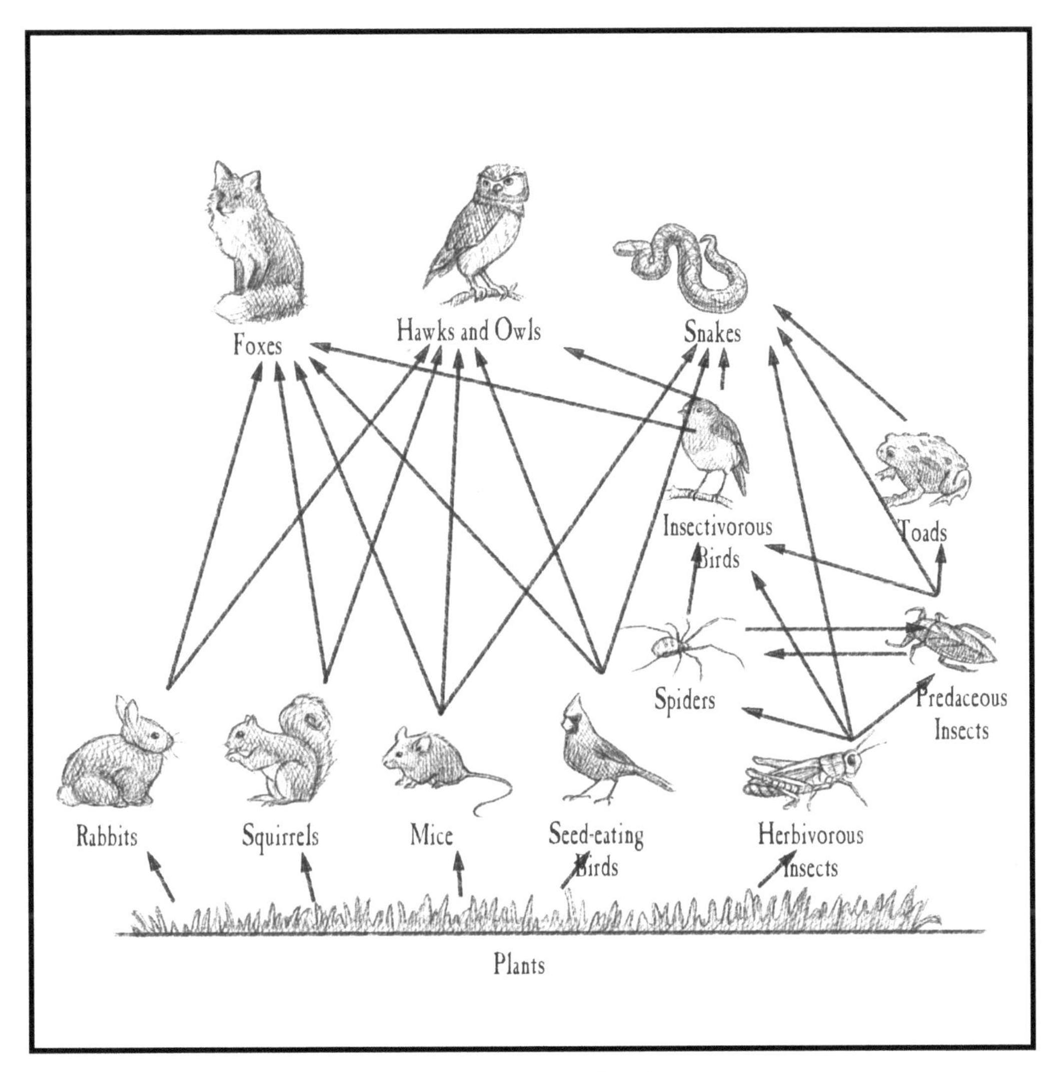

Figure 29.9 Food Web

Herbivores eat plants which provide them with food and energy to grow and reproduce. Carnivores eat herbivores or other carnivores for the same reasons. This familiar concept of energy flow through a community is called a **food chain** or **food web.** Food chains are simpler and look like a particular linear sequence of energy flow. For example,

grass → white-footed mouse → bull snake → red-tailed hawk.

But if we look at all the interconnected food chains that reflect the complexity of energy flow, it would look more like a web (Figure 29.9).

The direction of arrows indicates the direction of energy (food) flow from plants to herbivores to carnivores. Because plants or algae are the original source of food production in any food chain or web, they are collectively called **producers**. Animals that consume only producers are called **herbivores** or **primary consumers.** Animals that consume primary consumers are called **secondary consumers.** If they consume secondary consumers they are called **tertiary consumers.**

As you can imagine, food webs aren't that tidy. Many animals are general **carnivores** and aren't simply one level or the other. A carnivore may be a tertiary consumer today and a secondary consumer tomorrow. Also, **omnivores** eat both producers and consumers and can't be labeled as a primary, secondary, or tertiary consumer because they bounce around between all three categories.

Look at the figure below. Producer, primary consumer, secondary con-

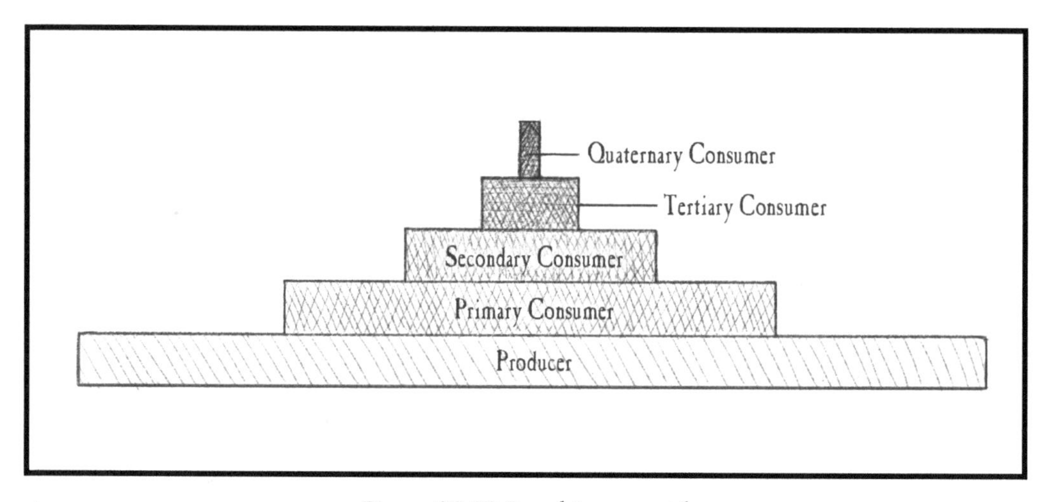

Figure 29.10 Trophic pyramid

sumer, etc., are called **trophic levels** ("trophic" refers to feeding). **Trophic pyramids** represent the relative abundance of energy (food) that is contained in each trophic level.

Because only a fraction of the available energy moves from one trophic level to the next, the number of trophic levels that can exist in a food chain is greatly limited. Of course, producers and consumers all die sooner or later. And when they do, certain critters consume them as well. Many fungi and bacteria consume the dead by the process of decay; when they do, they are called **decomposers.** Some animals also specialize in consuming large chunks of dead plants or carrion, and these are called **scavengers.** However, when the dead stuff is comprised of small fragments of plant and animal material, it is called **detritus.** Those that consume such matter are **detritovores** (earthworms, woodlice, amphipods, etc.).

BIOGEOCHEMICAL CYCLES

Biogeochemical cycles really highlight (from an ecological perspective) the first law of thermodynamics; i.e., the law that matter, apart from a miracle, cannot be created or destroyed. These cycles show how several key elements (or compounds, as in the case of water) are perpetually recycled. They don't spontaneously form somewhere, get used by living creatures, and then get permanently dumped.

The Water Cycle

The most familiar biogeochemical cycle is the **water cycle,** which you probably learned in elementary school. This cycle (hopefully) needs no detailed

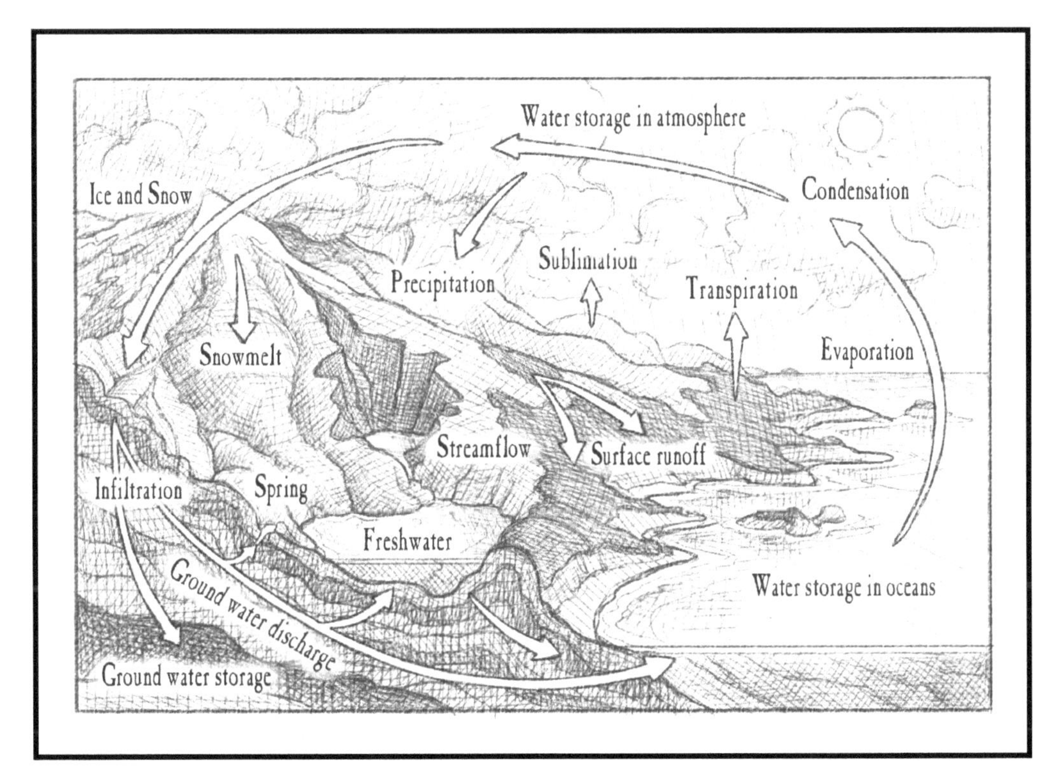

Figure 29.11 The Water Cycle

explanation. The diagram below shows how water is continually recycled through the environment. Evaporation from bodies of water or transpiration from plants adds moisture to the air. Through condensation, clouds form. Precipitation produces runoff in streams and rivers as well as flow of ground water. Eventually, the water returns to the surface where it can evaporate or transpire from plants, thus bringing it full circle.

The Carbon Cycle

To fully understand the **carbon cycle**, it is essential to know the composition of carbon-based biomolecules like carbohydrates, proteins, lipids, and nucleic acids. These biomolecules makes up a large portion of the fabric of living cells. How does it get there? Carbon dioxide (in the air) is absorbed by plants and converted into carbohydrates by photosynthesis ($6CO_2 + 6H_2O \rightarrow C_6H_{12}O_6 + 6O_2$). Plants also convert these carbohydrates into other biomolecules by other enzymatic pathways. When plants are eaten by herbivores, these biomolecules (containing carbon) are used for the creature's energy and growth. Herbivores are eaten and so the biomolecules in the prey are absorbed and reconfigured into the flesh of the predator. Thus carbon moves through the food chain.

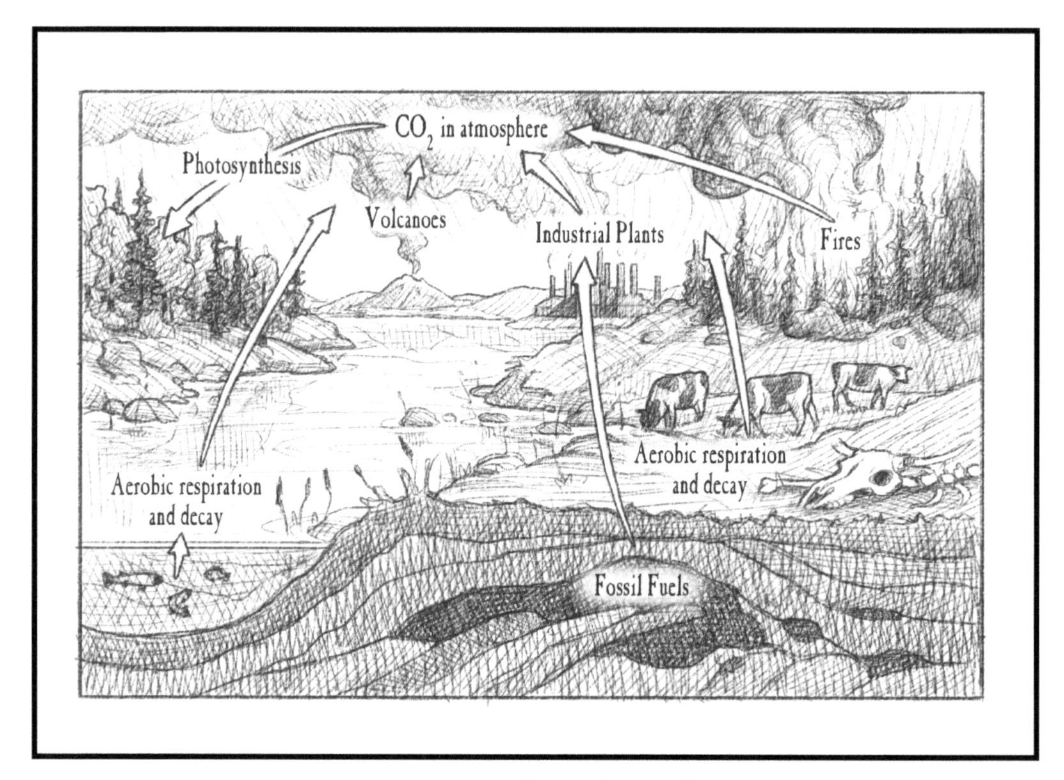

Figure 29.12 The Carbon Cycle

If the food is used for fuel in cellular respiration ($C_6H_{12}O_6 + 6O_2 \rightarrow 6CO_2 + 6H_2O$) by plant or animal, the carbon in the biomolecules can be released as carbon dioxide into the atmosphere. Once there, it can be taken up by plants again and made into carbohydrates by photosynthesis.

Carbon can also take the longer route through an entire food chain where the tertiary consumer dies. Decomposers (fungi and bacteria) consume the flesh and, by means of cellular respiration, release carbon dioxide into the atmosphere.

Carbon can take an even longer, more circuitous route if the creature is deeply buried, turned into oil or coal, eventually dug up, and turned into gasoline, burned, released into the atmosphere as carbon dioxide, and eventually back into plants to be converted into carbohydrates.

The Nitrogen Cycle

Nitrogen in biomolecules, though not as abundant as carbon, is still present and important in certain molecules like proteins and the amino acids that make them up. Nitrogen is also part of the nitrogenous bases of DNA, RNA, and ATP. As a result, they go through the food chain as well. However, nitrogenous wastes are not given off by exhalation like carbon dioxide.

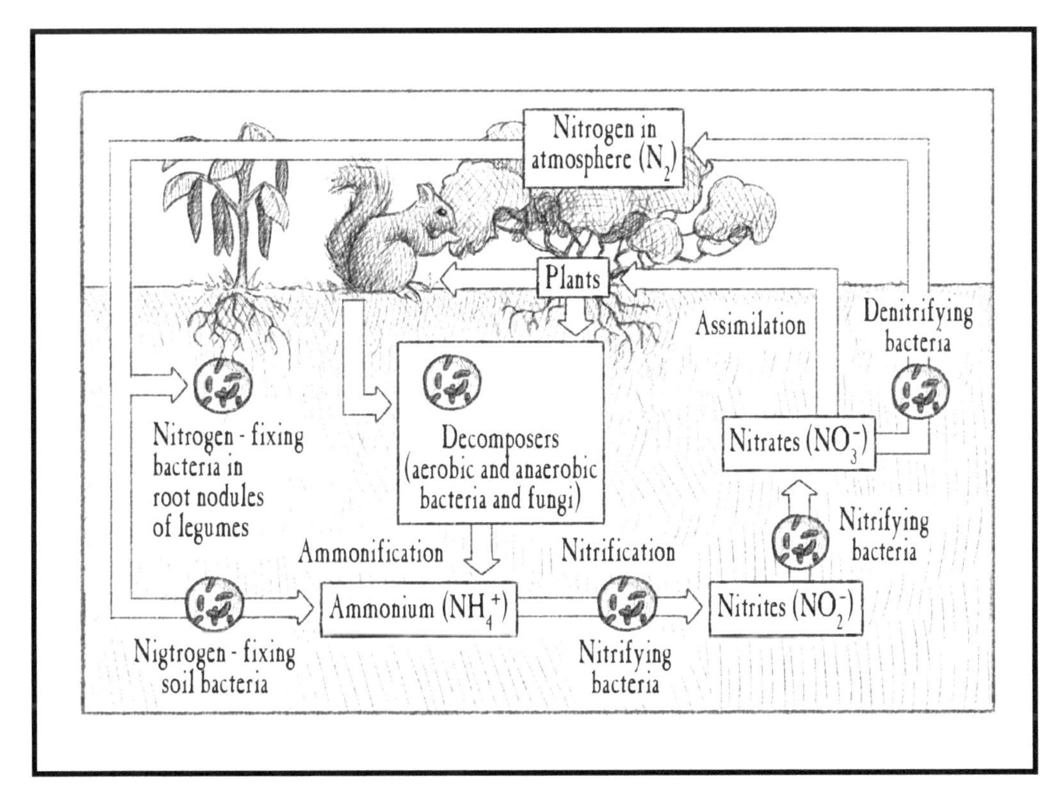

Figure 29.13 The Nitrogen Cycle

When excess proteins are broken down, the amino groups ($-NH_2$) are excreted as ammonia or incorporated into carbon containing compounds like urea and uric acid. These are excreted in both sweat and urine. If the creature dies, then proteins are broken down by decomposers into ammonia (by a process called ammonification) and released into the soil.

Several soil bacteria are involved in the **nitrogen cycle** as well. Atmospheric nitrogen (N_2) is converted into ammonia (NH_3) by certain **nitrogen-fixing bacteria**. This is the first step in getting nitrogen into a form usable by living creatures. **Nitrifying bacteria** are essential to convert ammonia (from nitrogen-fixation and **ammonification**) into nitrites (NO_2^-) and nitrates (NO_3^-). These compounds can be absorbed by plant roots and converted and incorporated into the structure of nucleotides (for DNA, RNA, and ATP), amino acids, and proteins in plant tissue. From there they can move through the food web. **Denitrifying bacteria** can convert excess nitrates (NO_3^-) not absorbed by plants, into atmospheric nitrogen (N_2).

THE BIOSPHERE

If you think an ecosystem is complex, think of studying the ecology of the whole earth. Our big-picture approach seeks to understand how all of life on earth interacts with nonliving factors on a global scale. This enormous, self-regulating system is called the **biosphere** and can be defined as the sum total of all the ecosystems present on the entire earth. At every level, the balance, the beauty, the bounty, and the bewildering complexities of biological life are mind-boggling. Whether we study life at the molecular level, the biosphere level, or any level in between. "The whole earth is full of His glory" (Is. 6:3b), and "Great are the works of the Lord, studied by all who delight in them" (Ps. 111:2, ESV).

Biblical Conservation

Many Christians are understandably leery of being pro-environment simply because they are used to being at odds with "the Left" or political liberals. Of course, most environmentalists are politically liberal and therefore it's easy to assume that we should be against whatever they are for, and since they are advocating the need to protect and conserve the environment, we have a knee-jerk tendency to be against their wants and desires.

But remember, "The earth is the LORD's and the fullness thereof, the world and those who dwell therein" (Psalm 24:1). Nature doesn't belong to the liberals; it belongs to God. Let's not be shallow in our thinking.

However, just as Christians shouldn't be reactionary towards liberals, neither should we be trend followers just to be cool. Christians are guilty of falling off both sides of this boat. While some Christians are opposed to protecting an endangered species because some extreme environmentalists are overly zealous trying to save it, other Christians are mindlessly following trends like, "It's cool to be green, so let's be green."

Good grief. We need to think like Christians regarding the diversity of life and the health of the local or global environment. A book could be written on this point, but I will try to be brief.[1] Who made all this wonderful diversity? It's not a trick question. And what was God's assessment after he made it all? Genesis 1:31: "And God saw everything that he had made, and behold, it was very good." This statement of God's should greatly influence our attitude toward all of creation, especially the parts of creation that are vulnerable to our actions. If God says it was very good, then we should simply adopt the same opinion. Don't worry if you discover that something you enjoy is also enjoyed by a pantheistic radical environmentalist. In fact, you should enjoy it *more*.

In short, we should think about this stuff like Christians. For example, we see God's perspective on the conservation of the biodiversity He created in Genesis 7:2-3, where He tells Noah: 'Take with you seven pairs of all clean animals, the male and his mate, and a pair of the animals that are not clean, the male and his mate, and seven pairs of the birds of the heavens also, male and female, to keep their offspring alive on the face of the earth." This huge ark that the Lord commanded Noah to build was the biggest biodiversity conservation effort in all of world history. Think about that for a while.

This biblical fact should shape our opinion about the diversity of life and the need to conserve what God created. Animals and plants were not put here for us to casually eliminate if we find that they are in the way of our desires or projects. As we learn more about ecology we see how much life on earth (including us) is interdependent. In other words, the diversity of life has more than just aesthetic appeal and nutritional value; it was also made to keep this planet habitable like a beautiful, living, breathing life-support system.

Now, if we conform our views to God's view of nature, we will still obviously differ from a secular environmentalist in at least one key area, and that is this: God made us in His image and *gave us dominion over all*

1. See Gordon Wilson, *A Different Shade of Green* (Canon Press, forthcoming).

creation. In Genesis 1:28, He said, "Be fruitful and multiply and fill the earth and subdue it and have dominion over the fish of the sea and over the birds of the heavens and over every living thing that moves on the earth."

But note: godly dominion is different than domination. It doesn't mean exploit, expend, or eliminate. Christ has *dominion* over the church, His bride, but to exploit, expend, or eliminate her isn't His goal. A marriage should also reflect this lovely kind of dominion. If properly understood, godly dominion conveys the idea of caring, nurturing, cultivating, enhancing, beautifying, and enriching. It never means diminishing, impoverishing, oppressing, or neglecting.

My hope is that this book, though I have just scraped the surface of God's wonderful creation, will not only instill a lifelong desire to learn more about the myriad creatures our Lord has made, but will also create a spirit of praise and gratitude along with a desire to exercise godly dominion over His lavish creation.

CHAPTER 29: REVIEW QUESTIONS

1. The study of the interactions between living creatures and their environment is called ______.

2. A naturally functioning system comprised of a living (biotic) community and its nonliving (abiotic) environment is a(n) ______.

3. Name the three types of symbioses and their corresponding symbols.

4. Give one example of a pair of creatures in a mutualistic relationship and state how both benefit each other.

5. Give one example of a pair of creatures in a parasitic relationship and state how one benefits and how the other is harmed.

6. In logistic growth what prevents a population from continuing to grow exponentially?

7. Which diagram more accurately represents the complex and variable energy flow in a community?
   a. Food web
   b. Food chain
   c. Trophic pyramid

8. Which diagram shows the relative abundance of producers, primary consumers, secondary consumers, etc.?
   a. Food web
   b. Food chain
   c. Trophic pyramid

9. What two major groups are decomposers?

10. Animals within the same population often compete for food, water, territory, sunlight, or mates. This is called ______ competition.

11. The total lifestyle of an organism including its habitat requirements (both biotic and abiotic) and how it uses these requirements to survive and reproduce are all part of its ecological ______.

12. When animals, plants, fungi, bacteria, and protists burn glucose during cellular respiration and release (or exhale) CO_2, it is a very important part of what biogeochemical cycle?

13. Name one other plant process that is also part of this cycle.

14. Ammonification, nitrogen fixation, nitrification, denitrification are all steps in the ______ cycle.

15. When atmospheric nitrogen is converted into ammonia by bacteria it is called ______.

APPENDICES

Appendix 1

A CREATIONIST MANIFESTO

If you've thumbed through this book, you've probably figured out that I'm a creationist of some sort. But since there is a number of different species of creationists, I thought it would be good to let you know exactly what sort I am. Before I do, you should also know that my primary goal in this book is to teach biology in such a way as to bring glory to God. I am a young earth creationist: in some places I touch on my views briefly but my young earth creationism is not glaringly obvious within the main text. This is because my goals do not include an argument for young earth creationism or a denunciation of Darwinism. Those goals are fine and have their place, but are best left for another book at another time. Nevertheless, I wanted to briefly and clearly present my foundational beliefs concerning the age of the earth, the origin of life, the fall, the curse, the flood, and the ultimate redemption of creation.

All Scripture is God-breathed and is useful for teaching, rebuking, correcting, and training in righteousness (2 Timothy 3:16). The Bible is true (from beginning to end) but must be interpreted carefully using hermeneutical principles appropriate for the genre. In other words history should be interpreted as history, poetry as poetry, etc. Because Genesis is written as straightforward history it shouldn't be reinterpreted into something contrary to what it obviously says even if mainstream secular scientific claims are contrary to its contents.

I believe the earth to be about six thousand years old based on the Hebrew meaning of the word *yom* and the genealogies of Genesis 5 & 11. Also several New Testament writers speak of the events and people of Genesis as historical not figurative.

I believe that plants, animals, and people were created during the creation week which lasted six ordinary days followed by one day of rest to set a pattern for our work week (Genesis 1:1-2:4).

I believe in a global flood in the days of Noah that destroyed all terrestrial animal life except for eight people and all terrestrial animals kinds brought into the ark (Genesis 6-8).

I believe that at the end of the creation week "God saw all that He had made and it was very good" (Genesis 1:31). It is clear from the context of Scripture that animal and human death was and is a result of the fall—God's curse against Adam's disobedience (Genesis 2:17). All animals and humans were vegetarians before the fall (Genesis 1:30). The fall also resulted in a curse that affected the entire creation. We know that the whole creation has been groaning as in the pains of childbirth right up to the present time (Romans 8:22). This is manifested through thorns and thistles, hard painful work for man, pain in childbirth, the transformation of benign creatures into predators, parasites, and pathogens and ultimate physical death to all creatures possessing *nephesh* (a Hebrew word basically meaning "breath of life"). Biological systems at all levels (molecular biology to ecology) are riddled with the consequences of the fall and it should be understood that even though it is glorious and wonderful in many respects, it isn't operating presently the way God originally created it. It will be utterly transformed to something that will be so glorious we currently are unable to grasp. "The creation itself will be liberated from its bondage to decay and brought into the freedom and glory of the children of God." (Romans 8:21)

Here I stand.

Gordon Wilson

Suggested Reading:

- *The New Creationism* by Paul Garner
- *Faith, Form, and Time* by Kurt Wise
- *Answers Magazine* by Answers in Genesis

Appendix II

NATURAL SELECTION

Natural selection is an important concept that creationists need to come to grips with. Unfortunately evolutionists successfully shanghaied the idea. After the Theory of Evolution became firmly established as the most popular explanation of how the diversity of life arose, many lay people simply thought that natural selection was a concept that only supported evolution. For the lay evolutionist, it was embraced as such. Some lay creationists who believe that 'molecules to man' evolution is false, have largely rejected natural selection. This is a classic case of "throwing the baby out with the bath water."

This is a brief attempt to clear up any misunderstandings. First, Edward Blyth (a creationist) was the one who pondered this idea before Darwin, though he never used the term 'natural selection.' He respected and corresponded with Darwin, but he believed that selection did not change types of creatures in any unlimited way. He believed that natural selection helped maintain the "perfection of the type" by weeding out members of a population who weren't able to survive under certain natural conditions (disease, competition, predation, climate, food availability, etc.).

What is natural selection? It is a fairly straightforward idea. I will break it down into four points.

1. In any population (a group of individuals of the same species living in a particular area) there is variation in phenotypes (different sizes, different color patterns, different behaviors, different internal and external characteristics, etc.). All of these differences make a given individual more or less vulnerable to certain natural conditions.

2. Reproduction in a population produces more individuals than a certain environment can support. Because of these differences, some individuals will have traits more suited for survival in a

particular set of natural conditions. So nature 'selects' which individuals are able to survive and which ones aren't (or aren't able to breed). The ones that aren't able to survive die from disease, predation, starvation, etc.

3. Many of these traits are heritable (passed to their offspring). The survivors pass on their 'winning' traits to their offspring thus bequeathing on them those traits that kept them alive and able to breed. Those that died or aren't able to breed are unable to pass their inferior traits to the next generation.

4. The effect of all this is that the population ends up possessing those traits most suited for survival and reproduction for a particular set of natural conditions. Those traits that aren't suited for survival and reproduction are eventually eliminated. Natural selection, therefore, enables a population (if there is enough variation) to adapt to a certain set of natural conditions.

AN ASSUMED EXAMPLE OF NATURAL SELECTION

(This example is not proven because it happened in the unobservable past.) Too much solar radiation (UV) is notorious for damaging DNA in our skin cells. Therefore, the heritable trait of darker skin color was advantageous for survival in the equatorial regions of the world (high solar radiation) and was a trait that was selected for. Why? It is because high melanin (the brown pigment) producing skin is able to absorb more of the damaging UV light, thus protecting the DNA of skin cells. Light-skinned individuals, on the other hand, were possibly selected against because they were vulnerable to frequent sun burns and higher incidences of skin cancer.

Fair-skin is a selective advantage for lower amounts of solar radiation. Low melanin production in fair skin people groups of higher latitudes (both north and south) enable them to allow lower levels of UV radiation to convert 7-dihydrocholesterol into vitamin D which is needed by our body. Melanin in dark-skinned people absorbs much of the UV, thus inhibiting the necessary conversion to vitamin D, leading to a possible deficiency in vitamin D at high latitudes.

CREATIONIST QUALIFICATIONS

There is nothing in the above concept that disagrees with creationism. All informed creationists believe that populations are able to adapt to a variety of different sets of natural conditions. But there are limitations. Natural selection 'selects'; it never creates novel traits from scratch to enable the population to increase in genetic information. Selection can only select traits that are already genetically present in the population. If a population has no member with a particular trait (nor gene(s) for that trait), then natural selection will not be able conjure that new gene or genes into existence.

What about mutations? Mutations are mistakes (typos) in the genetic code. Most mutations are either neutral (no effect), harmful (lethal to slightly negative), or beneficial (helps the individual in its struggle to survive). But even these 'beneficial' mutations are not an increase in novel genetic information. Usually they might help survival in extreme or unnatural conditions but if conditions return to normal, the mutants are less able to compete against the non-mutants. Yes, mutations can generate variability in genes (a new allele for example). But this is simply a new twist on a trait that already exists. This doesn't add a completely new trait (or apomorphy). Not only are mutation and natural selection incapable of generating novel genetic information, there is solid evidence that mutations ultimately reduce the amount of genetic information in existence. This is the exact opposite of what evolutionists claim mutations and natural selection can do over vast amounts of time.

Suggested reading:

- *Icons of Evolution* by Jonathan Wells
- *The Myth of Junk DNA* by Jonathan Wells
- *Genetic Entropy* by John Sanford

Appendix III

Periodic Table of the Elements

IA	IIA	IIIB	IVB	VB	VIB	VIIB	VIIIB			IB	IIB	IIIA	IVA	VA	VIA	VIIA	VIIIA
1 H Hydrogen																	2 He Helium
3 Li Lithium	4 Be Beryllium											5 B Boron	6 C Carbon	7 N Nitgrogen	8 O Oxygen	9 F Fluorine	10 Ne Neon
11 Na Sodium	12 Mg Magnesium											13 Al Aluminum	14 Si Silicon	15 P Phosphorus	16 S Sulfur	17 Cl Chlorine	18 Ar Argon
19 K Potassium	20 Ca Calcium	21 Sc Scandium	22 Ti Titanium	23 V Vanadium	24 Cr Chromium	25 Mn Manganese	26 Fe Iron	27 Co Cobalt	28 Ni Nickel	29 Cu Copper	30 Zn Zinc	31 Ga Gallium	32 Ge Germanium	33 As Arsenic	34 Se Selenium	35 Br Bromine	36 Kr Krypton
37 Rb Rubidium	38 Sr Strontium	39 Y Yttrium	40 Zr Zirconium	41 Nb Niobium	42 Mo Molybdenum	43 Tc Technetium	44 Ru Ruthenium	45 Rh Rhodium	46 Pd Palladium	47 Ag Silver	48 Cd Cadmium	49 In Indium	50 Sn Tin	51 Sb Antimony	52 Te Tellurium	53 I Iodine	54 Xe Xenon
55 Cs Cesium	56 Ba Barium	57-71	72 Hf Hafnium	73 Ta Tantalum	74 W Tungsten	75 Re Rhenium	76 Os Osmium	77 Ir Iridium	78 Pt Platinum	79 Au Gold	80 Hg Mercury	81 Tl Thallium	82 Pb Lead	83 Bi Bismuth	84 Po Polonium	85 At Astatine	86 Rn Radon
87 Fr Francium	88 Ra Radium	89-103	104 Rf Rutherfordium	105 Db Dubnium	106 Sg Seaborgium	107 Bh Bohrium	108 Hs Hassium	109 Mt Meitnerium	110 Ds Darmstadtium	111 Rg Roentgenium	112 Cn Copernicium	113 Uut Ununtrium	114 Fl Flerovium	115 Uup Ununpentium	116 Lv Livermorium	117 Uus Ununseptium	118 Uuo Ununoctium

57 La Lanthanum	58 Ce Cerium	59 Pr Praseodymium	60 Nd Neodymium	61 Pm Promethium	62 Sm Samarium	63 Eu Europium	64 Gd Gadolinium	65 Tb Terbium	66 Dy Dysprosium	67 Ho Holmium	68 Er Erbium	69 Tm Thulium	70 Yb Ytterbium	71 Lu Lutetium
89 Ac Actinium	90 Th Thorium	91 Pa Protactinium	92 U Uranium	93 Np Neptunium	94 Pu Plutonium	95 Am Americium	96 Cm Curium	97 Bk Berkelium	98 Cf Californium	99 Es Einsteinium	100 Fm Fermium	101 Md Mendelevium	102 No Nobelium	103 Lr Lawrencium

Alkali Metal · Alkaline Earth · Transition Metal · Semimetal · Nonmetal · Basic Metal · Halogen · Noble Gas · Lanthanide · Actinide

ACKNOWLEDGMENTS

I am very grateful to all those at Canon Press who gave me the green light on this project. I thank Brian Kohl, who oversaw the project, Forrest Dickison who did all the fantastic illustrations, Laura Storm (typesetter) who made the layout look snazzy, and Gwen Burrow who worked hard to make it squeaky clean grammatically. A general thanks to Brian Marr for indexing and proofreading and to anyone else at Canon who was enlisted in any way to get this published. I also thank a handful of photographers who donated some pictures to show folks what certain critters look like, while simultaneously lessening Forrest's illustration load. These talented photographers are Jonathan Blair (a Texan and sibling of an NSA grad), Yeran Torosyan (my niece), John O'Bryan (a friend), and Dane Wilson (my son). Thanks, y'all, for being good with a camera. I'm very grateful to Drs. Randy Davy, Joe Francis, and Scott Minnich who reviewed the scientific accuracy of certain chapters (I take full responsibility for any errors that remain). I am greatly indebted to my dear wife, Meredith who was a great cheerleader and encouragement through this long project. She made me believe that this kind of textbook needed to be written (even if it didn't). Above all I thank my Lord who created the beautiful unity, the rich diversity, and unfathomable complexity of biological life. I also thank Him for giving me the innate desire to hold forth incessantly about it to anyone willing to pay attention or pay tuition.

PHOTO CREDITS

See the list below for copyright holders. All photos used by permission of the photographer and/or in accordance with Creative Commons copyright licenses (CC BY 3.0 Unported and CC BY-SA 3.0 Unported; http://creativecommons.org/licenses/by/3.0/ or http://creativecommons.org/licenses/by-sa/3.0/), or are in the public domain. If you have any questions or concerns regarding this text's figures, please contact us in writing at Canon Press, Attn: Permissions, POB 8729, Moscow, ID 83843.

15.5 One of Family Coccinellidae; Jonathan Blair
15.7a *Anthonomus rectirostri*; copyright Stanislav Krejcik
15.7b *Anthonomus rubi* copyright Miroslav Deml
15.8 Black bear (*Ursus americanus*); Jonathan Blair
15.9 American toad (*Bufo americanus*); Gordon Wilson
15.11 Western fence lizard; Gordon Wilson
15.12 Eastern box turtle; Gordon Wilson
17.5 Kelp; Gordon Wilson
17.6 Red algae; Gordon Wilson
17.7 Green algae; Gordon Wilson
17.8 Green algae (Hydrodictyon); Gordon Wilson
18.2 Trypanosoma. This image is in the public domain and thus free of any copyright restrictions. Image #613 credit goes to the CDC/Dr. Myron G. Schultz
18.3 Ameba; Gordon Wilson
18.4 Live *Ammonia tepida* benthic foraminiferan collected from San Francisco Bay. Phase-contrast photomicrograph; copyright by Scott Fay, UC Berkeley, 2005.
18.6 *Carpocanium solitarium*; copyright John Dolan.
18.7 Paramecium; Gordon Wilson
18.8 Stentor; Gordon Wilson
18.10 Plasmodial slime mold; Gordon Wilson
18.12 Healthy versus blighted potatoes; Dr. Henk Shouten and Ronald Hutten, Laboratory of Plant breeding, Wageningen University
18.13 Sea-trout suffering from UDN with secondary Saprolegnia infections; copyright Velela
19.1 Rhizopus hyphae; Gordon Wilson
19.2 Mycelium; Gordon Wilson
19.6 Blue cheese; Gordon Wilson

19.8 Pilobolus; copyright Eduardo A. Esquivel Rios
19.12 Cup fungus; Gordon Wilson
19.13 Cross section of ascoma; Gordon Wilson
19.14 Basidiomycete; Gordon Wilson
19.15 Gill basiospores; Gordon Wilson
19.16a Two-Color Bolete downside; copyright Jason Hollinger, http://flickr.com/photo/7147684@N03/1011506605 (CC BY 2.0)
19.16b Puffball; copyright Jason Hollinger, http://www.flickr.com/photos/7147684@N03/1023701749 (CC BY 2.0)
19.16c Coral fungus; Gordon Wilson
19.18 Lichen thallus; Gordon Wilson
21.1 Sponge spicules; NOAA
22.2 Coral; Gordon Wilson
22.3 Obelia; Gordon Wilson
22.5 Hydroid colony; Gordon Wilson
22.6 Sea anemones; Gordon Wilson
22.4 Roundworms; Gordon Wilson
22.7 Leech; Gordon Wilson
22.9 Clamworm; Gordon Wilson
23.3 Diversity of bivalves; Gordon Wilson
23.4 Slug pneumostome; Gordon Wilson
23.5 Diversity of gastropods; Gordon Wilson
23.6 Chambered nautilus; Gordon Wilson
23.7 Diversity of jellyfish; Gordon Wilson
25.2 Arthropod features; Dane Wilson
25.3 Diversity of bivalves; Gordon Wilson
25.4 Millipede; Gordon Wilson
25.5 Centipede; Gordon Wilson
25.9 Isopod; Gordon Wilson
25.14 Dragonfly; Jonathan Blair
25.15 Dragonfly naiad; Gordon Wilson
25.16 Wings of grasshopper; Gordon Wilson
25.17a Variety of Orthoptera; Yeran Torosyan
25.17b Variety of Orthoptera; Gordon Wilson
25.17c Variety of Orthoptera; Jonathan Blair
25.18 Piercing-sucking mouthparts of stinkbug; Gordon Wilson
25.19a Variety of Hemiptera; Jonathan Blair
25.19b Brown Marmorated Stink Bug (*Halyomorpha halys*); David R. Lance, USDA APHIS PPQ, Bugwood.org

25.19c Variety of Hemiptera; Dane Wilson
25.20a Variety of Coleoptera; Gordon Wilson
25.20b Variety of Coleoptera; Jonathan Blair
25.22 Beetle on glass 2013-01-15 -copyright USGS Native Bee Inventory and Monitering Laboritory
25.25 Deerfly halteres; Gordon Wilson
25.26a Variety of Diptera; Jonathan Blair
25.26c Variety of Diptera; John O'Bryan
25.27 Wing scales of butterfly; Gordon Wilson
25.28b *Pholodes sinistraria*; copyright Donald Hobern
25.28c Butterfly larva; copyright Ajaykuyiloor
25.29b Moth versus butterfly, at rest; Dane Wilson
25.30 Hamuli; Gordon Wilson
25.31a Variety of Hymenoptera; Dane Wilson
25.31b Variety of Hymenoptera; John O'Bryan
25.32 Horseshoe crab; Gordon Wilson
25.37a Variety of Araneae; John O'Bryan
25.37b Variety of Araneae; Jonathan Blair
25.37c Variety of Araneae; John O'Bryan
26.1 Variety of Echinodermata; Gordon Wilson
26.5 Sea urchin; Gordon Wilson
26.6 Sea slug Pearsonothuria_graeffei.dREU_00566.UF6593; copyright Francois Michonneau
27.3 European Lancelet (*Branchiostoma lanceolatum*) from course sandy sediments (600 µm) on the Belgian continental shelf ; copyright Hans Hillewaert (Creative Commons Share Alike)
27.9 Spotted Eagle Ray (*Aetobatus narinari*); copyright john_norton
27.14 Caecilian; copyright Wilkinson M, Sherratt E, Starace F, Gower DJ (2013), "A New Species of Skin-Feeding Caecilian and the First Report of Reproductive Mode in Microcaecilia" (Amphibia: Gymnophiona: Siphonopidae). PLoS ONE 8(3): e57756. doi:10.1371/journal.pone.0057756
27.15b Variety of Caudata; Gordon Wilson
27.17 Spadefoot toad; Gordon Wilson
27.18 Tropical tree frog; Jonathan Blair
27.24b Painted turtle; Gordon Wilson
27.27 Eastern box turtle laying eggs; Gordon Wilson
27.28 Komodo dragon; Jonathan Blair
27.30 Rattlesnake; Dane Wilson

GLOSSARY

Abiotic factors: *The non-living portion of an ecosystem. 391*

Acetyl CoA: *Coenzyme A temporarily hooked to an acetyl group. 108*

Acetyl group: *A two-carbon molecule formed from the decarboxylation (removal of a carboxyl group) of pyruvate. 108*

Acid: *Any substance that gives off hydrogen ions; pH level < 7. 24*

Acidophilic: *Archaea that can live in highly acidic environments, usually below pH 2. 207*

Active site: *An indentation on an enzyme's surface where substrate(s) temporarily attach to the enzyme and react to form the product(s). 89*

Active transport: *The movement of a molecule from an area of low concentration to an area of high concentration; energy is required. 62*

Adenine: *A two-ringed base that pairs with thymine joining complimentary strands to form the DNA ladder. 116*

Against the concentration gradient: *When a substance moves from an area of low concentration to an area of high concentration. 63*

Agar: *An intercellular substance similar to alginate extracted from red algae. 217*

Algae: *Photosynthetic protists. 209*

Alginate: *An intercellular substance within brown algae tissue that contributes to the algae's rubbery texture. 215*

Allele: *A different version of the same gene. 154, 164-5*

Allosteric inhibition: *The shutting down of enzyme activity due to a non-substrate binding to the allosteric site. 92*

Allosteric site: *A crevice on the enzyme's surface where a non-substrate (often a heavy metal) may bind resulting in the distortion, and loss of function of the enzyme's active site. 92*

Alternation of generations: *A plant life cycle with two distinct generations: gametophyte and sporophyte. 367-72*

Ambulacral groove: *An area on the underside of an echinoderm's arms to the central disc from which tube feet emerge. 319*

Amino acid: *The building block or basic unit of proteins. 40*

Amino Acid Sequence: *The specified order of amino acids which determines the shape and function of each protein. 42, 88*

Ammonification: *The breakdown of proteins into ammonia and other products. 400*

Amebas: *A type of sarcodine that lacks a test. 223*

Amplexus: *The mating of frogs and toads by the male climbing on the female's back. 341*

Ampulla: *A tiny sac in an echinoderm's arms which helps control water movement in the tube feet. 320*

Anadromous: *Species which migrates to freshwater to spawn. 331*

Anal fin: *A single fin near a fish's anus. 332*

Analogous Structure: *An anatomical feature that has the same basic function in different groups of organisms (but, according to evolutionary theory, was not derived from the same structure in a common ancestor of the groups). 195*

Anaphase: *The third phase of mitosis in which the two copies of each chromosome separate from each other and move to opposite sides of the cell. 148*

Angiosperm: *A flowering plant. 378-85*

Anion: *A negatively charged ion. 19*

Annulus: *A spore-launching structure built into the sporangia of ferns. 372*

Anther: *The part of the stamen that produces and releases the pollen. 156, 383*

Antheridium: *The structure within a male gametophyte that produces haploid sperm by mitosis. 369-71*

Anticodon: *The three loose bases on tRNA which are*

designed to pair base-pair with the codons of mRNA. 126

Antony van Leeuwenhoek (1632-1723): *A Dutch tradesman who built a microscope with a single lens that was able to magnify objects over 200 times, allowing him to see many previously unobserved microbes. 48-9*

Apomorphy: *A completely new anatomical structure that, according to evolutionary theory, evolved from scratch from an ancestral population of creatures lacking both the structure and the genetic information to code for that structure. 198-9*

Archaea: *A kingdom of prokaryotes. 204*

Archegonium: *The structure within a female gametophyte that produces eggs by mitosis. 369*

Aristotle (384-322 BC): *Greek philosopher and naturalist who examined many living creatures to create natural groupings according to the features they have in common. 179*

Aristotle's lantern: *The feeding apparatus of a sea urchin consisting of five plate-like jaws. 323*

Arthropods: *Creatures in Phylum Arthropoda with an exoskeleton, a segmented body, jointed appendages, and periodic molting. 291*

Ascoma: *The fruiting body of an ascomycete. 245*

Ascospore: *The spore of an ascomycete. 246*

Ascus: *A cell that produces and contains ascospores in an ascoma. 246*

Aseptate: *Hyphae that lack partitions. 230, 242*

A site: *The second space on a ribosome that is aligned with the next codon to which tRNA binds. 26-7*

Asymmetry: *When no imaginary plane through the animal produces mirror-image halves. 255-6*

Atom: *The smallest part of an element. 15*

Atomic number: *The number of protons in one atom of an element. 18*

ATP: *Adenosine Triphosphate, a nucleotide that carries the chemical energy for metabolism in a cell, functioning as a portable and rechargeable battery. 44, 63, 73*

ATP synthase: *An enzyme/channel protein located in the thylakoid's membrane that allows the accumulated H+ ions to flow from the lumen to the stroma. It is designed such that ADP and P bind to its active site and are converted into ATP. 100*

Atriopore: *A hole through which a cephalochordate expels water from its atrium. 329*

Autotroph: *An organism that obtains food usually through photosynthesis. 209*

Bacillus: *Rod-shaped bacteria. 205*

Bacteria: *A kingdom of prokaryotes (can loosely refer to all prokaryotes). 205-6*

Bacteriology: *A subset of microbiology that focuses on prokaryotes. 20-24*

Bacteriophage: *A virus that infects and replicates within bacteria. 203*

Baramin: *A created kind. 193*

Barb: *A small filament that projects from the shaft of a feather. 353*

Barbule: *A tiny filament connecting the barbs of a feather together with microscopic hooks. 353*

Barnacle: *Phylum Arthropoda, subphylum Crustacea. 294-5*

Base: *Any substance that combines with or absorbs positive hydrogen ions; pH level > 7. 24-5*

Basidioma: *The fruiting body of basidiomycetes. 247*

Basidiospore: *The spore of a basidiomycete. 248*

Basidium: *A cell that produces and bears basidiospores in a basidiomycete. 248*

Bilateral symmetry: *A symmetry where only one imaginary plane passing through the central axis can produce mirror-image halves. 256*

Biogeochemical cycle: *A cycle in which key elements or compounds are perpetually recycled. 401*

Bioluminescence: *When a living creature produces light. 210*

Biosphere: *The enormous self-regulating system by which all life on earth interacts with nonliving factors on a global scale. 400*

Biosynthetic or anabolic reaction: *An endergonic reaction that joins molecules to form bigger molecules. 87*

Biotic factors: *The living portion of an ecosystem. 395, 391, 394*

Bipinnately compound: *A pinnately compound leaf blade whose leaflets are divided into smaller leaflets. 379*

Bivalve: *Phylum Mollusca, class Bivalvia. 283-6*

Blade: *The flattened photosynthetic part of a leaf.*

Bony fish: *Class Osteicthyes; a class of fish mostly having a skeleton of bone, operculum, and a mouth in front. 334-7*

Book lungs: *A series of air tubes surrounded by blood chambers in horseshoe crabs. 313*

Brown algae: *A group of algae, made greenish-brown by the pigment fucoxanthin and chlorophyll a and c. 214-6*

Brownian motion: *The innate ability of molecules to randomly move about. 58*

Buffer: *A chemical that slows down or resists changes in pH. 27*

Caecum: *A blind pouch off a lancelet's digestive track that can phagocytose food particles. 329*

Calcium carbonate: *Lime. 224*

Calvin-Benson Cycle: *The biochemical pathway in the stroma that produces glucose from CO_2 using various intermediates, NADPH, and ATP. 100-3*

Capsid: *A protein coat on a virus. 203*

Carapace: *The upper shell of turtles, terrapins, and tortoises; a decapod's single exoskeletal plate that covers its cephalothorax. 296, 345*

Carbohydrate: *A basic category of biomolecules that is the primary fuel source used to generate energy in the cells of most living creatures; also can serve as structural support for cells and tissues. 31*

Carbon cycle: *The process by which carbon is continually cycled between the biosphere and the atmosphere. 398-9*

Cardiac stomach: *The part of a starfish's stomach which is extruded out of its body to digest prey. 321*

Carolus Linnaeus (1707-1778): *Swedish naturalist and father of modern taxonomy who classified hundreds of animals, plants, and minerals in* Systema Naturae *and his botanical work in Species Plantarum. He developed the basic hierarchy of classification consisting of five ranks or taxa, as well as the binomial system of naming. 182-3*

Carrying capacity: *The maximum population size that a particular environment can sustain. 394*

Cartilaginous fish: *Class Chondrichthyes; a class of fish mostly having a cartilage skeleton and placoid scales. 331-4*

Cation: *A positively charged ion. 19*

Caudal fin: *The tail fin of a fish. 332*

Cell: *The smallest functional living unit of an organism typically consisting of a cell membrane, cytoplasm, and nucleus; can be prokaryotic or eukaryotic. 50*

Cell membrane: *the edge or boundary of the cell which plays a vital role in the import of oxygen and nutrients and export of cell products and waste. 53*

Cell plate formation: *A type of cytokinesis for plant cells in which Golgi bodies manufacture and pinch off cellulose vesicles that congregate along the plane of division and fuse to form a cell plate, creating two cells. 150-1*

Cell theory: *A theory consisting of three tenets: 1) all living things are composed of cells, 2) cells are the fundamental structural and functional unit of all living things, and 3) all cells arise from pre-existing cells. 50*

Cellulase: *An enzyme that breaks down cellulose into glucose. 222*

Cellulose: *Another polysaccharide made up of a linear chain of glucose units, used primarily as cell wall material in plants. 35, 71*

Cell wall: *The structure that provides external rigid or flexible support for certain cells. 79-81*

Centipedes: *Phylum Arthropoda, class Chilopoda. 293-4*

Central cell: *The middle cell of an angiosperm megagametophyte which contains the two polar nuclei. 383*

Central Dogma: *The flow of cellular information from DNA to DNA, DNA to RNA, or DNA to RNA to protein. It also includes the unusual flow of information from RNA to DNA. 115*

Cephalopod: *Phylum Mollusca, class Cephalopoda. 287-9*

Cephalothorax: *The head/thorax of a decapod. 295-6*

Chelicerae: *A small pair of feeding appendages in some arthropods. 309*

Chelipeds: *The pair of a decapod's walking legs enlarged as pincers. 296*

Chitin: *Cell wall material of fungi. 80*

Chloroplast: *An organelle found within plants and algae that is responsible for carrying out the process of photosynthesis. 74-5*

Chromatin: *DNA in its uncoiled state. 144*

Chromosome: *A skein of DNA. 118-9, 205*

Ciliates: *A group of protozoans possessing cilia and more than one nucleus. 225*

Cirripeds or Cirri: *The filter-feeding appendages of barnacles. 295*

Clade: *A group of organisms including both an ancestor and all its descendants. 196*

Cladistics: *The dominant current method of classification that attempts to classify organisms based on their evolutionary ancestry. 193*

Cladogram: *A diagrammatic representation of one or more clades. 196*

Clamworm: *A predatory polychaete. 280*

Claspers: *Copulatory organs on sharks or rays. 332*

Class: *The next taxon under Phylum. 182*

Cleavage furrowing: *A type of cytokinesis for animal cells in which cytoskeletal elements cinch up the membrane along the plane of division like a drawstring, creating two cells. 149*

Cnidocytes: *A cell type that contains nematocysts.*

CO_2: *The chemical formula for carbon dioxide. 266*

Coccus: *Spherical bacteria. 205*

Codominance: *A type of inheritance in which more than one allele is dominant. 169-71*

Codons: *Groups of three nitrogenous bases in RNA coding for one amino acid. 124*

Coenzyme A: *A conenzyme that binds to an acetyl group and delivers it to the Krebs Cycle. 108*

Coenzymes: *Non-protein molecules that assist in the proper function of an enzyme. 93*

Collar cell: *A cell that filters water and captures food in a sponge. 259-60*

Commensalism: *When two creatures live together and one symbiont benefits and the other neither reaps nor is adversely affected. 393*

Community: *All the populations of a given area. 390*

Competition: *When two or more creatures are after the same resources. 393*

Compound (leaf): *A leaf blade that is divided up into leaflets. 380*

Compound (molecule): *A molecule with two or more elements in it. 16*

Conidia: *Asexual spores produced by Ascomycete fungi. 245*

Conidiophore: *Branching hyphae bearing conidia. 245*

Conjugation: *A type of transformation whereby DNA is inserted into another bacterial cell through a pilus. 136*

Contractile vacuole: *A vacuole in unicellular creatures that ejects water from the cell through a membranous canal. 76*

Convergence: *When totally different structures evolve analogous functions. 196*

Coral: *Miniature sea anemone-like cnidarians that live and grow as colonies. 269-70*

Cotyledon: *An embryonic or seed leaf. 380-1*

Covalent bond: *A bond formed through the sharing of valence electrons. 20*

Cristae: *The highly folded inner membrane of the mitochondrion. 107*

Crossing over: *When homologous pairs of chromosomes swap equivalent pieces of their chromosomes. 157*

Crustose: *A growth form of lichen that is tightly affixed to the growth surface. 250-1*

Cuticle: *The nonliving outer portion of the exoskeleton. 291*

Cuttlebone: *A bony structure embedded in the mantle of cuttlefish. 287*

Cuvierian tubules: *An anti-predator device in which a sea cucumber ejects tubules out its anus at assailants. 325*

Cyanobacteria: *Bacteria involved in photosynthesis, contributing much food and oxygen for certain environments. 206*

Cyclosporine: *A chemical isolated from a certain fungus effective in suppressing our immune system which is necessary during organ transplants. 240*

Cytokinesis: *The actual dividing of the original cytoplasm into two separate compartments; concurrent with Telophase. 148-51*

Cytology: *the study of cells. 50*

Cytolysis: *The bursting of a cell due to an influx of water. 60*

Cytoplasm: *the fluid of the cell containing many functional compartments (organelles) and is the site of many biochemical pathways. 24, 38, 53, 67*

Cytoplasmic streaming: *The flow of cytoplasm, vesicles, and vacuoles about the cell's interior. 223*

Cytosine: *A two-ringed base that pairs with guanine joining complimentary strands to form the DNA ladder. 116*

Cytoskeleton: *The supporting framework of a cell which gives the cell its shape. 76-7*

Cytostome: *The mouth-like opening of a ciliate through which food enters a food vacuole. 226*

Decomposer: *Bacteria and fungi involved in breaking down dead organic matter into simpler inorganic substances. 206*

Degradative or catabolic reaction: *An exergonic reaction that breaks down larger molecules into smaller ones. 87*

Dehydration synthesis: *A reaction that occurs when two molecules are joined by removing an H from one molecule, an OH from the other (forming water) and covalently linking the molecules together to form a bigger molecule. 33-4*

Denaturation: *The process of an enzyme losing its proper shape due to heat or some other factor. 90*

Denitrifying bacteria: *Bacteria that can convert excess nitrates not absorbed by plants into atmospheric nitrogen. 400*

Desmosome: *A junction that looks like protein 'buttons' mounted on the inside surface of two adjacent cells with fibrous proteins stitching the proteins to each other and linking the two cells. 83*

Detritovore: *An animal that consumes small, dead fragments of plant and animal material. 397*

Detritus: *Dead organic matter. 237, 293, 397*

Diatom: *A large group of unicellular algae having beautiful glass-containing cell walls: responsible for about*

25% of the world's photosynthesis. 213-4

Diatomaceous earth: *Dried out diatomaceous ooze due to being above sea level. 214*

Diatomaceous ooze: *Fine ocean sediment composed of cell walls of dead diatoms that have sunk to the bottom. 214*

Diffusion: *The movement of a substance from an area of high concentration to an area of low concentration. 56-8*

Diglyceride: *Two fatty acids bonded to a glycerol. 37*

Dihybrid cross: *When both parents in a cross are heterozygous for two traits. 167-9*

Dikaryotic hyphae: *Hyphae with two nuclei per cell. 245*

Dinoflagellate: *A unicellular flagellated protist found primarily in marine waters. 211-3*

Dipeptide: *Two amino acids bonded together. 40*

Diplo-: *A prefix denoting a paired-grouping pattern in bacteria. 205*

Diploid (2N): *When a cell has two complete sets of chromosomes. 154*

Diploid zygote: *What is produced when one haploid sperm fertilizes a haploid egg (1N + 1N = 2N). 228*

Disaccharide: *A carbohydrate formed by linking two monosaccharides together. 33*

Divergence: *According to evolutionary theory, when a homologous structure is modified into different functions through variation and selection. 194*

DNA ligase: *An enzyme designed to splice any matching sticky ends of DNA together. 135*

DNA polymerase: *An enzyme that slides down single-stranded DNA unzipped by Helicase, reads the exposed bases, and builds a complimentary strand from the nucleotide stockpile in the nucleoplasm. 144*

DNA replication: *The process by which DNA is used as a template (pattern) to copy itself. 121*

Dominant: *An allele which is expressed in the presence of another allele. 166*

Dorsal fin: *A fin on the back of a fish. 332*

Dorsal nerve cord: *A nerve cord above the notochord in chordates. 327*

Duplicated chromosome (two-copy chromosome): *two identical copies of a chromosome hooked together resulting from DNA replication. 144*

Earthworm: *Phylum Annelida, class Oligochaeta. 279*

Ecological niche: *A particular organism's entire way of life. 391*

Ecology: *The study of interactions between living creatures and their environment. 389*

Ecosystem: *A naturally defined area comprised of all its biotic and abiotic factors that function as an integrated whole. 390-1*

Ectoparasite: *A parasite that resides on the outside of their host. 393*

Ectothermic: *Attains body heat from the environment. 338*

Electron: *A subatomic particle with a negative electrical charge. 17*

Electron transport system: *Various molecules embedded in the thylakoid membrane or cristae that pass electrons along at lightning speed. 97*

Element: *A substance that has distinct chemical properties and cannot be broken down into simpler substances by normal chemical means. 15*

Elytra: *Thickened forewings that protect the membranous hindwings of a beetle. They do not overlap, but meet in the middle and form a straight line down their back. 304*

Embryonic sporophyte: *The embryo of a plant (2N) often contained within a seed. 385*

Endergonic: *When a chemical reaction requires an input of energy. 86-7*

Endocytosis: *The entry of an object (large molecules or a cell) across a cell membrane. The object attaches to membrane receptors causing an inpocketing to form. The objects is then engulfed when the inpocketing is internalized as a vacuole. 63*

Endoparasite: *A parasite that lives within and feeds on its host's tissue or ingested food. 393*

Endoplasmic reticulum (ER): *A maze-like network of membranes filled with many enzymes designed to process and modify newly made proteins or lipids. 69-70*

Endosperm: *What is produced when the triploid cell of an angiosperm divides by mitosis; serves as food for the developing embryonic sporophyte. 385*

Endothermic: *Creatures that generate heat internally through metabolic processes. 352*

Energy: *The ability to do work. 88*

Energy levels or shells: *The area in which one or more electron orbitals surround the nucleus of an atom. 17*

Entropy: *A measure of disorder. 86*

Environment: *A creature's living and nonliving surroundings. 389*

Enzyme: *A protein whose shape and chemical properties give it the ability to greatly speed up particular chemical reactions. 88*

Epidermis: *The outermost layer of cells on cnidarians. 266*

Epistasis or polygenic inheritance: *A type of inheritance in which two or more genes contribute to one trait. 172*

Equilibrium: *The even distribution of a substance such that the concentrations are equal everywhere in an area. 57*

Eudicot: *A flowering plant having two cotyledons in the embryo and seedling. 380-1*

Euglenoid: *A unicellar torpedo-shaped protist ranging from less than 10μm to 500μm. 210*

Eukaryotic cell: *A cell usually larger than 10μm and containing membrane-bound organelles and a membrane-bound nucleus. 53*

Evisceration: *A defense mechanism in which a sea cucumber ejects internal organs out of its anus or mouth at an assailant. 325*

Exergonic: *When reactants release energy during a chemical reaction. 87*

Exocytosis: *The ejection of waste or exportation of a product needed outside a cell membrane. The material is packaged within a vesicle which is then transported to the cell membrane.The vesicle membrane fuses with the cell membrane and then releases its contents outside. 64*

Exoskeleton: *A rigid or flexible external covering found on arthropods. 183*

Exponential growth: *The increase of a population assuming no limits to resources and no accumulation of factors that hinder reproduction. 394*

Extracellular digestion: *Digestion which takes place outside the fungus by exocytosis of lysosomes from the hyphae. 238*

Extracellular material: *Material that is not cell membrane or cell wall and is outside the cell. 81*

Extremophile: *Archaea that live in the most inhospitable environments imaginable. 207*

F1 generation: *The generation which results from crossing the parental generation. 164*

F2 generation: *The generation which results from crossing the F1 generation. 164*

$FADH_2$: *(Flavin adenine dinucleotide) A coenzyme, working in concert with enzymes, that swipes electron pairs from certain molecules and transfers them to other molecules in cellular respiration. 44*

Family: *The next taxon under order. 182*

Fatty acid: *A linear carbon molecule that ranges from four to eighteen carbons long. One end is a carboxyl group; the remaining atoms are hydrogen. 36*

Filament: *The stalk of the stamen. 381*

Filarial worm: *A roundworm that causes elephantiasis by obstructing the flow of lymph, resulting in grotesque swelling. 278*

First law of thermodynamics: *Matter cannot be created or destroyed, though it can be converted from one form to another. 86*

Flagellated chambers: *A series of tiny rooms in leuconoid sponges that are lined with collar cells which generate the water current through the sponge. 260*

Flagellate or mastigophoran: *A creature that has at least one eukaryotic flagellum. 221-3*

Flagellum: *A lash-like appendage that serves as a locomotive organelle of prokaryotic and eukaryotic cells. 205*

Fluid mosaic model: *A description of a cell membrane in which various membrane proteins are floating in a phospholipid bilayer. 56*

Fluke: *A flatworm parasite that causes many horrible diseases; its first host is a mollusk and its last host is a vertebrate. 275*

Foliose: *A growth form of lichen with a flakey or leafy appearance. 250*

Food chain or web: *Energy flow through a community. 395-7*

Food vacuole: *A vacuole formed during the endocytosis of food. 72*

Foraminiferan ooze: *The old tests of dead foraminiferans that sink to the bottom of the ocean, accumulating into large deposits. 224*

Foraminiferans: *A sarcodine that produces a test made of calcium carbonate, often diminutive with spirals like snail shells and perforated so that their pseudopods (called reticulopods) can protrude. 223-4*

Francis Crick (1916-2004): *Discoverer of the three-dimensional structure of DNA with James Watson, which they published in the prestigious journal* Nature *in 1953. Awarded the Noble Prize in 1962. 115*

Frond: *A fern leaf which grows from the rhizome. 372*

Fruit: *The mature ovary of a flowering plant that contains seeds. 385*

Fruticose: *A growth form of lichen with a bushy or branchy appearance. 250*

Gametangium: *A gamete container. 243*

Gametes: *Cells that unite to produce a zygote. 156*

Gametophyte: *In plants with alternating generations: the plant phase that produces either sperm or eggs or both. 368-9*

Gap 1 (G1): *The period of interphase in which normal cell growth and activity occur. 146*

Gap 2 (G2): *The period of interphase in which cell growth and synthesis of proteins* *occur in preparation for mitosis. 146*

Gap junction: *A group of proteins that forms a tunnel spanning both the membranes of adjacent cells. 82*

Gastrodermis: *The inner layer of cells facing the gastrovascular cavity in cnidarians. 266*

Gastropods: *Phylum Mollusca, class Gastropoda. 286-7*

Gastrovascular cavity: *The internal cavity of cnidarians. 265*

Gemmule: *A little capsule made from spongin and spicules containing sponge cells employed in asexual reproduction in sponges. It is designed to ride out harsh environmental conditions that may kill the parent sponge. 262*

Gene: *A gene is a segment of DNA that codes for a specific protein or for a specific RNA. 121*

Gene gun: *In bioballistics, a device which shoots a DNA-coated microscopic metal particle into a cell. 137*

Gene of interest: *The gene that the scientist is interested in expressing in another cell. 137*

Generative cell: *One of two cells in a pollen grain which divides to produce two sperm. 383*

Genotype: *The combination of alleles for any given trait or traits. 165*

Genotypic ratio: *The ratio of genotypes in a given generation. 166*

Genus: *The next taxon under Family. 182, 185*

Gill-rakers: *Comb-like structures on fish gills for filtering plankton out of water. 335*

Glucose: *A monosaccharide with the molecular formula* $C_6H_{12}O_6$*. 16, 32-3*

Glycerol: *a linear three-carbon molecule with three OH groups on one side; the remaining atoms are hydrogen. 36*

Glycogen: *A branching polysaccharide (similar to starch) used as short-term food storage in animals. 34-5*

Glycolysis: *A biochemical pathway in the cytoplasm whereby glucose is split by a battery of enzymes into two pyruvates. 105-7*

Glycosidic linkage: *A covalent bond linking two monosaccharides together. 34*

Golgi Body: *An organelle involved in modifying, packaging, and shipping various biomolecules to other organelles or the cell membrane. 70-1*

Granum: *A stack of thylakoids. 96*

Green algae: *A group of algae made green by its pigments, which includes chlorophyll a & b and carotenoids. 217-8*

Gregor Mendel (1822-1884): *a monk from the Czech Republic who figured out inheritance patterns from pea plants and proposed the Law of Segregation and the Law of Independent Assortment. He is considered the Father of Genetics. 163*

Guanine: *A two-ringed base that pairs with cytosine joining complimentary strands to form the DNA ladder. 116*

Guard cells: *A pair of wiener-shaped cells that form little pores to allow gas exchange between the interior and exterior of the leaf (usually in the lower epidermis). 95-6*

Gymnosperm: *A plant with seeds produced in cones; the majority are conifers. 375*

H_2O: *The chemical formula for water. 16*

Habitat: *Where a creature naturally lives. 391*

Hagfish: *Phylum Chordata, Superclass Agnatha. 330*

Halophilic: *Salt-loving Archaea. 207*

Halteres: *Club-shaped gyroscopic organs on dipterans involved in balance during flight. 306*

Haploid (1N): *When a cell has one complete set of chromosomes. 154*

Helicase: *An enzyme that unzips the double helix of DNA into two single strands. 144*

Hemelytra: *Protective forewings of suborder Heteroptera; the proximal half is leathery and the distal half membranous and overlapping. 302*

Hemipenes: *Paired male copulatory organs of snakes and lizards. 348*

Hemolysis: *The cytolysis of red blood cells. 60*

Herpetology: *The study of reptiles and amphibians. 344*

Heterodont teeth: *Mammalian teeth having a variety of shapes and functions. 358*

Heterotroph: *Organisms that obtain food from sources other than themselves. 221*

Heterozygous or hybrid: *Having two different alleles in their genotype. 165*

Histones: *Spool-like proteins around which the Double Helix of DNA is wrapped. 119*

Holdfast: *The root-like base that anchors brown algae to the sea floor. 215*

Homologous chromosomes: *A pair of chromosomes that are very similar to each other in size, shape, and the genes they carry. 153-6*

Homologous Structure: *An anatomical feature that various groups of organisms share because of common design or, according to evolutionary theory, common ancestry. 194-5*

Homozygous or purebred: *Having two identical alleles in a genotype. 164-5*

Hydra: *Small cnidarians that prey on tiny crustaceans in freshwater habitats. 265-9*

Hydrogen bond: *A weak bond between partial*

positively charge areas and partial negatively charged areas within the same molecule or between different molecules. 22

Hydroid colonies: *Colonies of connected polyps. 269*

Hydrolysis reaction: *A reaction that occurs when a molecule is cut in two through water splitting into OH and H. 34*

Hymenium: *The spore-producing surface of an ascoma or basidioma. 245*

Hypertonic: *When the solute concentration is high outside the cell relative to inside. 59*

Hyphae: *Long, thin, branching filaments in a fungus; used to refer to several threads visible under a microscope. 230*

Hypotonic: *When the solute concentration is low outside the cell relative to inside. 60*

Incomplete dominance: *A type of inheritance in which one allele is not completely dominant over the other allele. 171-2*

Incurrent and excurrent siphons: *Two apertures that allow water to flow in and out of a bivalve's mantle cavity. 284*

Incurrent canal: *Areas in syconoid sponges into which water first flows before entering the radial canals. 284*

Ink sac: *An ink-excreting sac attached to the rectum of a cephalopod. 288-9*

Inner and outer membranes: *Two separate phospholipid bilayers that surround both chloroplasts and mitochondria. 96, 107*

Instars: *The stages between moltings in an arthropod life cycle. 299*

Insulin: *The protein hormone that enables body cells to take up glucose from the blood stream. 137-9*

Intermediate filament: *A cytoskeletal element that contributes to the supporting framework of the cell (rather than provide transportation). 78-9*

Intermembrane space: *The space between the outer and inner membranes in a mitochondrion or chloroplast. 107*

Internode: *A section of a herbaceous stem in between leaf nodes. 380*

Interphase: *The period of time when the DNA is uncoiled and in which normal cellular activity and cell growth occur. 145-6*

Interspecific competition: *Competition between species. 393*

Intraspecific competition: *Competition between individuals of the same species. 393-4*

Intrinsic rate of increase: *The rate of increase of a population found by subtracting death and emigration rates from the birth and immigration rates. 394*

Ion: *An atom with a positive or negative charge due to the number of electrons and protons being unequal. 19*

Ionic bond: *A bond formed when certain kinds of atoms rob one or more electrons (to fulfill the octet rule) and consequently make themselves negatively charged; because the robber atom becomes negatively charged and the robbed becomes positively charged, they stick together. 19*

Isotonic: *The solute concentration is the same both inside and outside the cell. 60*

Isotopes: *Different forms of an element that have a variable number of neutrons in their atomic nuclei. 18*

Jacobson's Organ: *An organ in a snake's mouth that detects odor molecules in the environment sampled by the forked tongue. 349*

Jacque Monod (1910-1976) and Francois Jacob (1920-2013): *French molecular biologists that discovered the lac operon, a mechanism in E. coli of how genes are turned off and on. 131*

James Watson (1928-present): *Discoverer of the three-dimensional structure of DNA with Francis Crick, which they published in the prestigious journal* Nature *in 1953. Awarded the Noble Prize in 1962. 131*

Jellyfish: *A cnidarian with the medusa body form. 270-272*

Karyotype: *An orderly picture of an organism's chromosomes isolated from a single cell. 155*

Kinetochore: *The point of attachment between chromosomes and spindle microtubules. 147*

Kingdom: *The most general taxon after domain, consisting of Plantae, Animalia, Protista, Fungi, Archaebacteria, and Eubacteria. 182*

Krebs Cycle: *A very important biochemical cycle occurring in the mitochondrion that breaks down acetyl groups into CO_2 and directly produces ATP, NADH, and $FADH_2$. 108-9*

Lac operon: *A set of genes in E. coli that was turned on if lactose was available as a food source. 131-3*

Lamprey: *Phylum Chordata, Superclass Agnatha. 330-1*

Lancelet: *Phylum Chordata, Subphylum Cephalochordata. 328-9*

Late blight of potatoes (Phytophthora infestans): *A water mold that caused the Great Potato Famine of 1845-1852 in Ireland. 230*

Lateral or axillary bud: *A bud located at the leaf axil. 380*

Law of Independent Assortment: *When an organism produces gametes, alleles on one pair of homologous chromosomes separate independently compared to how alleles separate on another pair of homologous chromosomes* *(so more combinations of gametes can be produced). 168*

Law of Segregation: *When an organism produces gametes (during meiosis), the two alleles separate so that each gamete gets only one of the two. 165*

Leaf: *The petiole and the blade; grows from a main plant stem or branch. 380*

Leaf axil: *The upper surface where the petiole meets the stem. 380*

Leaflet: *The leaf-like subdivisions of a leaf blade. 380*

Pinnae: *Leaflets of a fern frond. 376*

Leech: *Phylum Annelida, class Hirudinea. 279-80*

Lichen: *A mutualistic relationship between ascomycete fungi and green or blue-green algae. 250-1*

Light dependent reaction: *A reaction of photosynthesis that uses pigments (in the thylakoid membrane) to capture light energy. This indirectly causes electrons to be removed from water. Electrons are passed through an electron transport system, thus producing NADPH. Water is split in the process into oxygen and H+ ions. H+ ions accumulate in the lumen and flow through ATP synthase producing ATP. 97-100*

Light independent reactions: *The same as the Calvin-Benson cycle which is the light independent part of photosynthesis. 100-103*

Lipid: *A basic category of biomolecules consisting of neutral lipids (fats, oils, and grease), waxes, steroids, and phospholipids. 35-9*

Logistic growth: *The pattern of population growth in a highly stable environment. 394-5*

Lugworms: *A polychaete that lives in a burrow and eats sand. 280*

Lumen: *The fluid-filled space inside a thylakoid disc. 96*

Lysosome: *A vesicle filled with a variety of digestive enzymes that breaks apart most of the major biomolecules. 71-2*

Mammary gland: *A specialized epidermal gland on the chest and abdominal region of all mammals that produces milk for their young. 359*

Mandible: *The chewing mouthparts of a decapod. 294*

Mantle: *Epidermis of a mollusk. 283*

Mantle cavity: *The space between the visceral mass and the mantle of a bivalve. 283*

Matrix: *The space inside the cristae of the mitochondrion. 107*

Matthias Schleiden (1804-1881): *A German Botanist who developed the cell theory with Theodor Schwann. 50*

Maurice Wilkins (1916-2004): *Scientist whose experiments formed the basis of Watson and Crick's breakthrough discovery in DNA. Awarded the Noble Prize in 1962. 115*

Maxillae: *The mouthparts used by a decapod to handle and sort food. 296*

Maxillipeds: *Appendages modified for feeding behind the maxillae of a decapod. 296*

Medusa: *One of two body types for cnidarians (e.g., jellyfish). 265-272*

Megagametophyte: *The haploid generation in conifers and flowering plants which produces eggs. 376-8, 383*

Megaspore: *The larger spores on the female cone or flower, one of which grows into a megagametophyte. 376, 383*

Meiosis: *A special kind of nuclear division for sexually reproducing creatures that insures that the resulting cells have the haploid number of chromosomes. 153*

Meiosis I: *The first division of Meiosis. 156*

Meiosis II: *The second division of Meiosis. 156*

Mesoglea: *A jelly-like substance found between the epidermis and gastrodermis in cnidarians. 266*

Mesophyll: *Photosynthetic tissue of leaves between the upper and lower epidermis. 96*

Metabolism: *The sum total of all the chemical reactions in an organism. 88*

Metaphase: *The second phase of mitosis in which chromosomes neatly align along the spindle equator with the identical copies of each chromosome facing towards opposite sides of the cell. 147*

Methanogen: *Archaea that live in deoxygenated muck in swamps and produce a gaseous waste product called methane. 207*

Microfilament: *The smallest of the cytoskeletal elements. It is shaped like a thin rod that serves as part of the cytoskeleton, or it helps with the complex contraction system within all types of muscle cells. 79*

Microgametophyte or pollen grain: *A two- to four-celled male structure in conifers and flowering plants that produces sperm. 376, 383*

Microhabitat: *A specific portion of a habitat. 391*

Micropyle: *A small opening in an ovule through which pollen enters for fertilization. 376-378, 383*

Microsporangium: *A sack carried by a male cone that contains cells that go through meiosis to produce microspores, which eventually become microgametophytes. 376*

Microspore: *A spore that goes through mitosis to create a two- to four-celled microgametophyte. 376, 383*

Microtubule: *A cytoskeletal element that forms the "trolley cables" for the movement of organelles and, during meiosis and mitosis, chromosomes. They also form the internal framework of flagella and cilia. 77*

Millipede: *Phylum Arthropoda, class Diplopoda. 293*

Mitochondrion: *A jelly-bean shaped organelle that generates ATP through the oxidation of food molecules. 73*

Mitosis: *The process by which one nucleus divides into two nuclei. 143*

Mitotic spindle: *The specialized assemblage of microtubules upon which the chromosomes haul themselves along. 147*

Molecule: *Two or more atoms hooked together by some kind of chemical bond. 15*

Mollusk: *An animal from Phylum Mollusca with a mantle, mantle cavity, gills or lungs within the cavity, a visceral mass, a head-foot, and a shell secreted by the mantle. 283-9*

Monocot: *A flowering plant with one cotyledon in the embryo and seedling. 380-381*

Monoglyceride: *A fatty acid bonded to a glycerol. 37*

Monohybrid cross: *When both parents in a cross are heterozygous for one trait. 166*

Monokaryotic hyphae: *Hyphae with one nucleus per cell. 245*

Monophyletic group: *A clade containing the ancestor and all of its descendents. 196*

Monosaccharide: *The basic building block or simplest unit of a carbohydrate. 32*

mRNA (messenger RNA): *The type of RNA that contains the information encoding a protein. 123*

Mutualism: *Two different species living together in a way that benefit each other. 206, 213, 251*

Mycelium: *Larger quantities of fungal hyphae when visible to the naked eye. 235*

Mycorrhizae: *"Fungus roots"; a certain group of fungi that form mutualistic relationships with plant roots. 241, 251*

Myxomycota: *The phylum of plasmodial slime molds. 228*

NADH: *(Nicotinamide adenine dinucleotide) A coenzyme, working in concert with enzymes that swipes electron pairs from certain molecules and transfers them to other molecules during cellular respiration. 44, 93*

NADPH: *(Nicotinamide adenine dinucleotide phosphate) Another coenzyme that works and looks much like NADH except that it does its job in the context of photosynthesis rather than cellular respiration. 44, 93*

Natural history: *The study of life in its natural habitat (more observational than experimental). 200, 389*

Natural law: *The way God usually runs the universe. 85*

Nauplius: *The larval stage of a crustacean. 295*

Nematocysts: *Stinging organelles within cnidocytes. 266*

Nematodes or Roundworms: *A non-segmented worm that has a complete digestive system, is round in cross section, and ranges from microscopic to over 1 meter in length. 277-8*

Neutrons: *A subatomic particle with no electrical charge. 17*

Nitrifying bacteria: *Bacteria that can convert ammonia into nitrates and nitrites. 400*

Nitrogen-fixing bacteria: *Bacteria that convert nitrogen gas into ammonia. 400*

Nitrogen cycle: *The process by which nitrogen is continually cycled between the biosphere and the atmosphere. 399-400*

Node: *The part of a stem from which leaves and lateral buds emerge. 384*

Non-polar covalent bond: *A bond formed when two or more atoms have an equal pull on the shared electrons; consequently the electrons are equally distributed between the atoms involved. 21*

Notochord: *A stiffening dorsal protein rod found in the embryos of all chordates; develops into the backbone in vertebrates. 327*

Nuclear envelope: *An envelope that serves as the boundary of the nucleus and is formed by two phospholipid bilayers. 68*

Nucleic acid: *A basic category of biomolecules consisting of DNA or RNA. 31, 43-4*

Nucleoid: *A hoop of DNA in a prokaryote containing most of its genome. 205*

Nucleolus: *An area within the nucleus that is actively engaged in the manufacture of certain parts of ribosomes. 69*

Nucleoplasm: *The watery fluid of the nucleus. 68*

Nucleosome: *A small spool of DNA and histones. 119*

Nucleotide: *The basic unit of DNA and RNA that is made up of a sugar, phosphate, and nitrogenous base. 43, 116*

Nucleus (of a cell): *master control center of the cell in which is housed the DNA. 53, 68-9*

Nucleus (of an atom): *The center of an atom containing protons and neutrons. 17*

Octet rule: *The outermost shell of an atom can be filled with eight electrons and is most stable when it contains eight. 18*

Oligopeptide: *A few amino acids bonded together. 40*

Oligosaccharide: *A chain of a few to less than a hundred monosaccharides linked by glycosidic linkages. 34*

Omnivore: *An animal that eats both producers and consumers. 396*

Operator: *A region of DNA where a repressor protein binds and blocks RNA polymerase. 131-2*

Operculum: *A stiff flap that covers the gills of bony fishes. 336*

Operon: *Any gene or set of genes that is turned off or on as a single unit. 131*

Oral cirri: *Thin finger-like strands in lancelets that serve as sensory structures and filter water for food. 329*

Oral groove: *The funnel-shaped area in which ciliates collect food prior to phagocytosis. 226*

Orbital: *A subset within an energy level or shell that contains at most two electrons. There may be one to several orbitals with an energy level or shell. 17*

Order: *The next taxon under Class. 182, 184*

Osculum: *The opening at the top of a sponge where water flows out. 260*

Osmosis: *The diffusion of water across a semi-permeable membrane. 58-9*

Osteoderm: *A bony, dermal plate in reptiles. 345*

Ostium or Dermal Ostium or Prosopyle: *A sponge pore. 259*

Ovary: *In flowers, the base of the pistil containing the ovules or seeds. 382*

Oviparity: *Egg-laying; embryos are nourished by the yolk. 336*

Ovoviviparity: *Eggs hatch inside the mother after the embryos are nourished by the yolk; live birth. 336*

Ovule: *An immature seed. 375, 382*

Ovuliferous scale: *A seed-carrying scale on a pine cone. 375*

Oxidized: *When a molecule or atom loses electrons. 101*

Palmately compound: *A blade having multiple leaflets where all radiate from one point. 380*

Papulae: *Thin-walled, finger-like projections used for gas exchange on the outer surface of an echinoderm. 321*

Parabronchi: *A system of tubes that serves as a gas-exchange area in bird lungs. 351*

Paramecium: *A ciliate ranging from 150 to 300 µm and sporting approximately 10,000 to 14,000 cilia in parallel bands running lengthwise over its entire surface, allowing it to move up to 1,000 µm/second. 226-7*

Paraphyletic group: *A subset of a monophyletic group. 196-7*

Parasitism: *Two different species living together in a way that benefits one and harms the other. 393*

Parental generation: *The starting generation for a particular series of genetic experiments. 164*

Passive transport or facilitated diffusion: *The movement of a molecule through a protein gate that receives it on one side of the membrane and deposits it on the other side through a variety of ways; no energy is required. 602*

Pathogenic bacteria: *Disease-causing bacteria. 200*

Pectoral fins: *A pair of fins just behind a fish's head on either side of its body. 332*

Pedal disc: *The flat bottom of a polyp that sticks to surfaces with secreted mucus. 266*

Pedicellariae: *Microscopic pincer-like structures on echinoderms that remove debris, larvae, and tiny animals that might otherwise settle on the echinoderm's surface. 321*

Pedipalps: *The second pair of appendages attached to an arachnid's cephalothorax. 310*

Pellicle: *A sophisticated network of proteins beneath the cell membrane. Contractile pellicles enable certain unicellular protists to change their shape. Some pellicles do not contract but grant the cell a certain shape. 210*

Pelvic fins: *A pair of fins on the pelvic region of a fish. 332*

Pen: *A thin, flexible, supporting rod embedded in a squid. 287*

Penicillin: *An antibiotic produced by the fungus* Penicillium *which is used against certain bacterial diseases. 240*

Petiole: *The stalk of a leaf. 380*

Phagocytosis: *Endocytosis on a large scale in which a cell attempts to engulf entire cells or cell fragments for food. 63*

Pharyngeal slit: *A slit found in the pharynx of some chordates that acts like a filter for feeding. 327, 329*

Phenotype: *The outward expression of a genotype. 165*

Phenotypic ratio: *The ratio of phenotypes in a given generation. 166*

Phloem: *Cellular pipes in plant veins that transport photosynthates through the plant body. 103*

Phospholipid: *A molecule similar to a diglyceride (two fatty acids bonded to a glycerol) except having a unique molecular group with a positive and negative charge on the third carbon. 35, 37*

Phospholipid Bilayer: *Two-layers of phospholipids. The hydrophobic tails of phospholipids (the fatty acid portion) form an inner water-free area, while the hydrophilic heads (the unique charged portion) form the two surfaces of the membrane and interact with water. 38*

Phosphorylation: *The process whereby ATP synthase*

converts ADP and P to ATP. 100

Photosynthate: *Any product of photosynthesis (often sugars). 103*

Photosystem: *A pigment cluster embedded within the thylakoid's membrane. 97*

pH scale: *A measure of a solution's acidity or alkalinity. 25*

Phylum: *The next taxon under Kingdom. 182-3*

Pilus: *A tiny tube constructed by the bacteria that can temporarily link two cells together. 136*

Pinnately compound: *A blade divided up into leaflets on either side of the rachis (the stem-like continuation of the petiole). 380*

Pinocytosis: *Endocytosis in which the cell engulfs dissolved molecules that are too small to be considered phagocytosis but too big to bring in by passive or active transport. 64*

Pinworm: *A roundworm that grows to about 1 cm and lives in the intestinal tract of infected humans; symptoms are minor. 277-8*

Pistil: *The female reproductive structure of the flower. 382*

Pit organs: *Infrared sensors on certain snakes that allow them to detect warm-blooded prey in complete darkness. 349*

Placoid scales: *Small, tooth-like scales on a shark's skin. 332*

Planarian: *A free-living flatworm that is a predator and scavenger in freshwater, marine, or moist terrestrial environments. 276-7*

Planula: *A ciliated larva in the lifecycle of cnidarians. 271-2*

Plasmid: *A small hoop of DNA in a prokaryotic cell (compared to the nucleoid) containing extra genetic information. Often used as a vector to introduce a gene of interest into a recipient cell in recombinant DNA technology. 136, 205*

Plasmolysis: *The shriveling of a cell due to loss of water. 60*

Plastron: *The lower shell of turtles. 345*

Platyhelminthes or Flatworms: *Worms with a dorsoventrally flattened body, no body cavity, and an incomplete digestive system. 275-7*

Plesiomorphy: *A structure already present in the ancestor of a particular clade. 199*

Pliny the Elder (23-79 AD): *Roman natural historian who wrote* Naturalis Historia, *which is full of his accumulated knowledge of zoology, botany, geology, mineralogy, and astronomy. 181*

Pneumatized bone: *A strong and hollow bone unique to birds. 354*

Pneumatocyst: *An air filled-flotation device that helps brown algae buoy its stipe and blades up to well-lit surface water. 215*

Pneumostome: *A lung-like cavity found in land-dwelling gastropods. 286*

Polar covalent bond: *A bond formed when the "strong" atom (high electronegativity) cause the shared electrons to move closer to it than to the "weak" atom (low electronegativity). 21*

Polar nuclei: *The two nuclei in an angiosperm megagametophyte which are in the central cell. 383*

Pollen grain: *A two- to four-celled haploid microgametophyte formed when a microspore divides in the microsporangium in conifers and angiosperms. 383*

Pollen sac: *The portion of an anther which develops and contains microspores (which become pollen grains). 383*

Pollination: *The transfer of pollen to a receptive stigma in a flower; when pollen lands near the micropyle of an ovule in a female cone in a conifer. 377*

Polychaetes: *Phylum Annelida, class Polychaeta. 279-80*

Polyp: *One of two body types for cnidarians (e.g., hydra). 265-72*

Polypeptide: *Fewer than one hundred amino acids bonded together. 40-41*

Polyphyletic group: *Portions of two or more clades but not including the ancestors that would unite them all into a single clade. 197*

Polysaccharide: *A chain of a hundred or more monosaccharides linked by glycosidic linkages. 34*

Population: *All members of the same species in a certain area. 390*

Primary consumer or herbivore: *An animal that consumes only producers. 396*

Proboscis: *The feeding siphon of lepidopterans. 307*

Producer: *The original source of food production in a food chain or web; usually algae and plants. 396*

Product: *The resulting molecule(s) of a chemical reaction. 86*

Proglottid: *A segment of a tapeworm's body that contains both egg and sperm. 276*

Prokaryotic cell: *A cell usually smaller than 10µm and lacking membrane-bound organelles or a membrane-bound nucleus. 53*

Promoter: *The segment of DNA to which RNA polymerase initially binds before constructing an RNA strand. 122*

Prophase: *The first (and longest) period of mitosis in which the following occur: DNA coiling, the disintegration of the nuclear envelope, the formation of the mitotic spindle and the movement of chromosomes toward the spindle equator. 146-7*

Protein: *A basic category of biomolecules that performs most jobs in a cell; each protein is a chain of one hundred or more amino acids. 39-42, 88*

Protein translation: *The process by which a ribosome makes a protein according to the instructions contained in mRNA. 121, 124-7*

Prothallus: *A bisexual gametophyte in ferns that develops both antheridia and archegonia. 374*

Protist: *A kingdom of life that lacks any suite of features that would place it in one of the other three eukaryotic kingdoms. 209*

Protonema: *Algae-like threads that result from the germination (and mitosis) of moss spores. 371*

Protons: *A subatomic particle with a positive electrical charge. 17*

Protozoan: *A protist that is animal-like in that it is motile and heterotrophic, but since it is unicellular it is not classified as an animal. 221*

Pseudopod: *A little cellular protrusion in sarcodines used for locomotion and for feeding through phagocytosis. 63, 223*

P site: *The first space on a ribosome that is aligned with a codon to which tRNA binds. 126*

Punnett Square: *A square devised by Reginald C. Punnett which graphically shows the possible genotypes of the offspring of a particular cross.*

Pupa: *An inactive instar, such as a chrysalis. 301*

Purines: *Adenine and Guanine. 116*

Pygidium: *The tail region of a trilobite. 292*

Pyloric stomach: *The central upper stomach of a starfish. 321*

Pyrimidines: *Cytosine, thymine, and uracil. 116*

Pyruvate: *A three-carbon molecule which is the product of glycolysis. 105*

Quill: *The shaft of a feather that is rooted in the skin follicle of a bird. 353*

Radial canal: *Areas in syconoid sponges that are lined with collar cells which generate the water current through the sponge. 260*

Radial symmetry: *A symmetry where two or more imaginary planes passing through a central axis can produce mirror–image halves. 256*

Radiolarians: *A sarcodine with tests made of glass-containing compounds, whose radial symmetry and beauty makes them microscopic jewels. Their tests have holes that allow pseudopods (called axopods) to extend from their cell bodies, but unlike the reticulopods their axopods do not connect with one another. 223-5*

Radula: *The rasplike tongue of many gastropods and cephalopods. 286*

Reactant: *Chemicals that react with each other. 86*

Recessive: *An allele which is unexpressed in the presence of a dominant allele. 166*

Red algae: *A group of algae made red by the pigment phycobilin. 216-7*

Red tide: *A massive toxic bloom of certain kinds of dinoflagellates that produce neurotoxins. 212-3*

Reduced: *When a molecule or atom receives electrons. 101*

Reduction division: *The division in meiosis when a reduction in ploidy occurs (meiosis I). 157-8*

Reduction in ploidy: *When a cell goes from diploid (2N) to haploid (1N). 157-8*

Release factor: *An anticodon which causes the mRNA, tRNA, and newly translated protein to fall off the ribosome. 127*

Repressor protein: *A protein supplied by the cell that serves as a roadblock to prevent RNA polymerase from transcribing a particular gene or set of genes. 131-2*

Reservoir: *An indentation on a Euglenoid that contains two flagella. 210*

Respiratory tree: *A sea cucumber's breathing system consisting of internal branching tubules. 325*

Restriction enzyme: *An enzyme that cuts DNA at specific sequences and restricts foreign DNA from successfully invading the cell. Used often in recombinant DNA technology. Opposite of DNA ligase. 135*

Reticulopods: *Net-like pseudopods of foraminiferans. 224*

Rhizoids: *Root-like fungal hyphae that grow into and consume food discovered by stolons. 243*

Rhizome: *A horizontal underground stem of a plant from which roots grow to anchor the plant to the soil and absorb water and nutrients. 372*

Ribosome: *A complex assembly platform for making proteins within the cell. 69*

RNA: *Ribonucleic Acid; "Xeroxed" copies of certain sections of DNA. 43-4, 68*

RNA polymerase: *An enzyme with the ability to temporarily unzip the double helix so as to read a segment of the DNA strand and enzymatically construct an RNA strand by base-pairing RNA nucleotides with the exposed DNA bases. 122*

RNA transcription: *The process by which a segment of DNA (a gene) is used as a template to make a copy of RNA. 122-3*

Robert Hooke (1635-1703): *An English scientist who developed a microscope and published the book* Micrographia *in 1665, in which he coined the term 'cell' to* *describe the square or rectangular chambers he saw in cork tissue with his microscope. 47-9*

Rosalind Franklin (1920-1958): *Scientist whose experimental data formed part of the basis of Watson and Crick's breakthrough discovery of DNA's structure. 115*

Rostrum: *Nose. 332*

Rough ER: *ER having a bumpy surface due to its coating of ribosomes. Involved in the modification of proteins. 70*

rRNA (ribosomal RNA): *The type of RNA that is woven together with certain proteins to form the highly complex structure of the ribosome. 123*

Rudolf Virchow (1821-1902): *A German biologist who contributed to the cell theory by suggesting that all cells arise from pre-existing cells. 50*

Salt: *Any substance resulting from mixing equal amounts of an acid and a base. 26-7*

Saprobe: *decomposer. 230*

Sarcodine: *A protozoan that has the ability to make pseudopods of some sort. 223-5*

Scavenger: *An animal that specializes in consuming large chunks of dead plants or carrion. 397*

Scolex: *A head-like structure that enables a tapeworm to attach to the lining of a host's gut. 276*

Sebaceous gland: *An oil gland in the skin of a mammal. 358*

Secondary consumer: *An animal that consumes primary consumers. 396*

Second law of thermodynamics: *Any system left to itself goes from order to disorder. 86*

Seed: *A plant embryo encased in a seed coat that has ceased growth and has dried up. 164*

Seed coat or integument: *A tough, protective layer around a plant embryo. 377*

Segmented worm: *A worm with a body divided into segments with bristles and sometimes fleshy appendages sticking out of their sides for locomotion. 279-280*

Sepal: *The outermost leafy part of the flower which encloses the petals. 382*

Septate: *Hyphae having partitions. 245*

Shaft: *The extension of the quill that forms the central axis of the feather. 353*

Sharks: *Phylum Chordata, Class Chondrichthyes. 331-3*

Sieve plate *or* **Madreporite:** *A plate on the upper surface of the central disc that serves as a filtering gateway for sea water to enter the internal water vascular system. 320*

Simple leaf: *A leaf whose blade is not divided up into leaflets. 380*

Simple diffusion: *The movement of molecules through a phospholipid bilayer, not facilitated by proteins. 61-2*

Sister chromatid (one-copy chromosome): *one half of a duplicated chromosome. 144*

Slug: *In the slime mold lifecycle: when the amebas of a slime mold congregate into a clear, elongate, motile blob several millimeters long. 229*

Smooth ER: *ER having a smooth surface due to its lack of ribosomes; does some protein modification, but mostly involved in the synthesis and modification of lipids. 70*

Solenoids: *The arrangement of nucleosomes into larger coils. 119*

Solute: *The solid, liquid, or gas dissolved into a liquid (the solvent). 59*

Solution: *The mixture of one or more solutes dissolved in a solvent. 59*

Solvent: *The liquid into which a solid, liquid, or gas (the solute) is dissolved. 59*

Sorus: *A cluster of sporangia that forms a spot on the underside of a fern leaflet (several to many sori per leaflet). 372*

Spawning: *The reproduction of fishes, whether oviparous, viviparous, or ovoviviparous. 336*

Species: *The next taxon under Genus, not to be confused with baramin, the created kinds of Genesis. 182*

Specific epithet: *The second part of a scientific name or binomial. 186*

Spermatophore: *A tiny proteinaceous stalk produced by salamanders that is capped with a packet of sperm. 339-40*

Spicules: *Glassy or calcareous particles forming a brittle extracellular matrix in many sponges. 259*

Spindle equator: *The plane of division within the cell when mitosis is taking place. 145*

Spinnerets: *The organ through which spider silk is ejected. 314*

Spiracles *An opening into the mouth and behind the eyes of certain fish. 314-5*

Spirillum: *Corkscrew shaped bacteria. 205*

Spirochaete: *Tightly coiled bacteria. 205*

Sponge: *An animal belonging to the phylum Porifera. 259-62*

Spongin: *An elastic protein that makes up a flexible skeleton-like extracellular network of fibers in many sponges. 259*

Spongocoel: *The centrally located cavity of a sponge. 260*

Sporangiophore: *A specialized fungal hypha that bears the sporangium. 242*

Sporangium: *A structure that contains spores.* 228, 241, 371

Spore: *A reproductive unit of many organisms composed of one cell that is often dispersed through the air.* 228-9

Sporocarp: *A spore-bearing body of cellular slime molds.* 227

Sporophyte: *In plant life cycles with alternating generations: the diploid (2N) plant generation that produces spores through meiosis.* 273

Stamen: *The male reproductive structure inside the flower.* 386

Staphylo-: *A prefix denoting a cluster-grouping pattern in bacteria.* 203

Starch: *A type of polysaccharide composed of a linear chain of glucose units and primarily used for food storage in plants.* 32

Stentor: *A ciliate shaped like a hairy fanfare trumpet that can stretch over 2mm in length. To move, it uses its muscle-like pellicle to round up like a hairy rugby ball and spirals through the water.* 225

Stigma: *The end of the style, which receives pollen.* 386

Stigma or Eyespot: *A light-sensitive spot of red pigment in Euglena and some other euglenoids.* 208

Stipe: *The flexible stem-like structure of brown algae.* 213

Stipules: *Paired leafy growths on both sides of a petiole's base.* 384

Stolon: *A fungal hypha that grows over the surface of a food source prospecting for new sources of food.* 241

Stomates: *The little pores that allow gas exchange between the interior and exterior of the leaf.* 94

Stop codon: *A codon that signals the end of translation.* 125

Strepto-: *A prefix denoting a chain-grouping pattern in bacteria.* 203

Stroma: *The chloroplast's interior fluid.* 94

Style: *The structure in a pistil between the ovary and the stigma.* 386

Substrate: *The reactant that temporarily attaches to an active site of an enzyme in which the reaction occurs.* 89

Sucrose: *Table sugar which is a disaccharide composed of the monosaccharides, glucose and fructose.* 34

Symbiont: *An organism involved in a symbiotic relationship.* 392

Symbiosis: *Two different species living together.* 213, 392

Symmetry: *When an imaginary plane through the central axis of an animal produces mirror-image halves.* 255-6

Synthesis (S phase): *The period of interphase in which DNA replication occurs.* 146

Tapeworm: *Parasite with no digestive tract that often hangs onto the lining of a host's gut and absorbs the predigested nutrients through its body surface.* 275-6

Tegmina: *The protective forewings of an orthopteran.* 302

Telophase: *The fourth (and final) phase of mitosis in which a new nuclear envelope forms around the two clusters of one-copy chromosomes, which then uncoil, and the spindle disappears.* 148

Telson: *The middle piece of the tail of a decapod.* 296, 310

Temperature-dependent sex determination: *The temperature of the nest determines the sex of hatchling turtles; higher temperatures generate females and lower temperatures generate males.* 346-7

Tertiary consumer: *An animal that consumes secondary consumers.* 396

Test: *A miniature shell that surrounds the single-celled body of a foraminiferan or radiolarian.* 224

Theca: *An internal lattice of cellulose plates just beneath the cell membrane of free-living dinoflagellates.* 210

Theodor Schwann (1810-1882): *A German Physiologist who made several biological discoveries and is considered the father of cytology. He developed the cell theory with Matthias Schleiden.* 50

Thorax: *The middle region of an arthropod.* 292

Thylakoid disc: *A membrane-bound disc-like structure suspended within the stroma of a chloroplast.* 96

Thymine: *A one-ringed base that pairs with adenine joining complimentary strands to form the DNA ladder.* 116

Tight junction: *Special membrane proteins on adjacent cells that bind and link the cells together wherever the proteins are.* 82

Tonicity: *A measure of the concentration of a solute in water outside the cell relative to inside the cell.* 59-61

Transduction: *A type of transformation that uses virus particles as a vector to insert foreign DNA into a cell.* 136

Transformation: *When a gene of interest has been inserted into and been expressed by the recipient cell. Usually refers to naked DNA taken up by a cell. Other types go by different names like transduction or conjugation.* 136

Triglyceride: *Three fatty acids bonded to a glycerol.* 37

Trilobites: *An extinct group of arthropods having a head, a thorax, and pygidium; Phylum Arthropoda, Class Trilobita.* 292

Tripeptide: *Three amino acids bonded together.* 40

Triple fusion: *When one sperm from a pollen grain fuses with the two polar nuclei in the central cell of an ovule to produce a triploid cell (1N + 1N + 1N = 3N). 385*

tRNA (transfer RNA): *The type of DNA that performs the task of capturing specific amino acids and delivering them to the ribosome for assembly into proteins as specified by the mRNA. 123*

Trophic level: *A feeding level in a trophic pyramid. 396*

Trophic pyramid: *A representation of the relative abundance of energy that is contained on each tropic level. 396*

Tube cell: *One of two cells in a pollen grain which develops into the pollen tube to carry the sperm from the pollen grain through the stigma, down the style, and along the ovary's wall to the micropyle of an ovule after pollination. 383-4*

Tubeworm: *A polychaete that builds a tube for itself. 280*

Tunicate or Sea squirt: *Phylum Chordata, Subphylum Urochordata. 327-8*

Turgid: *When plant cells are plump and firm because of turgor pressure. 61*

Turgor pressure: *The water pressure within the plant cell due to the influx of water. 61*

Umbo: *The bulge on the two valves next to the hinge on a bivalve. 283*

Upper epidermis: *The upper layer of cells on a leaf. 95*

Uropod: *A terminal pair of a decapod's appendages that form part of the tail. 296*

Vacuole: *Any membrane bound organelle of various sizes and shapes that acts as a storage container for a variety of contents such as food or wastes. 75-6*

Valence Electrons: *The outermost electrons in an atom. 20*

Valves: *The two hinged shells of a bivalve. 283*

Vascular bundles: *A bundle of long cells in a stem that transport water, minerals, and photosynthate. 379*

Vertebrate: *An animal with a backbone. Examples include jawless, cartilaginous, and bony fish, as well as amphibians, reptiles, birds, and mammals. 256*

Virology: *The subset of microbiology that focuses on viruses. 203*

Visceral mass: *The part of a bivalve containing most of the organs. 284*

Viviparity: *Live bearing; embryos are nourished directly from the mother's tissues. 336*

Waste vacuole: *A vacuole containing waste (usually a food vacuole after the nutrients have been absorbed by the cell). 75-6*

Water cycle: *The process by which water is continually recycled through the environment. 397-8*

Water mold: *a fungal-like protist. 229-32*

Water vascular system: *An internal hydraulic system that controls the movement of tube feet in echinoderms. 319*

With the concentration gradient: *a substance is moving from high to low concentration. 61*

Xylem: *Vascular tissue that transports water and minerals in a stem. 379-80*

Zooxanthellae: *A group of dinoflagellates living as mutualistic symbionts in other sea creatures. 213*

Zygosporangium: *In zygomycetes, when two gametangia merge into one compartment and form a thick wall that can withstand adverse environmental conditions. 244*

Zygote: *A fertilized egg that divides by mitosis to form an adult. 153, 369*

INDEX

CPSIA information can be obtained
at www.ICGtesting.com
Printed in the USA
LVHW070902211221
706739LV00002B/132

* 9 7 8 1 5 9 1 2 8 1 2 3 8 *